KU-342-744

Geomorphology

THE MACMILLAN COMPANY
NEW YORK · BOSTON · CHICAGO · DALLAS
ATLANTA · SAN FRANCISCO
MACMILLAN AND CO., Limited
LONDON · BOMBAY · CALCUTTA · MADRAS
MELBOURNE
THE MACMILLAN COMPANY
OF CANADA, Limited
TORONTO

[1942]

TWO THOUSAND YEARS BEFORE PLAYFAIR

"Nothing under heaven is softer or more yielding than water; but when it attacks things hard and resistant there is not one of them that can prevail."

From the Chinese: *Tao Tê Ching,* Chapter LXXVIII, 240 B. C.

Translation by Arthur Waley in: *The Way and Its Power,* George Allen and Unwin Ltd., London, 1934, p. 238. (Courtesy George Sears, C. U., '40.)

TABLE OF CONTENTS

LIST OF ILLUSTRATIONS

PLATES

Geomorphology

Chapter One

CONTENT AND BACKGROUNDS

Content. Geomorphology is ordinarily understood to comprise the science of land forms. But this conventional restriction of the field, to the discussion of land forms only, is in complete disregard of the constitution of the word and fails in appreciation of the real scope of the subject. Geomorphology is made up of the Greek terms, *ge* meaning "earth," *morphe* meaning "form," and *logos* meaning "a discourse." It is obvious that if the discourse is to be about the form of the earth something more than the forms of the land must be given consideration. The earth's configuration as a whole and the shape and disposition of its larger units will also have a place.

It is easy to discern why the content of geomorphologies has been so much given over to analyses of land forms. These are the items that may be realized through human experience and are of immediate and popular interest. The shape of the earth as a whole, the make-up of continents and ocean basins as units, are, by contrast, phenomena beyond the powers of direct observation. For their comprehension data must first be collected piecemeal, then assembled, mentally, as a concept, or by representation in a map, model, or diagram. The larger view should not, however, be neglected simply because it has these difficulties. In this book the endeavor is made to provide an inclusive treatment of geomorphology.

Student Preparation. It is assumed that the student who uses this book has had the training to be got in an elementary course in geology. He should be acquainted with the commoner minerals and rocks, and with the nature and operation of geologic processes and the results of their action. He will also have learned some elementary geomorphology.

As this further study in geomorphology is begun it is, accord-

1

ingly, expected that the student will be familiar with such words as "feldspar," "anticline," "base level," "syenite," "strike," "pothole." In general, such terms are used in this book without definition. If a word is encountered that is not in the student's vocabulary he should turn at once to an unabridged dictionary, preferably Webster, or to a textbook in general geology for the explanation of its meaning.

Historical. Geomorphology, in the broadest sense of the term, is in debt to all observers of geographic phenomena from the time when the earliest of such records was made. Geomorphology, so regarded, is a part of geography.

But geomorphology as an explanatory science had its beginnings in geology. Abraham Gottlob Werner (1749–1817), generally regarded as the founder of modern geology, is reported (Adams, F. D., 1938, p. 213) to have lectured on the influence which the character of the rock underlying a district or country exerts upon its surface features. Many of the classical names in the golden age of geology are those of personages who made important contributions in the field of geomorphology.

In 1795 James Hutton published a book called *Theory of the Earth* in which he proclaimed that "The mountains have been formed by the hollowing out of the valleys, and the valleys have been hollowed out by the attrition of hard materials coming from the mountains" (Vol. II, p. 401). In 1802, John Playfair provided his *Illustrations of the Huttonian Theory,* a much easier book to read than Hutton's, which defined and exemplified the Huttonian principle of gradual, slow development of land forms. This idea became the chief concept of Charles Lyell's *Principles of Geology* (1830–32), "being an attempt to explain the former changes of the earth's surface by reference to the causes now in operation," and this doctrine has since been called **uniformitarianism.** Lyell carried his advocacy of uniformitarianism to such extremes that he became known as its "high priest." A. C. Ramsay, at a later date, championed marine erosion as an extremely potent agency in the leveling down of lands, and introduced glaciers as sculptors of lake basins. Like Lyell, he swayed opinion too much in favor of these agencies and processes in particular, and it took some time before the wider general significance of degradation by weathering and stream action was again fully realized.

Still later the foundations were laid in America for what has become the leading school of geomorphic study. Beginning with J. W. Powell (*Exploration of the Colorado River of the West*, published in 1875), followed by C. E. Dutton (*Report on the Geology of the High Plateaus of Utah,* 1880), G. K. Gilbert (*Geology of the Henry Mountains,* 1877), and W. M. Davis (b., 1850, d., 1934) there was gradually established through the field studies and interpretations of these men an appreciation of the evolutionary development of land forms.

Powell recognized the validity of Hutton's, Playfair's and Lyell's principle of uniformitarianism and added the concept of base-leveling. Given enough time, said Powell, the relief of any region, however great its original volume and altitude, will be reduced by subaerial degradation to a low-lying plain for which the sea will be the ultimate base level. Gilbert, somewhat after the manner of Playfair's support of Hutton, found examples to confirm Powell's concept and elucidated the processes involved. Gilbert worked out histories of land sculpture for many areas, and besides made highly original and significant contributions in other branches of geology. To W. M. Davis (Fig. 1), how-ever, must go the credit for systematizing all that had been done before. It was he who invented the term *peneplain* to designate the end result of Powellian base-leveling. Davis also introduced the cycle-of-erosion concept, and the idea that distinctive stages are recognizable in the course of the reduction of a region from an original constructional form, and elevation resulting from uplift, to the peneplain at the close of the cycle.

Davis was indefatigable in this work throughout his long career. Between the time of a first publication in 1880 to the year of his death, 1934, there came from his pen some four hundred papers and books. A very large proportion of these works was devoted to geomorphic science and for the most part to studies of land forms.

Davis had many devoted students and adherents. By his own inspired and great efforts, and with the aid of his followers, the American school of geomorphology achieved its first-rank position. Davis was not, however, unaware of other aspects of geographic and geologic study. He covered much of the field of geography in his writings, and made contributions to branches of geology

FIG. 1. THE MASTER
Drawing, by Hope Sawyer from photographs.

other than geomorphology. But Davis, more than any other man, is to be regarded as the father of American geomorphology. This distinction may be accorded him with full awareness of the place of Hutton and Playfair as the founders of geomorphology.

It should be said that Davis considered geomorphology to be a phase of geography rather than of geology. In arguing for association with geography he distinguishes (Davis, W. M., 1924, p. xiv) between geomorphogeny and geomorphology to the effect that geomorphogeny has primary significance for the geologist because it directs attention to the past, whereas geomorphology (or to use the term he preferred, *geomorphography*) tends to place the present in the foreground, hence adopts the geographic attitude. He also

FIG. 2. THE CHALLENGER
Drawing, by Steve Barker from a photograph.

maintains (p. vii) that in a geologic description the time sequence must be the dominating theme, no epoch may be ignored simply because it has no landscape expression. But elsewhere in the same book he writes: "All landforms whether simple or complex may best be described by going back to their origins." This is clearly geomorphogeny. In another place (Davis, W. M., 1909, p. 253, originally published in 1899) Davis asserts: the geologist "examines the changes of the past for their own sake," the geographer (geomorphologist) "examines the changes of the past only so far as they serve to illuminate the present, for geography is concerned essentially with the earth as it now exists." It is true that, to the last, Davis, in geomorphic studies, always had his eye on the end form and gave little or no attention to the nature of processes or the manner of their functioning. But Davis found it difficult to divorce geomorphology from geology, and the trend of modern geography for some time was to disavow any connection with or responsibility for geomorphology. Latterly American geographers have manifested a renewed interest in geomorphology.

From the preceding paragraphs the reader will get the impression that the science of geomorphology has been built up by the work of English-speaking students. Such is the fact with reference to nearly all the basic principles of the science. Persons in other lands have made noteworthy contributions in amplification and application of these principles. The French, Scandinavians, Dutch, Finns, Swiss, and Italians have in general followed the lead of the American school. In Germany, S. Passarge and J. Walther in their investigations of desert lands have accepted its teachings. But two famous German geographers, F. v. Richthofen and Albrecht Penck, developed an independent approach to the study of land forms, and they and their followers have sought persistently to escape from the British-American geomorphic frame.

The German attacks on the American concepts, even when not soundly based, have served to call attention to neglected factors, and have prevented a too facile acceptance of all the conclusions of the American school. The most complete departure from the American approaches and results was that formulated by Albrecht Penck's son, Walther Penck (b., 1888, d., 1923, Fig. 2). The younger Penck's attempt to establish geomorphic study on a different basis from that of the American school did not succeed. But his untimely death deprived geomorphology of a scholar of great promise, because his formulations, even when found untenable, have proved to be very stimulating. It is interesting to note that the Pencks, father and son, were close friends of W. M. Davis, despite the fact that they were his resolute opponents in geomorphic controversy.

Interpretation versus Description. Before Davis, the account of the land forms of a region, even when supplied by a scientific observer, was of necessity in terms of sense experience. It contained what the observer saw, a deep, narrow valley; or endured, a heartbreaking climb; nothing more. Hutton, Playfair, and Lyell had supplied the principles for an understanding appreciation of landscape but these principles were concerned with processes rather than with results. The topography was still hills, lakes, spurs, sea bottom, land surface; not breached anticline, glacial rock basin, intrenched meander, ocean basin, continental platform, volcanic island, atoll. What Davis conceived (though he may never have stated it in exactly this way) was that if earth forms, large and small, are the product of slow, long, evolutionary change under the same processes that are at present operative, there must be characteristic stages in their development. He recognized, further, that processes of a given intensity operating on one kind of material would not in a given time produce the same amount of change as they would on another kind. Also (and this, perhaps, should not be attributed to Davis) that it would be probable, in view of the vast age of the earth, that some very nice adjustments in its larger features would have been achieved through the action of forces having throughout geologic time the same direction of application and the same intensity.

If an observer is compelled to depend on experience, that is, to use only empirical terms in his descriptions of topography, every feature he discusses must be unique in all respects. If it is a hill, there immediately come the questions, round, pointed, or ridge hill? steep, moderate, or gentle slopes? and so on until every attribute directly observable is named and evaluated. If, then, all the elements of the landscape are similarly treated the account will be almost interminable and utterly wearisome.

Empirical terms must be used in geomorphology; they are the common heritage of language. But even these, in their scientific application, can be employed in strict senses. Thus the word "valley" may be limited to a depression sloping in one direction over all its length. Then the Valley of California and Death Valley are not valleys at all. They should, instead, be referred to, respectively, as an intermont basin and a graben.

In these examples the clue is supplied for the explanatory descriptions which Davis first formulated and always advocated. If "valley" is used in the geomorphic sense indicated, then many of the features common to all valleys are immediately implied, and empirical description to that degree becomes unnecessary. The history of valley development is also suggested, that is, the geomorphogeny. From the more exact use of the empirical terms the invention and employment of technical, explanatory terms appropriately follows. When one sees Davis's word "peneplain" in print there opens to the mind all the long vista of change required for the production of a plain of such origin. Most of the matter of a strictly empirical description becomes unnecessary. Once "peneplain" is said, all that is required is to indicate how the peneplain referred to departs from other known peneplains or from the type concept of a peneplain.

Here it is to be noted that the science of geomorphology is largely a matter of comparisons. There is a more or less standardized type concept, such as that of the peneplain, or perhaps an actual example that serves as the type form, thus monadnock from Mount Monadnock, N. H., with which specific occurrences or other instances are matched to make note of resemblances and differences.

The competence of the geomorphologist, especially in the field, depends very much on how well he is informed in regard to the established and accepted nomenclature. The fund of such terms is now very considerable. In possession of this vocabulary every word, every phrase of the geomorphologist's account summons up a long train of circumstances all contributing to the understanding and appreciation of the prospect under consideration.

Davis (1912, p. 201) has himself supplied an illustrative example of what an explanatory description should be like. "In northeast Italy, south of Ancona, there is a well-dissected coastal plain approximately 20 or 30 kilometers wide. It is built up of unconsolidated sand and clay layers, and has reached the stage of late maturity in development due chiefly to erosion by its primarily consequent streams and their short insequent tributaries. The largest streams are extended consequents from the oldland, and these have attained old age. The altitude of the inner border of the dissected plain is 200 or 250 meters; the greater heights of the oldland Appenines rise immediately behind this boundary line. A row of cliffs, 50 to 100 meters high, marks the present outer edge of the dissected plain. These cliffs, in turn, are maturely dissected by marine erosion. The plain has moderate relief, the spacing (texture) is rather coarse. In consequence of a small recent uplift, which is of increasing significance as one proceeds inland, the revived major streams have converted their wide valley floors into terraces by excavating new mature valley floors below the level of the earlier one. During approximately the same period the sea retreated from the base of the mature cliffs, and permitted the emergence of a strand flat 200 to 300 meters wide. This flat is somewhat wider at the sites of the blunt deltas. From this fact it would seem that during their short new youth and maturity the streams had conveyed so much more debris to the sea than during the preceding stage of extreme old age as to permit outbuilding to prevail for a time over the former recessional erosion activity of the sea."

Thus conceived the study and application of geomorphic science becomes a fascinating pursuit. So much so that a word of caution is not inappropriate. It should not be too quickly assumed that the interpretation which seems obviously to fit is the true one. Further study may suggest an alternative explanation, or several other possibilities, which must be considered before a conclusion not subject to contravention is reached.

Geology and Geomorphology. "The present is the key to the past" has been the slogan of geologists since Lyell's time. While the extreme uniformitarianism that Lyell preached is now discredited, the principle which the phrase emphasizes is still entirely valid.

If the present is the key to the past, competence in geomorphic interpretation is clearly a fundamental for sound training in geology. It is the study of existing conditions, as expressed in the relief of the lands, the form and distribution of the continents and oceans, that constitutes the field of geomorphology. In other words, geomorphology is the geologic present which must be mastered before the geologic past can be understood.

Literature. Undergraduate students ordinarily have neither the time nor the disposition to do wide reading of source material. It is nevertheless deemed worth while to authenticate the textbook assertions in many instances. This is done in order that readers may gain an appreciation of the makers and the manner of original contributions to geomorphology even if none or only few of these works are actually consulted. It is appropriate, also, to direct the attention of the student to the classical books and papers. Finally he should be made aware of the contemporary contributors, for such acquaintance will insure his realization of the active growth of geomorphology as a present-day science.

To best serve these several purposes a uniform plan of reference notations is used. In accordance with the practice that is gaining increasing acceptance in scientific papers, authentication is made by inserting the name of the authority in parentheses, together with the year of publication and page number, at the place where the citation is made. All authors so quoted are listed alphabetically in the general bibliography at the end of the book with the titles of their books and papers arranged in chronological order. This system has been found less cumbersome than footnote references.

Topical bibliographies are printed at the end of each chapter. These are intended to provide a background for the content of the chapter to which they are appended. Unless they have been specifically referred to somewhere in the book, items in the chapter lists do not appear in the general bibliography. The chapter bibliographies ordinarily have two parts. The first part is devoted to a listing of papers and books of classical significance (not necessarily ancient) on the subject matter of the chapter. The second part is a listing of works, in general, of more recent date, for the most part of contributions made by living authors. This second list is intended to be representative, but because of space limitations must be selective. The selection does not profess to be a judgment on the comparative importance of those included, either as to author or paper, in relation to persons or contributions that are omitted. The purpose, rather, is to be catholic, and so to provide a survey of the type of papers and of workers in the field of geomorphology.

Contributors to scientific journals commonly have reprints made of their papers. On request the author will ordinarily be glad to present a copy of such reprint of his work to school libraries. Authors may best be addressed in care of the editor of the publication in which the paper appeared. Some journals, notably the Bulletin of the Geological Society of America, New York City, keep on hand stocks of reprints of articles appearing in their pages and sell them at prices slightly above the cost of printing. A little enterprise in following up these suggestions in regard to reprints should result in the acquisition of a fairly representative collection of modern source material for class use.

There is normally a considerable curiosity in regard to the geomorphic features of the school region or about the student's home area. If this curiosity is to be satisfied by reading, special bibliographies will be needed. It is now relatively easy to compile bibliographies for specific localities or, similarly, on particular topics.

The United States Geological Survey has indexed all the literature on the geology of North America from 1785 to the present. These indexes to date are contained in bulletins numbered 746,

757, 823, 858, 869, and 892 of the United States Geological Survey, Washington, D. C. These bulletins are sold by the Superintendent of Documents, Washington, D. C., for nominal sums. New bulletins are issued biennially. The Director of the United States Geological Survey, Washington, D. C., will mail any applicant a monthly list of new publications. In these lists the new bibliographies will be noted as they appear. From 1933 on the Geological Society of America, New York, has published annually a bibliography of all geologic literature pertaining to continents and islands other than North America. These bibliographies are priced at $2.00 to $3.00 each.

By using these two sets of publications a bibliography for any locality in the world or on any topic may readily be compiled. It is usually better to work back from the more recent publications to those of earlier date, unless the chief interest in the special topic studied is its historical aspect.[1]

Background and Textbook Materials. In conformity with the pattern described above, appropriate topical bibliographies appear at the end of this chapter.

But as this arrangement does not provide for any reference to background literature in geology, topical and historical, nor to other textbooks on geomorphology, such a list is inserted here with explanatory notes.

For consultation in regard to geologic topics generally the following textbooks will be found most informative:

Chamberlin, T. C., and Salisbury, R. D. (1906) *Geology,* Vol. I, *Geologic Processes and their Results,* 2d ed., rev., Henry Holt and Company, Inc., New York, 1906.

[1] When a particular publication that is costly, or out of print, or not available locally is of special interest to a school because of its regional significance, resort may be had to the Library of Congress, Washington, D. C., for the loan of the book or journal in question. Such loans are made only through a library organization, which must make the application and accept responsibility for the safe return of the material. While it is in his possession the borrower should make notation of those pages which present the matter of greatest interest and significance for the study he is making. On return of the paper or book the Library of Congress will, on request, make photostat copies of such pages at small expense. Such photostat material, appropriately titled and bound, will make the school library adequate to the normal demand for information in regard to the local geomorphology. By the same means samples, at least, of some of the classical contributions to geomorphology, for example Playfair's (1802) *Illustrations of the Huttonian Theory of the Earth,* William Creech, Edinburgh, may be included in the reference collection.

Schuchert, C., and Dunbar, C. O. (1941) *Textbook of Geology*, Part II, *Historical Geology*, 4th ed., rev., John Wiley & Sons, Inc., New York.

Scott, W. B. (1932) *An Introduction to Geology*, 3rd ed., Vol. I, *Physical Geology*, Vol. II, *Historical Geology*, The Macmillan Company, New York.

The treatment in the first two books is more philosophic than that by Scott, but the latter is rich in references to specific examples.

Fuller treatment of geomorphic topics than that given in textbooks of general geology has, in the past, regularly found its place in books on physiography. Physiography includes a consideration of the phenomena of the hydrosphere and of the atmosphere, as well as of the surficial configuration of the lithosphere which is the distinctive province of geomorphology. Of broad physiographic content are:

Tarr, R. S., and Martin, L. (1914) *College Physiography*, The Macmillan Company, New York.

Martonne, E. de (1926) *Traité de Géographie Physique*, three volumes, 5th ed., revised and corrected. Armand Colin, Paris.

Braun, G. (1930) *Grundzüge der Physiographie*, Bd. 1 and Bd. 2, B. G. Teubner, Leipzig.

Two more recent books called "geomorphologies" are much like the physiographies just listed in that they include discussion of minerals, rocks, rock weathering, underground water, etc., and are planned for introductory courses in geologic science. These are:

Lobeck, A. K. (1939) *Geomorphology*, McGraw-Hill Book Company, Inc., New York.

Worcester, P. G. (1939) *A Textbook of Geomorphology*, D. Van Nostrand Company, Inc., New York.

Lobeck's book may be consulted to advantage when a topographic sheet illustrating a particular land form is sought, as it contains comprehensive classified lists of the available material of this nature.

Two regional physiographies are of special interest to students in the United States because they treat the whole area of the country systematically. They are:

Bowman, I. (1911) *Forest Physiography*, John Wiley & Sons, Inc., New York.

Fenneman, N. M. (1931) *Physiography of Western United States;* (1938) *Physiography of Eastern United States,* McGraw-Hill Book Company, Inc., New York.

In Bowman's book considerable attention is given to the climatic factor, in Fenneman's books climate is given only incidental mention; the broader implications of the word "physiography" are largely ignored in the one on western United States; the discussion is devoted almost exclusively to land forms.

Two shorter books cover somewhat the same ground as Fenneman's volumes. They are:

Loomis, F. K. (1937) *Physiography of the United States,* Doubleday, Doran and Company, Inc. New York.

Atwood, W. W. (1940) *The Physiographic Provinces of North America,* Ginn and Company, Boston.

Atwood's book is to be commended because it is a unit treatment of all North America and because it provides a succinct one-volume account of the regional geomorphology directly accessible to American students, and may, accordingly, be used to advantage as a supplement to the systematic exposition of the book in hand.

Several books bridge the gap between those which are of the physiographic or regional type and those which are strictly geomorphic in content:

Hobbs, W. H. (1931) *Earth Features and their Meaning,* 2d ed., The Macmillan Company, New York.

Wooldridge, S. W., and Morgan, R. S. (1937) *The Physical Basis of Geography: An Outline of Geomorphology,* Longmans, Green & Company, New York.

The first of these is a semipopular account in which the phenomena, as such, are given prominence by description; in the second, interpretation of the phenomena occupies the chief place.

Davis provided the first systematic exposition of the principles of geomorphology, but not in English. His German book, listed below, is an expansion of his lectures on land forms delivered at the University of Berlin. The first English textbook of geomorphology to appear was that by Cotton. Cotton's book is a government publication, and from its title would be expected to have only local interest and application. But because there was no systematic English account of geomorphology available, Cotton could not hope for success in apprising his New Zealand audience about the geomorphology of their homeland without first instructing them in the principles of the subject. His book, accordingly, although it makes constant reference to New Zealand features, is also a concise and complete manual of general geomorphology and has been much used as a reference work outside New Zealand.

The other systematic books that have appeared since Cotton published his are all in German. Maull is encyclopedic, over four hundred pages of fine print, and presents conflicting viewpoints, usually without taking a positive stand in support of any particular contention. Machatschek has provided a concise compendium, Aigner an introductory handbook on geomorphology. W. Penck's book challenges fundamental concepts of the Davis school of thought and seeks to substitute for them a geomorphic science based chiefly on correlations between diastrophism and topography.

Davis, W. M. (1912) *Die erklärende Beschreibung der Landformen,* B. G. Teubner, Leipzig.

Cotton, C. A. (1926) *Geomorphology of New Zealand,* Part I, *Systematic,* New Zealand Board of Science and Art, Wellington, N. Z.

Maull, Otto (1938) *Geomorphologie,* Franz Deuticke, Leipzig.

Machatschek, Fritz (1934) *Geomorphologie,* 2d ed., B. G. Teubner, Leipzig.

Aigner, Andreas (1936) *Geomorphologie,* Walter de Gruyter & Company, Berlin.

Penck, Walther (1924) *Die morphologische Analyse,* J. Engelhorn's Nachfolger, Stuttgart.

SUMMARY

Geomorphology is defined as comprehensive of all aspects of science dealing with the surface configuration of the solid earth. In geomorphology chief attention is given to land forms because these are directly observable and are the sites of human experience. Geomorphology is a division of geologic science and had its beginnings coincidentally with modern geology. The principle of progressive change in the development of surface features was introduced early in the history of the science and is still valid. The contributions of Hutton, Playfair, Lyell, Ramsay, Powell,

Dutton, and Gilbert were systematized and added to by Davis, and American leadership in geomorphology resulted from Davis's formulation of the concept of the geomorphic cycle. The endeavor of a German school to discredit the basic significance of the cycle scheme has not succeeded.

A feature of geomorphic science is its special terminology which makes possible concise explanatory and comparative descriptions, and makes it incumbent on the geomorphologist to have preliminary training in geology. As few compendiums of geomorphology are available, special competence in searching the original literature of the subject is essential for acquisition of full knowledge of the progress that has been made.

BIBLIOGRAPHY

CLASSICAL

Hutton, James (1795) *Theory of the Earth,* 2 vols., William Creech, Edinburgh.

Playfair, John (1802) *Illustrations of the Huttonian Theory of the Earth,* William Creech, Edinburgh.

Lyell, Charles (1830–32) *Principles of Geology,* 2 vols., 1st ed., John Murray, London.

Ramsay, A. C. (1846) *On the Denudation of South Wales,* Memoir Geological Survey of Great Britain, Geological Survey of Great Britain, London, Vol. I, pp. 297–335.

Powell, J. W. (1875) *Exploration of the Colorado River of the West,* Smithsonian Institution, Washington.

Gilbert, G. K. (1877) *Report on the Geology of the Henry Mountains* (Utah), 1st ed., United States Geographical and Geological Survey of the Rocky Mountain Region (Powell), Washington.

Dutton, C. E. (1880) *Report on the Geology of the High Plateaus of Utah,* United States Geographical and Geological Survey of the Rocky Mountain Region (Powell), Washington.

Dutton, C. E. (1889) *On Some of the Greater Problems of Physical Geology,* Bulletin of the Philosophic Society of Washington, Bull. 11, pp. 51–64. (Reprinted in the Journal of the Washington Academy of Sciences, Vol. 15, pp. 259–369, 1925.)

Davis, W. M. (1909) *Geographical Essays,* Ginn and Company, Boston.

HISTORICAL

Geike, Archibald (1897) *The Founders of Geology,* 2d rev. and enl. ed. (1905), The Macmillan Company, London.

Merrill, G. P. (1904) *Contributions to the History of American Geol-*

ogy, United States National Museum, Annual Report, Washington, pp. 189–733 (issued 1906).

Adams, F. D. (1938) *The Birth and Development of the Geological Sciences,* The Williams and Wilkins Company, Baltimore.

Various authors (1941) *Geology 1888–1938, Fiftieth Anniversary Volume of the Geological Society of America,* Published by The Society, New York. (This contains accounts of progress in the various branches of geologic science during the fifty years following the founding of the Society in 1888. Geomorphology, as such, and its particular aspects are given a prominent place in the book.)

Chapter Two

RELIEF FEATURES OF THE FIRST ORDER

Introduction. The phrase, "relief features of the first order," used as the heading of this chapter, is adopted from R. D. Salisbury (1919, pp. 5, 11, 14).

The relief forms of the earth may be divided into three classes, or orders, primarily on the basis of size. The forms of the solid earth as a whole, of the continents, and of the ocean basins are relief features of the first order. Plains, plateaus, and mountain ranges comprise the second order of relief; valleys, ridges, cliffs, basins, etc. make up the third order. The sorting which this classification requires is readily done, and the classification has significance because, as a group, the items of each order have an origin and a measure of permanence different from those of the other two orders.

The geological formula, "The present is the key to the past," is a concise way of saying that if what is going on, geologically, at present is understood, the geologic past will become clear, because things were shaped in the past by the same forces and processes as those now acting, and, in general, the rate of change, under similar climatic conditions, and the kinds of material affected, are the same now as they were in the past. This principle, indeed, is basic to all modern geology. There must, however, be flexibility in applying the principle if it is to have general validity.

Relief features of the first order seem to have a considerable degree of permanence. They constitute, as it were, the theaters in which geologic dramas are enacted. Stages, which in theaters are frequently altered and rebuilt to fit the succession of productions, may be figuratively compared with the plains, plateaus, and mountains of the second order of relief, and stage scenery, which may be many times shifted during the progress of a single play, matches the items of the third order of relief (Fig. 3).

FIG. 3. "SCENERY"— DOE RIVER GORGE, TENNESSEE
Photograph from the United States Geological Survey.

The rule that the present is the key to the past applies to relief features of the first order in the sense that the undeviating application of the same forces and processes throughout the eons of geologic time can be expected by now to have achieved an ap-

proximation of their ultimate effect. A considerable degree of
permanence may be looked for in relief features of the first order
because an equilibrium between very great forces and very great
masses would probably be attained from such long interaction.
If the relief features of the first order are to be affected by further

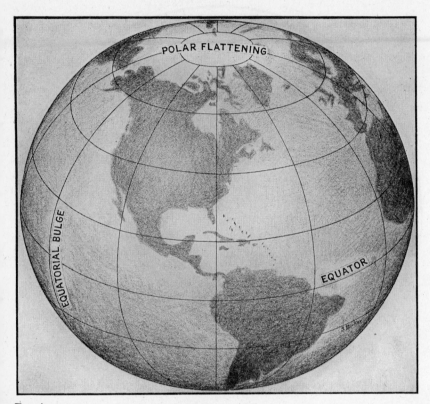

FIG. 4. THE EARTH AN OBLATE SPHEROID
Drawing by Steve Barker.

change, it must be assumed either that the great forces have not
been able to come to an enduring balance, or that the masses are
acquiring new characteristics. The stability of the present is
indicative of the obduracy of the masses, and warrants the inference that their modification was no more rapid than now for a
long time past. It may be deduced from these circumstances that
the items of the largest order of relief are relatively permanent
features.

The Oblate Spheroid. The polar diameter of the earth is between 26 and 27 miles shorter than an equatorial diameter. The earth, geometrically, is an oblate spheroid (Fig. 4); more exactly, an ellipsoid of rotation. That is, in its case, the solid developed

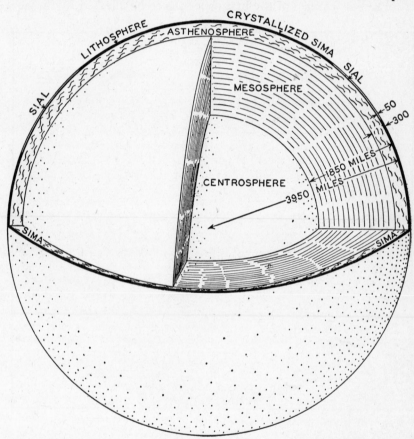

FIG. 5. THE STRUCTURE OF THE EARTH

After a drawing by Reginald A. Daly in *The Changing World of the Ice Age*. By permission of the publishers, Yale University Press.

by an ellipse rotating on its short axis. This shape may be visualized by recalling that many varieties of apples have the oblate-spheroid form in an exaggerated degree. In the case of the earth, departure from a perfectly spherical form is very slight.

If it is sought to account for the nearly spherical form of the earth, and the kind of departure from the perfect globular shape it exhibits, a number of factors must be considered. There is, first, the nature of the earth's substance and the manner of aggregation of this substance. Second, there is the force of gravity, and third, centrifugal force due to the earth's rotation.

The solid earth, as a whole, has a rigidity about twice as great as that of steel. That is, the earth resists change of form, in that

FIG. 6. THE EARTH AS A TRIAXIAL ELLIPSOID
Drawing by Laurence Nugent.

degree, to a force instantaneously applied. Although it opposes such high measure of strength to forces suddenly applied, the solid earth can and does yield elastically to forces of very small magnitude when these are slowly or continuously acting. Such is its yield to tidal force. Elastic yield is like that of a rubber ball. When the deforming force is removed the ball returns to its original shape. If, however, the small force acts persistently in one direction a permanent warp may result. The material, in effect, suffers from fatigue, and, due to localized rearrangement of materials, acquires a new set.

Modern ideas in regard to the structure and strength of the earth are reviewed by R. A. Daly (1939, 1940). He postulates the existence of an outer, rock shell, the *lithosphere,* which has strength (in part because of its domed form) and residual rigidity so that it breaks if stresses are too great (Fig. 5). The lithosphere is thought to have an average thickness of 50 miles. Under the lithosphere is the *asthenosphere,* which, if not utterly devoid of strength, yields under very low shearing stresses. The asthenosphere is conjectured to be about 225 miles thick. It rests on a *mesosphere,* slightly stronger, about 1500 miles thick. The remainder, nearer 4000 miles, of the diameter of the earth is comprised in the *centrosphere.* The centrosphere is presumed to be chemically like the asthenosphere and mesosphere, but in a crystalline instead of a vitreous state, hence denser and possessed of considerable strength. Further, the centrosphere may be asymmetrical, possessed of humps, so that the form of the smoothed *geoid* (earth form) is a triaxial ellipsoid with the long axis of the equatorial ellipse emerging at 25° West Longitude, and the antipodal point, the short axis, similarly, at 65° East Longitude (Fig. 6). If these speculations are representative of the facts, then the difference in length of the semiaxes, 2300 feet, is perhaps indicative of the measure of the failure of the long-effective earth forces to bring the earth form to a perfect ellipsoid of rotation. Because the amount of the distortion is so very slight, its cause is more probably local and recent; and perhaps results from differential radioactivity. There may be energies as yet quite unknown.

Although theories in regard to the origin of the earth are no longer based on purely imaginative considerations the subject is mainly one of speculation still.

K. F. Mather (1939), in a review of modern knowledge of the genesis and structure of the earth, concludes that the assumption of an encounter between the sun and some other celestial body is the most promising hypothesis of origin. The demonstrated stratiform structure of the earth then seems to point to a tidal theory of disruption, with consequent condensation to a molten stage, during which there was gravity separation into a dense central core surrounded by successive shells of progressively less dense substances. But as interior earth yield of vitreous and crystalline materials to continuously applied stress is indicated by seismic and isostatic evidence to be very easy, reorganization of a heterogeneous mass to a specific gravity assortment is feasible, in time, without recourse to development of a molten state.

The conjecture that the earth is an agglomerate built up gradually by slow accretion of fragments, large and small, collected from space is, hence, as well warranted as any other. If such was its origin, gravitation would bring about the shaping of the accumulating aggregate to the form of a sphere, (a) because the attraction at any given stage would be greater at those sites which were nearest the center of the mass; (b) because, as water flows downhill, so would any projection of greater than average diameter tend to be leveled down to conform to the spherical shape.

The force of gravity, the presumed high viscosity of the interior of the earth, and the rigidity of its outer shell together give strength to the earth. Collectively these constitute centripetal force. Because of centripetal force the earth resists deforming stresses. But deforming stresses are not without effect. There is an elastic response on part of the solid earth to the gravitative attraction of the moon and sun. This earth tide is a recurrent phenomenon. Another stress has been continuously applied to the solid earth for billions of years, perhaps from the time of its earliest origins, that due to the centrifugal force of rotation.

The numerical value of this centrifugal force is seemingly low in comparison with the force of gravitation. An object weighing 288 pounds at the equator by a spring balance, weighed on a non-rotating earth would be one pound heavier. Centrifugal force, at the earth's equator, lightens a mass; offsets gravitation, by 1/289 of the whole. At the poles centrifugal force is zero. This seemingly small amount of differential stress has sufficed to constrain the earth from a true sphere to the form of an oblate spheroid. In consequence of the so-induced bulging in the equatorial belt and flattening at the poles, the force of gravity is diminished at the equator and increased at the poles (because of the greater distance from the center of gravity in the first instance, and lesser in the second) so that the reduction of gravity at the equator is actually 1/195 of the whole. That is to say, on an oblate spheroid earth, at rest, every 195 pounds of matter on the surface of the earth at the equator would be subject to a gravitative pull of one pound more toward the center of the earth than it now experiences. The 1 pound in 195 is the measure of the lightening effect of centrifugal force at the equator. (If a spherical earth is assumed, then the ratio is 1 pound in 289.) In other terms, if, at the equator, the inward acceleration due to gravity is 385 inches a second, the outward acceleration due to centrifugal force is 1 1/3 inches a second.

Whether centripetal force is mainly gravity or earth strength is a question beyond the scope of this analysis. The differential stress from centrifugal force appears arithmetically to be of low value but is actually very great. That the deformational yield of the earth has been so slight indicates a close approach to balance between the opposing forces. The earth has yielded, but not much. If the centripetal strength were significantly greater the earth would be a perfect sphere; if it were significantly less, its form would be that of a lozenge, or even that of a disk. Perhaps the adjustment is even now not complete as referred to the mass of the earth.

The assumption of nearly complete equilibrium in respect to form is based on the concept of a homogereous mass, or of one in which differing materials are now symmetrically and concentrically distributed, and will stay put. If these conditions are not met deformation can be expected to continue because the deficiency is on the side of the earth's strength. The outer lithosphere shell of the earth is of especially heterogeneous composition. Some of these surface materials may lack the strength necessary for conformity with the average oblate spheroid form. Such units should yield to the stress arising from centrifugal force. The result would be shift from high latitudes toward lower latitudes. This concept gets vivid expression in the German term *polflucht* (flight from the poles) and is said (Staub, Rudolf, 1928, pp. 168, 170, 246, etc.) to be counterbalanced by subcrustal streamings, which may, using a similar word form, be called *polsucht* (pole-seeking), resulting from the isostatic unbalance the polflucht engenders. These circumstances are held by some students to account for the occurrence of east to west mountain chains girdling the earth north of the equator. As when covers on a bed slide off and wrinkle at its foot, so the weaker rock sheets, impelled by the centrifugal pull, creep equatorwards and eventually crumple into mountain folds in the lower latitudes.

The Continental Platforms and the Ocean Basins. The continental lands and the oceanic expanses are distinctive areas of the earth's surface. That they are distinctive units is indicated by the fact that the transition from continental surface levels to ocean-bottom floors is abrupt. In other words, the outer surface of the solid earth is not simply corrugated into gradual swellings and downbends such as would permit some of its areas to appear as dry lands and the remainder to constitute broad troughs to hold the ocean waters.

It has been pointed out that there are two dominant levels of the earth's solid surface. Over 21 per cent of the earth's surface area occurs between sea level and 3300 feet elevation; over 23 per cent between 13,000 and 16,000 feet below sea level. The

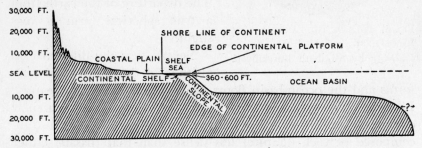

FIG. 7. THE TWO DOMINANT LEVELS OF THE EARTH'S SOLID SURFACE
Drawing by Elizabeth Burckmyer.

percentage distribution at the other intervals is in every instance much lower. These two levels may be regarded as representative of the altitudes of the continental platforms and the ocean floor respectively (Fig. 7).

The maximal relief of the surface is much greater. Altitudes of over 29,000 feet are reached in the Himalaya Mountains (Mount Everest) and depths of more than 35,000 feet in the western Pacific Ocean. The greatest known declivity within a short horizontal distance is that between the summit of Mount Llullaillaco in Chile, altitude 21,450 feet and the Atacama Deep in the adjacent Pacific Ocean with a depth of 24,700 feet. This is a total of over 46,000 feet within a distance of 180 miles.

These heights and depths, together with the difference in length of the polar and equatorial diameters of the earth while impressive in magnitude from the viewpoint of human experience, are very small in comparison with the dimensions of the earth. The radius of the earth is approximately 4000 miles long; the maximal sur-

FIG. 8. POLE OF THE LAND HEMISPHERE

Drawing by Elizabeth Burckmyer.

ficial declivity is less than 9 miles, or not 1/400 of the radius length. If a globe were constructed 10 feet in diameter this relief could be shown by less than 1/5 inch difference in the level of the surface. On the same globe the polar axis would need to be less than 1/2 inch shorter than equatorial axes. The departure of the earth from a true spherical form is very slight.

Nevertheless the difference in altitude of the continental platforms and the ocean-basin floors is a real and persistent feature. Like the oblate-spheroid form it is the consequence of particular circumstances. Broadly speaking, the continental platforms are composed of rock (granite) less dense than that (basalt) either composing the ocean floor, or present there under a thin cover of granitic rock. The continental platforms may be likened to rectangular blocks of ice floating in a lake. The difficulty with this comparison is that the water of the lake will be regarded as matching the water of the oceans. Instead the water of the lake represents the solid, basalt floor of the ocean basins. This basalt shell is conceived to extend without interruption under the continental platforms. But just as the ice blocks interrupt the continuity and depress the surface of the lake water, so do the continental platforms press down the level of the sea of basalt in which they float in isostatic equilibrium.

Isostasy. The conjectural answers to the question: How, in the course of the earth's evolution as a planet, was the segregation of the granitic materials which were to become the continental platforms brought about? were suggested in preceding paragraphs. That the granitic (technically, *sial)* continental platforms float in an underlying sea of denser basaltic rock *(sima)* is the broadest application of the principle of *isostasy.* A density of 2.7 is commonly attributed to the continental platforms; that of 3.0 to 3.15 to material below them and composing the ocean floor. By isostasy

(Greek, *isostasios,* "in equi-
poise") is meant balance, a state
of equilibrium. The adjustment
that such a balance between the
light and the dense implies again
bespeaks a yield and shifting of
materials ordinarily regarded as
solid and rigid. Probably the
adjustment is not perfect Some
of the seeming load suggested
by the height of the continents is
upheld by the height of the
earth. In part the yield may be
elastic. In any event it is slow
and not immediately perfect like
that between the ice blocks and water. The ultimate geophysical
problems here approached are outside the scope of geomorphology. The geomorphic forms, continents and ocean basins, derive
from the differences in density of their component materials
brought into approximate isostatic balance by yield and flow
of the subcrustal stuff.

FIG. 9. POLE OF THE WATER
HEMISPHERE
Drawing by Elizabeth Burckmyer.

Distribution of Land and Sea. If, in the matter of the oblate-
spheroid form of the earth and the isostatic adjustment of continental platforms and ocean basins, "the past is the key to the
present," then it is also appropriate to consider the plan of the
earth, that is, the arrangement and form of its surface features, to
be similarly conditioned. Otherwise stated, this means that if
accretions, gravity, and rotation unceasingly and undeviatingly
operating from the beginnings of the planet have brought about
geometric and isostatic equilibria, they may be supposed to be
effective also in ordering the distribution and shapes of the enduring units of its relief.

This a priori approach has, it is true, an a posteriori origin.
There is a discernible pattern of distribution that calls for explanation. The arrangement of continental platforms and ocean
basins is not haphazard and the repetitions of form are conspicuous.

The ocean waters occupy 70.8 per cent of the earth's surface,
the lands 29.2 per cent. If the submerged continental shelves are

included with the lands the relation becomes 65 per cent actual oceanic basins, 35 per cent continental platforms. About 75 per cent of all the land is situated north of the equator and is grouped about the small Arctic Ocean. If the earth is divided into hemispheres by locating one pole in the English Channel, the other at the Antipodes Islands near New Zealand, the northern one will be a land hemisphere (Fig. 8) with 83 per cent of the land surface of the earth; the water hemisphere in the south (Fig. 9) will be 90.5 per cent water.

Such concentration would seem to have significance. Even more arresting is the fact of the antipodal arrangement of the continental platforms and ocean basins. This is most perfectly attained in the opposed positions of the Arctic Ocean and the Antarctic Continent around the North and South Poles respectively. While the antipodal relationship is not so exact elsewhere, still 75 per cent of all the land is opposite the broad southern Pacific Ocean. The only marked exception to the rule is southern South America, which is opposite a part of China.

Further, the oldest or nuclear parts of the continents in the Northern Hemisphere are disposed about 120° of longitude apart; these are the Laurentian Shield in North America, the Baltic Shield in Europe and the Angara Shield in Siberia. The continents characteristically taper southward. Gravity observations indicate less mass in the Southern than in the Northern Hemisphere.

These facts led Lowthian Green to propose his Tetrahedral Theory. It is, in brief, that a contracting sphere, possessed of an outer crust not participating in the shrinking, in the case of the earth due to heat loss, would tend toward a tetrahedral form. That is to say, the change would be from the geometrical solid having the minimal surface area for a given volume toward one having the minimal volume. It is the volume that changes with contraction, the surface area remains the same. According to this scheme the Arctic Ocean constitutes one face of the tetrahedron; the old lands of the Northern Hemisphere are located at the corners where this and the three other faces come together; the Antarctic Continent constitutes the other point of the tetrahedron (Fig. 10).

It is to be noted that these forms and relations indicate only a *tendency* toward a tetrahedral shape. Centrifugal force of rotation would probably counteract any large departure toward tetrahedral collapse. Indeed the tetrahedron may, in earlier geologic ages, have been upside down as compared to the present. Then there was a preponderance of lands and mass in the Southern Hemisphere.

Further pursuit of this question leads to geologic correlations and influences outside the special field of geomorphology, defined as the science of the existing forms of the earth. It remains that,

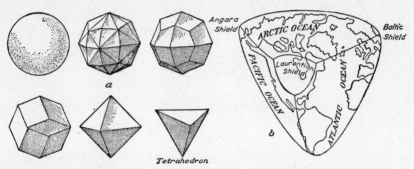

FIG. 10. THE TETRAHEDRAL THEORY OF THE EARTH'S SURFACE FEATURES

If it is assumed that the surface areas of the geometrical solids in *a* are alike, then it is clear that the cubic content decreases as the number of sides decreases. In *b* this idea is applied to the earth.

whatever cause or principle governs, relations, repetitions, and correspondences exist to indicate an evolutionary development in the distributional plan.

Acceptance of the reversing tetrahedron theory involves collapses of once continental areas, that is, foundering of wide regions of sial density. This is in accord with orthodox geologic interpretation of former land bridges between now widely separate continents and islands. But on the isostatic basis such sinking is not feasible; the continents and ocean basins are, in a large sense, permanent features.

Continental Drift. Modern thought is hospitable to theories of rifting and drifting continents. These theories would retain the sial masses undiminished in area, but shifting in position over the surface of the planet by the fragmentation (and subsequent drifting apart) of one or more extensive original units. The pieces sundered off slowly plow their way through the underlying highly viscous sima.   The factors of mass and force and time in this performance are of such great magnitude that the yield of the sima becomes comparatively no more difficult than that of the

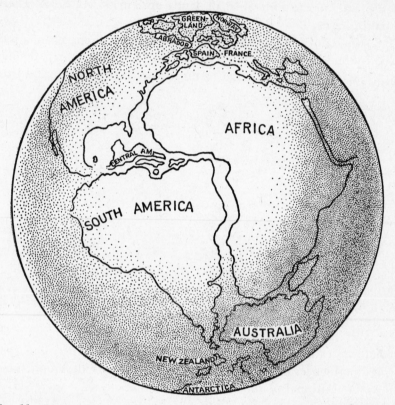

FIG. 11.   THE THEORY OF CONTINENTAL DRIFT

   The former associations of the continents as conceived by H. B. Baker. After a drawing by Alexander L. Du Toit in *Our Wandering Continents*. By permission of the publishers, Oliver and Boyd, Edinburgh.

ocean water through which an air-inflated rubber life raft, propelled by an outboard motor, makes its way.   The chief barrier to general acceptance of the theory of continental drift is that an adequate force to bring it about has not been demonstrated.   Its chief support comes from the possible dovetailing (Figs. 11 and 12) as to contour and structure between lands now widely separated by water, and which, as indicated by fossil forms, are matched

in geologic age.   The validity of much of this dovetailing is greatly
disputed (Du Toit, A. L., 1937, Chaps. I and II).   Precise observations of longitude are being made to discover whether drifting is now in progress.   It is reported (Guyot, E., 1935) that the
records of modern observatories give little if any indication that

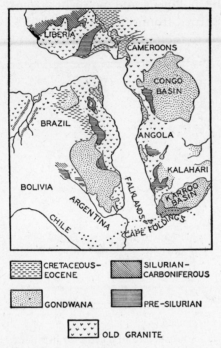

CRETACEOUS–
EOCENE

SILURIAN–
CARBONIFEROUS

GONDWANA

PRE-SILURIAN

OLD GRANITE

FIG. 12.   THE THEORY OF CONTINENTAL DRIFT: GEOLOGIC MATCHING OF AFRICA
AND SOUTH AMERICA

The Cretaceous-Eocene materials may have been deposited after the continents were sundered; and part of the cover of other rocks may have been
stripped off the Old Granite after that time.   After a drawing by Alexander
L. Du Toit in *Our Wandering Continents*.   By permission of the publishers,
Oliver and Boyd, Edinburgh.

continental drift is in progress.   Bucher (1940, pp. 490–491) sum-
marizes the available evidence and concludes that local horizontal
displacement is taking place but that there is no proof that large
units are shifting as wholes.   But if such change should later be
demonstrated, drifting in the past could be reasonably inferred.
In that event the perfection in pattern of distribution of continents and ocean basins, that is so completely in accord with the

tetrahedral hypothesis, is seemingly reduced to merely coincidental significance. The only direct relationship then remaining between the gravitative adjustment of differentiated materials of the earth's mass and the earth's rotational spin on the one hand, and the movement and distribution of the continents on the other, is that suggested in the polflucht and polsucht hypothesis. Attention, accordingly, is turned from consideration of the form and placing of the continents to the problem of the origin of ocean basins.

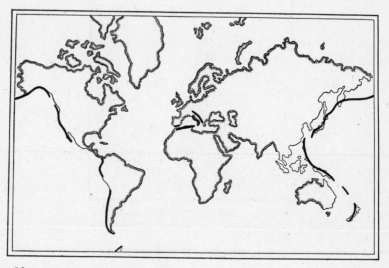

FIG. 13. TYPES OF COAST LINE

Atlantic (discordant) notched, and Pacific (concordant) straight. Drawing by Elizabeth Burckmyer.

Origin of the Ocean Basins.   When an answer is sought to the question: What was the origin of the ocean basins? the fact of first importance to be noted is that the floor of the greatest ocean, the Pacific, is made up almost wholly of basaltic rock, sima. By contrast the floors of the Atlantic and Indian oceans are veneered with sial. The sial shell under these oceans is probably less than half as thick (12 miles as compared to 30 miles) as that under the continental platforms, but it is present. The Pacific Basin is uniquely oceanic, the others have continental correlations. Thus under the young sediments off the Atlantic coast of the United States south of New York City, the granitic surface of the old land appears to slope smoothly down to oceanic depths (Fig. 19). Seismic observations indicate that seaward from Cape Henry, Virginia, 12,000 feet in thickness of young layers overlie the old rock 150 miles out from the point on land where the basement formation emerges from under the sedimentary cover. The sediments may actually be much thicker (Leet, L. D., 1940, p. 885). There is no break in continuity between the continental top and the oceanic basement.

Of almost equal importance with the difference in composition of the oceanic floors is the difference in type of the oceanic borders. Suess (1888, p. 256) first made note of this difference and distinguished between Pacific and Atlantic types of coast line. W. H. Bucher (1939, p. 426) proposed the use of the terms *concordant* and *discordant* (Fig. 13) to indicate the distinction. The whole ring of the outline of the Pacific Basin extends parallel, concordantly, with the land structures forming the margin. By contrast the coasts of the Atlantic and Indian basins, and corresponding parts of the Arctic and Antarctic basins run transverse to the structure lines of the land; they are discordant.

From these circumstances it is reasonable to infer that the Atlantic Basin was created by some process of stretching and thinning down of the sialic shell. The Pacific Basin, on the other hand, appears to be an original hole toward which the continental blocks are crowding. Its bottom constitutes an unyielding shield (Staub, Rudolf, 1928, p. 165) against which the inmoving continental margins have been crumpled in great folds. The structure of the Andes shows thrust from the west.

No better explanation for the presence of the Pacific hole is known than that of attributing it to the detachment of the moon from this site. As Staub points out, the basaltic sima could be exposed to quick cooling to great depth (without the differentiation of the rock materials that occurs with slow cooling) only through the sudden tearing loose of a great mass of the outer sialic shell.

If the departure of the moon could be given a comparatively recent geologic date the drifting apart of the continents and the formation of the discordant "tension" basins would find a ready explanation in the movement of the surface shell toward infilling of the depression. A variety of uninterrupted geologic sequences that would not exist if this cataclysm had been of recent occurrence, and the great destruction of life that would also mark it, make this inference improbable in the highest degree.

But it may be that the detachment, though of geologically very ancient time, started a deep and slow pulsation of the earth's interior substance which has not yet ceased. Various geologic authorities subscribe to the idea of pulsation on different grounds. Bucher (1939, pp. 428–430) has elaborated the pulsation hypothesis in relation to ocean basins and with reference to specific evidence. He deduces that the outer granitic shell of the earth is subject to alternate compression and tension. In the tensional phase the subcrustal volume of the earth expands. In consequence of such expansion the granitic sial crust is stretched and sags.

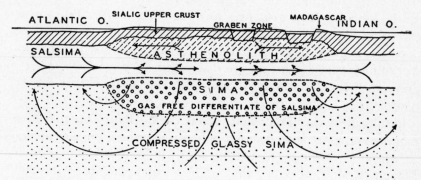

FIG. 14. THE UNDATION (WAVE) OR PULSATION HYPOTHESIS OF OCEAN BASINS AND CONTINENTAL PLATFORMS AS APPLIED TO AFRICA

The arrows show the direction of convection currents in the subcrustal section of the earth. Such flow alternately brings about expansion and compression of the sialic upper crust, uplift and rifting of the continents, sagging of the ocean basins. After R. W. Van Bemmelen. Drawing by Laurence Nugent.

This sagging, Bucher holds, has given rise to the discordant Atlantic Basin. It is here suggested that the stretching may be accompanied by actual rupture and drifting toward the Pacific depression.

According to R. W. Van Bemmelen (1930) the continents rise and sink, in accordance with the periodic expansion of a salsima layer, by magmatic differentiation and diffusion. This causes the continents to rise, and their upper crust to stretch, with resultant graben faulting; the faulted blocks sinking into the weak astheno-lith mass. The movement of the magma currents is upward. But as the expanded salsima is less dense than the sial, a foundering of the continents follows and a reversal of the currents takes place; the salsima moves out from under the continents. The diagram (Fig. 14) shows this system applied to Africa which is represented as at present undergoing expansion. The Atlantic Ocean is re-garded as a foundered continental area, with the Mid-Atlantic Ridge (Fig. 16) beginning to rise as a wave at its center. The magma currents are convectional, the heat energy is supposed to be supplied by radioactive elements, with cooling along the con-tinental borders.

Attention has been directed (Keindl, J., 1940) to the results that would follow if the earth has been expanding in volume through the geologic ages instead of shrinking or remaining substantially unchanged in size during that period of its history, as is generally thought to be true. An expanding earth could be expected to bring about the sundering, and progressive separation of the split parts, of a rigid, surficial, continental, sialic shell. Such splitting and separation would appropriately be induced and accompanied by tremendous upwelling of convectional sima currents. This concept appears to have a prospect for exploration of its possibilities by ex-periment. A hollow globe made of thick elastic rubber (so that it could be made to expand by inflation) covered with a completely or partially rigid shell would be a promising device for a first at-tack on this problem.

It will be appreciated that if the earth has been expanding progressively the concept of an established equilibrium from long time adjustment of force and mass, as related to the first order of relief, and that of the permanency of continental platforms and ocean basins, are largely vitiated.

From this discussion it will be easily understood that the prob-lem of the origin of the ocean basins is one in which there is a groping for understanding with approaches from many directions. Its solution requires the reconciliation of varied, complex, and often contradictory evidence.

SUMMARY

The configuration of the solid earth, as a whole, and the phe-nomena of continental platforms and oceanic basins are the items of the first, or largest, order of relief of the earth classified in three orders of greatness.

Relief features of the first order appear to have a high degree of permanence and to be the product of forces acting unremittingly in the same direction over extremely long periods of time.

The earth is an oblate spheroid because its strength, centripetal force, is slightly inferior to the centrifugal force of rotation. The close approach to a balance, as between these opposed forces, is an impressive example of the many nice adjustments that prevail in earth relations.

Continental platforms and oceanic basins are distinctive units. The simplest explanation of their unlike altitudes is that which attributes the higher stand of the continental masses to their less dense substance. In this, the theory of isostasy, it is asserted that the light continents float in a shell of denser rock which is continuous under them and under the ocean basins. Other theories seek to account for the distribution and shape of the continents as well as for their higher altitude. In the tetrahedral theory, the distribution, shapes and make-up are held to be the result of collapse due to heat loss. That the continents are pieces of formerly larger continuous expanses, first fragmented, then drifted apart is the thesis of the theory of continental drift.

The Pacific Basin is floored with denser rock than that composing the continents. The other ocean bottoms have a veneer of the light continental rock covering the denser material. Because of its floor, and because the Pacific shores are structurally concordant with the outline of the Pacific Basin it is held that this depression is in some sense original, while the discordant Atlantic shores are thought to attest some manner of tearing apart of areas formerly joined.

BIBLIOGRAPHY

CLASSICAL

LaPlace, P. S. (1796) *Système du Monde,* 1st. ed., Cercle-Social, Paris.
Green, W. L. (1875) *Vestiges of a Molten Globe,* E. Stanford, London.
Pickering, W. H. (1907) *The Place of Origin of the Moon,* Journal of Geology, Vol. 15, pp. 23–38.
Taylor, F. B. (1910) *Bearing of the Tertiary Mountain Belt on the*

Origin of the Earth's Plan, Bulletin, Geological Society of America, Vol. 21, pp. 179–226.

Chamberlin, T. C. (1916) *The Origin of the Earth,* University of Chicago Press, Chicago.

RECENT

Wegener, A. (1924) *The Origin of Continents and Oceans,* E. P. Dutton & Company, Inc., New York.

Bucher, W. H. (1933) *The Deformation of the Earth's Crust,* Princeton University Press, Princeton, N. J.

Russell, H. N. (1935) *The Solar System and its Origin,* The Macmillan Company, New York.

Du Toit, A. L. (1937) *Our Wandering Continents,* Oliver and Boyd, Edinburgh.

Willis, B., (1938) *Asthenolith (Melting Spot) Theory,* Bulletin, Geological Society of America, Vol. 49, pp. 603–614.

Daly, R. A. (1940) *Strength and Structure of the Earth,* Prentice-Hall, Inc., New York.

Chapter Three

RELIEF OF THE OCEAN BOTTOMS

Introduction.   Before 1900 knowledge of the relief of the ocean bottoms was extremely limited.   It was based on soundings laboriously made with rope or steel wire at scattered points, or along special lines; soundings extremely few in number, in view of the immensity of the oceanic areas, remote from each other, and not accurately located.

Since the beginning of the twentieth century, very rapid progress has been made in many fields of science that can contribute, and have contributed, to the expeditious and accurate gathering of data in regard to the form and nature of the ocean floors. The invention and perfection of echo-sounding devices have enormously facilitated such investigations.   Sound waves travel through water at a fixed velocity.   A sound impulse sent out from the hull of a ship is echoed back from the bottom.   The time required for its travel to the bottom and for the echo to return is recorded automatically by electrical devices.   Great and shallow depths are measured with equal facility and in such rapid succession that a ship may steam full speed along its course as the soundings are made.   Intersection of radio beams permits very exact fixing of the location of each sounding.   Deep cores of the soft bottom materials are obtained by explosion borings, and hard rock differences at great depths are explored by seismic means.

Equipment for rapid collection of precise information about the ocean bottoms is now available and is in process of being further perfected.   It remains to do the immense survey work the vast expanses of ocean make necessary.   Enough has already been accomplished to make clear that many of the concepts derived from the meager observations procured by the old-time methods must be given up or greatly modified.

It was formerly thought that the general aspect of the ocean bottoms was that of a monotonous, nearly level plain.   It now appears that this is certainly not true of the Atlantic Basin (Bucher, W. H., 1940, pp. 492–493). In the light of such knowledge statements about other relief features of the oceanic areas can be only tentative and general at present. Nevertheless the existence, and some of the characteristics, of items of the second and third orders of relief on the ocean floors are established and are found to be of much geomorphic significance.

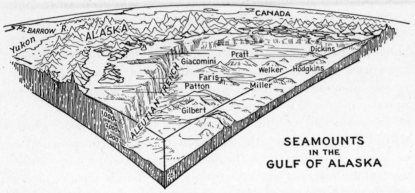

FIG. 15. MAP DIAGRAM OF THE SUBMARINE TOPOGRAPHY OF THE GULF OF ALASKA

Echo soundings reveal unsuspected seamounts rising above the ocean floor at 12,000 feet depth. The sharp outlines of the Aleutian Trench indicate that it is a graben fault. A wide expanse of continental shelf appears, and submarine canyons are cut into the continental slope. Depths indicated on the side of the digram are fathoms. The region shown is about 1000 miles east to west, 800 miles north to south. Drawing (based on a map by H. W. Murray) by Steve Barker.

Islands. The continuity of the ocean basin floors is interrupted by islands far from continental shores that rise from the sea bottom to altitudes, in some instances, high above sea level (Fig. 15). The question at once arises: Are these islands miniature continents composed of sial, sustained in their elevated positions, like the larger continental land blocks, in isostatic equilibrium because of the density deficiency of their masses?

LARGE BASALTIC ISLANDS

The fact that earthquake waves propagated through the floor of the Pacific Ocean gain about 18 per cent in speed is held to warrant the inference that the material traversed has sima composition. This inference is in accord with the interpretation that the low elevation of the Pacific floor results from a condition of isostatic equilibrium due to its superior density.

In conformity with the deduction that the material of the Pacific Ocean bottoms is basaltic sima is the finding that the Pacific islands are almost all volcanic and composed of basaltic rock. That is to say, if the bottom substance is basaltic it could be expected that volcanic extrusion would pile up basaltic cones.

In the case of the smaller islands this circumstance is not of great moment. But the large island of Hawaii rising 30,000 feet above the ocean floor and made up of the dense basaltic material presents a problem. Isostatically considered it would appear to be an immense unadjusted load, difficult to account for if the isostatic principle is assumed to be valid.

Two solutions of this problem have been suggested. One is that Hawaii, and other islands of similar size and composition, are of so recent origin that the isostatic adjustments they should necessitate have not yet taken place; the islands are destined to sink beneath the waves and their mass to be distributed broadly in the general underlying sima shell. The other is that the lavas of the island, though composed of the sima type of rock, are so porous as to be actually of less density than granitic sial. Computations having this idea as their basis indicate that so made up Hawaii could stand at a level 20,000 feet above the ocean floor in complete isostatic adjustment. It is an appropriate assumption that both solutions may apply: there will be some sinking; the excess of load is not so great as the composition of the rock would suggest. These interpretations are confirmed by the findings of Betz, Jr. F. and Hess, H. H. (1942, pp. 108–111).

SMALL ISLANDS AND THE MID-ATLANTIC RIDGE

The great majority of other Pacific mid-ocean islands are also volcanic in origin and are composed of basaltic rock. If the great masses of the Hawaiian Islands can be sustained, as described, it is clear that the existence of these smaller islands may be similarly accounted for. In the Atlantic the isolated Bermudas with a lime rock surface were found by boring to have a basaltic volcanic base. Where, in other islands, the rock is sialic in nature, composed of

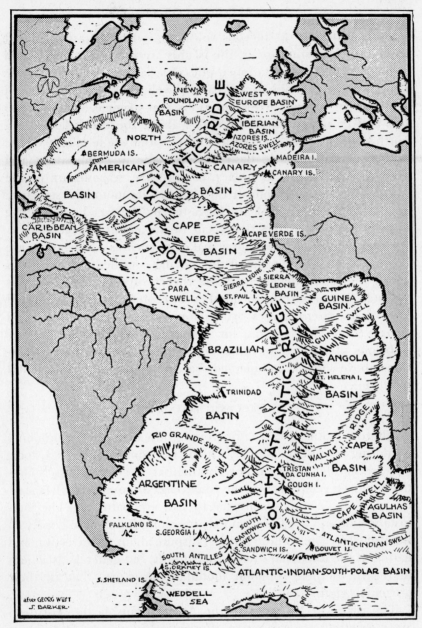

FIG. 16. TOPOGRAPHY OF THE FLOOR OF THE BASIN OF THE ATLANTIC OCEAN
Based on the soundings of the "Meteor"— German Atlantic Expedition.
Drawing by Steve Barker.

granitic materials or siliceous volcanics, it may be assumed that isostatic equilibrium exists, the islands are light enough to stand so high. This interpretation applies especially to the Mid-Atlantic Ridge (Fig. 16). This is a broad upswell of the Atlantic Ocean bottom that extends with elevations that average 3000 to 6000 feet and in places 18,000 to 20,000 above the ocean floor, in a north-south line for 9000 miles through the whole length of the middle of the Atlantic Basin. It is sialic in composition and perhaps represents a secondary, compressive, warping up of the stretched granitic bottom of this ocean. Its mountain structure and recency of upheaval are suggested by the fact that it is the locus of the earthquakes that occur in the Atlantic area.

Other islands of continental make-up, such as Madagascar, are fragments left in the wake of the moving continental block from which they were detached, if the theory of continental drift is accepted, or, according to another interpretation, are separated from their parent masses by the foundering of the intervening areas. Some large islands, for example, Newfoundland, appear to belong in this class of sundered islands but actually are projections above shallow, submerged, border areas of the continental platforms.

OROGENIC ISLANDS

There remains a very numerous group of islands, commonly bordering continental shores, which rise from the deep sea floor, and are neither volcanic nor continental fragments. As a class these may be referred to as the *island arcs* although strictly speaking not all examples conform to the arc pattern. The best instances of arcs are the island chains along the Asiatic border of the Pacific Ocean. There is much dispute about the direction and nature of the force that caused their uplift, but general agreement in regard to their common mountain structure, that is, their orogenic origin.

The island of Barbados in the Atlantic outside the Antillean arc is selected to serve as an illustration of the possibilities of such upheaval from the deep sea floor. Barbados has, it is true, certain characteristics unlike those representative of orogenic islands in general, but these very differences afford significant evidence indicative of the probable sequences in such uplifts.

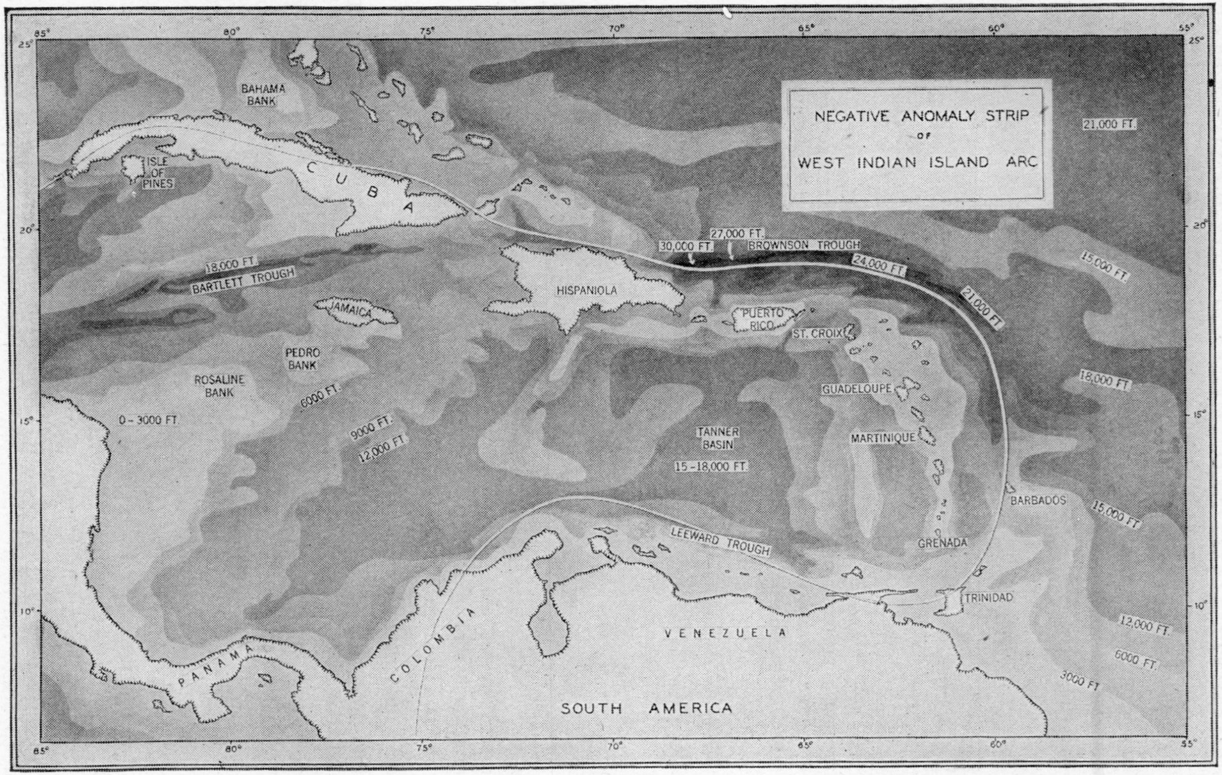

The axis of the strip (white line) is inferred to mark the axis of the geotectocline in this region.
Based on maps by H. H. Hess.
Drawing by Elizabeth Burckmyer.

FIG. 17. MAP OF THE WEST INDIAN ISLAND ARC AND NEGATIVE ANOMALY STRIP

43

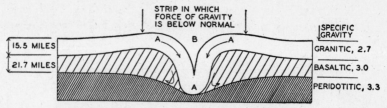

A-A-A IS CRUSTAL DOWNBUCKLE OR TECTOGENE (KUENEN)

B IS BASIN OR GEOTECTOCLINE (HESS) DEVELOPED BY DOWNBUCKLE. (AFTER HARRY H. HESS)

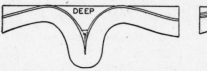

TECTOGENE DEVELOPS BELOW SEA LEVEL AND GEOTECTOCLINE FORMS AN OCEAN DEEP. (AFTER HESS)

UPBENT LIMBS OF TECTOGENE ARE SUB-AERIALLY ERODED AND SEDIMENT FILLS GEOTECTOCLINE (AFTER HESS)

A FURTHER COMPRESSION BRINGS THE LIMBS OF THE TECTOGENE TOGETHER AND FORCES OUT THE SEDIMENTS TO FORM A MOUNTAIN-UNIT LIKE THAT OF THE ALPS, HERE SUGGESTED IN SECTION. THE VERTICAL AND HORIZONTAL SCALES ARE THE SAME. (AFTER HESS)

FIG. 18. DIAGRAMS OF A TECTOGENE

The force of gravity is below normal (negative anomaly strip) because the crustal downbuckle introduces an excess of the less dense granitic material in the lithosphere section along its axis. Drawings, after H. H. Hess, by Elizabeth Burckmyer.

The discovery by gravity measurements of great deficiencies in mass in the vicinity of island arcs afforded F. A. Vening Meinesz (1934) and H. H. Hess (1938) a basis on which to construct a theory of the origin and manner of such uplifts (Fig. 17). In the West Indies the belt of deficiency, called the *negative strip*, swings as a convex loop around from north of Cuba, past Hispaniola over Barbados and Trinidad. It is in places marked by exceptionally deep ocean tracts, at other places is over a ridge with islands like

Barbados and Trinidad projecting above sea level. Behind it there is a main uparching, Hispaniola, Puerto Rico, the Lesser Antilles, that has an excess of mass. It is inferred that over the negative strip the upper 15 miles of sialic crust is bent vertically downwards to a total depth of 36 miles. This crustal downbuckle, as a structure, is called a *tectogene* (Fig. 18), and the basin between the two limbs of the downbend a *geotectocline*. Sediments from the exposed portions of the swell behind it tend to fill the geotectoclinal basin. A further compression of the tectogene brings the limbs of the geotectocline into contact and results in the upward outsqueezing of the sediments to form an orogenic island.

In Barbados an emergent upswell, on the west, furnished coarse sediments that were deposited in shallow water. Above the coarse beds of such origin there is a breccia containing large blocks of sandstone. Overlying these two formations are found the Oceanic Series composed of such materials as are normally accumulated on deep-sea floors.

Following the deposition of the shallow water sediments in the Barbadian area, a great downbuckle, tectogene, developed, according to Hess (1938). Into the depression, geotectocline, so formed, the breccia materials slid. During an interval of quiet the deep-sea Oceanic beds were laid down. A succeeding tectogenic deformation folded and squeezed out the sediments and the Oceanic Series so that they now form the core of the island of Barbados. Trinidad appears to have experienced the same succession and to possess the same structure. Barbados is one of a very few places in the world where deep-sea beds appear as land rocks. Although this interpretation is elaborately theoretical it fits the known facts and provides a mechanism by which orogenic islands may be developed.

Deeps and Troughs. The exceptionally deep places of the ocean floors are of much greater areal extent than are equivalent high altitudes on the continental surfaces. Only 0.1 per cent of the continental areas rises above 18,000 feet above sea level, whereas 3 per cent, 30 times as much, of ocean bottom is inferred to be 18,000 feet or more below sea level. There are 57 *deeps* under more than 3 miles of water; 11 of these are under 4 miles and 5 are below as much as 5 miles of water. But it should be realized that the areal extent of these deeps is mapped from a very inadequate number of soundings. A detailed survey of a representative ocean deep has yet to be made.

Some of these deeps are broad, gradual depressions in the central areas of the ocean. These may be regarded as regions of even greater density than the average sima, and are depressed accordingly. But others, such as the Swire Deep, 35,433 feet deep, north and east of Mindanao, one of the Philippine Islands (the greatest depth known), the Emden Deep, also in the Pacific, 34,125 feet deep (Machatschek, F., 1938, p. 1); the Nares Deep north of Puerto Rico, 29,220 feet (Milwaukee depth, *New York Times,* April 19, 1939), and the Bartlett Trough, south of Cuba, 1000 miles long and 21,000 feet deep, are relatively narrow, steep-sided troughs, located near continents or associated with island arcs. These are referred to as *foredeeps* and probably result either from graben faulting, or are geotectoclines.

Even if the foredeeps were all demonstrated to be regions of exceptionally high gravity the sharpness of their boundaries and their close association with lands of notably great elevation suggest a relationship other than slow isostatic adjustment. The conspicuousness of the deeps, in general, is in part accounted for by the absence on the ocean bottoms of denudational or depositional processes comparable, in a quantitative sense, with those subaerially operative. In the light of present knowledge the foredeeps appear to be unfilled geotectoclinal basins of the negative strip of island arcs as described above; that is, sharply downfolded and downfaulted belts of the sialic crust.

The Continental Shelves. In general the edges of the continental platforms do not correspond with coast lines. Instead the descent, *continental slope,* to the deep ocean basins is usually a considerable distance off-shore and begins at an average depth of 600 feet. The area of shallow-water bottom, more or less wide, between the shore line and the top of the relatively steep continental slope is called the *continental shelf* (Fig. 15). The continental shelves are probably not all the same in structure and origin. Shepard (1933) maintains that the upper surfaces of the continental shelves are generally irregular and were developed antecedent to the present conditions; further, that most of the continental slopes are too steep to be composed of unconsolidated fine sediment. It suffices here to assume that the continental shelves apparently comprise downbent, border portions of the basement rock of the continental platforms upon which thick masses of more recent sedimentary beds have accumulated (Leet, L. D., 1940) (Fig. 19).   In sum these slightly submerged areas

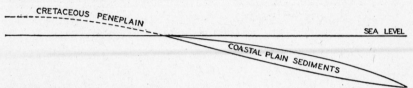

FIG. 19. THE SEDIMENTARY LENS

Constituting the Atlantic Continental Shelf and Continental Slope off the South East Atlantic Coast of the United States.   After A. C. Veatch and P. A. Smith.   Drawing by Elizabeth Burckmyer.

constitute about 5 per cent of the earth's surface. Along the eastern coast of North America they extend outward 100 miles from the shore, around Newfoundland 500 miles, off northwestern Europe they extend beyond the British Isles.   The islands of the Arctic area south and west of Greenland rise above the general level of the continental shelf there.   The continental shelves are narrow or lacking all around Africa and along all the western coasts of North and South America.

The rather uniform depth, 600 feet, of the outer termination of the continental shelves appears to be governed by the presence of the water. If so, 600 feet represents the maximal depth to which the water can be sufficiently agitated by wave motion and currents, set up by surface agencies, to move sedimentary materials. Beyond that depth, with no motion, suspended and dragged particles sink to the bottom; hence accumulate on the steep continental slope. The top of the continental shelf may be built outward very slowly at the 600-foot depth, but beyond this depth the angle of rest for the materials being deposited determines the angle of the continental slope extending from the edge of the continental shelf down to the floor of the deep oceans.

As an outcome of their detailed soundings over, and study of the Atlantic Coastal Plain, A. C. Veatch and P. A. Smith (1939, pp. 33, 37) are of the conviction that the Coastal Plain formations there constitute a thick lens of sediments resting on a uniformly sloping floor of peneplaned basement rock (Fig. 19).   The steeper continental slope, according to this concept, is simply the thinning,

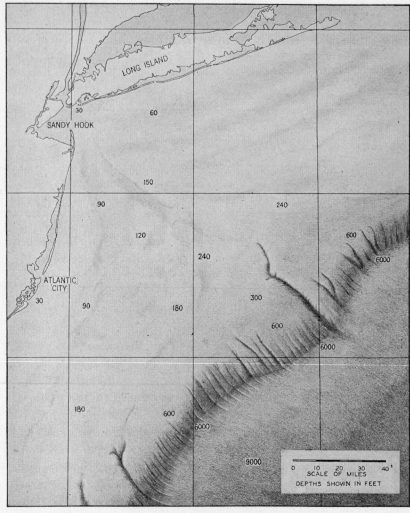

FIG. 20. SUBMARINE CANYON OF THE HUDSON RIVER

Based on the maps of detailed soundings by A. C. Veatch and P. A. Smith. The Hudson Canyon was cut through well-consolidated beds. Note the numerous lesser channels eroded in the continental slope of this area. Drawing by Elizabeth Burckmyer.

seaward edge of the sedimentary lens. Further, Veatch and Smith conclude that from a depth of about 400 feet shoreward the surface of the continental shelf has been developed by wave planation; presumably at a time of rising sea level following the Pleistocene Ice Age.

Submarine Canyons.   In view of these circumstances the presence of *submarine canyons,* extending partly across the continental shelves, partly, and more profoundly, cut into the continental slope is a very puzzling geomorphic phenomenon.

Such channels are found off the coasts of all the continents. From this fact it may be inferred that the circumstances of their origin were of world-wide incidence.   The canyon off the mouth of the Hudson River is the best known example in eastern North America (Fig. 20).   Accurate surveys made in 1936 by modern methods provide exact information in regard to bottom conditions for 125 miles out from New York harbor.   A channel extends across the continental shelf for about 90 miles where it attains a depth of 300 feet.   The remaining 35 miles is a canyon, about one half cut into continental shelf, the other half into the continental slope.   Where the survey ends this gorge is 6600 feet deep.   It is nearly straight, has no conspicuous tributaries, and has a width of nearly 5 miles, with walls 3000 feet high.

The Foss de Cap Breton is a submarine channel continuing the course of the Adour River off the coast of France at the southeast corner of the Bay of Biscay.   It becomes a true rock canyon 4000 to 6000 feet deep and ends at the base of the continental slope 9000 feet below sea level.   For 35 miles offshore from its mouth the channel of the Congo River, Africa, has a submarine continuation in the form of a gorge 6 miles wide and 6000 feet below the level of the sea bottom along the sides of the canyon.   Less definitely than in the case of the Congo, the continuation of the Monterey River, California, is the canyon at the head of Monterey Bay; a canyon which has been traced seaward to a depth of 11,000 feet.

A cut into the weak muds composing the outer slope of the Mississippi River Delta is a deep, broad, gulflike depression (Fig. 21).   Its form is in sharp contrast with the relatively narrow, steep-sided submarine channels found elsewhere.   This difference in topography would seem to be significant for the problem of the origin of the submarine channels.   It suggests that both forms result from current erosion with the nature of the valley cross section governed by the kind of material cut into.

Even more remarkable is the submarine topography around the volcanic island Bogoslof, in the Bering Sea, which rises 5000 feet above the floor of the ocean and has its summit practically at sea level. This underwater area has been surveyed by echo sounding in such detail that it was possible to make a small-interval

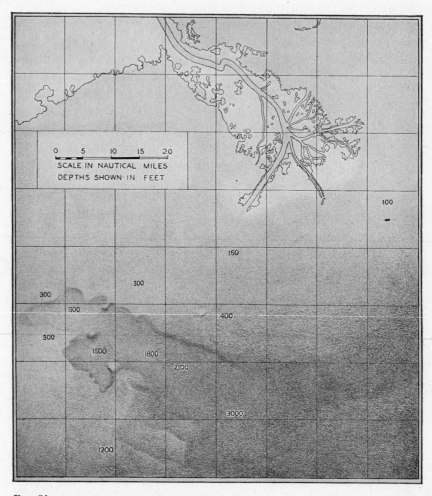

FIG. 21. MISSISSIPPI SUBMARINE TROUGH

Cut into unconsolidated sediments. Based on two maps by F. P. Shepard. Drawing by Elizabeth Burckmyer.

contour map of the bottom there which presents the relief with nearly the same accuracy as that of a carefully surveyed map of a land area of similar topography (Fig 22). The underwater portion of the Bogoslof volcanic cone is found to have concave slopes like those that would be developed subaerially. (In the East Indies it has been found that the subaerial portions of volcanic cones all have concave slopes while their submarine slopes are invariably straight lines with an inclination of about 25 degrees.) Around the Bogoslof cone there is a pattern of stream valleys of

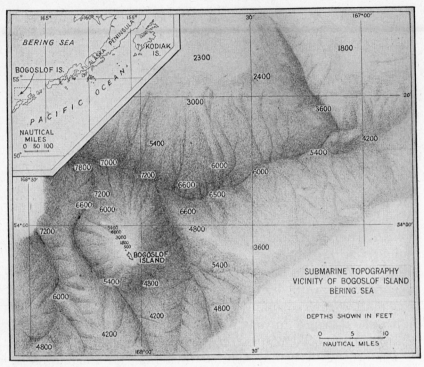

FIG. 22. PATTERN OF SUBMARINE VALLEYS ON THE SEA BOTTOM IN THE VICINITY OF BOGOSLOF ISLAND, BERING SEA

Note how perfectly this pattern of drainage conforms to those of valley systems developed subaerially. Based on a map by P. A. Smith. Drawing by Elizabeth Burckmyer.

entirely subaerial aspect fitted to the presence of the cone. One of these is a widely open valley which attains a depth of 7800 feet below sea level and is over 60 miles long. Numerous tributaries make a dendritic drainage pattern. The whole system is incised in the floor of the Bering Sea and has apparently no connection with existing land drainage. It is the development that could be expected if the flat bottom of the Bering Sea were uplifted 8000 feet above sea level and subjected to subaerial erosion. It has proved difficult to escape this implication.

The submarine canyons, in general, are not mere slumpings of oozy sediments at the outer edges of the continental shelves. Their walls have been sampled by dredging and proved to be made up of consolidated rock. Fossils in some of these samples *(New York Times,* Oct. 2, 1937, H. C. Stetson, Harvard) indicate that formations of Pliocene age, hence geologically of extraordinary recency, have been cut through. The canyon making must, in part at least, have been post-Pliocene. The forms of the canyons and the pattern of the Bogoslof valley system make graben faulting an improbable explanation. If the Bogoslof area were an isolated occurrence it could be regarded as the localized sinking of an unstable volcanic region. But the world-wide presence of the submarine canyons makes it more probable that this region derives its characteristics from the same general cause that led to the other developments.

Surveys, as detailed as that of the Bogoslof area, made along the Atlantic coast of the United States disclose the existence of canyons at sites unrelated to modern river courses and in such numbers within short reaches that the volume of present-day precipitation would be quite inadequate to supply enough continental rivers with drainage for their cutting. In the narrow area of the Georges Banks, off Cape Cod, Massachusetts, there are at least 30 V-shaped canyons, 5 to 12 miles long, 2 to 6 miles wide, going down to 8000 to 10,000 feet below sea level.

The evidence at hand, especially that from the Bogoslof area, seemingly points to a hitherto unsuspected episode of the most extraordinary kind in the recent geomorphic history of the earth. The simplest solution of the problem and the one which is in harmony with established geomorphic science is to infer that the canyons were eroded subaerially. Then two possibilities are open. One is that during the Pleistocene Ice Age all the continental platforms as such were raised 8000 feet or more above sea level. (Some lowering of sea level by withdrawal of water to make the ice sheets might contribute to such an emergence.) This would do very nicely for the erosion of the canyons but would have other consequences that do not seem to have followed. Perhaps the continents were not lifted as wholes. Du Toit (1940) has suggested an orogenic upwarping of the borders of the continents. But tilting upward of the outer edges of the continental shelves (with hinge lines along present shores), supplemented by regional uplift of coastal belts to supply gradients for eroding streams, is hardly credible as a universal synchronized program of diastrophism. In any event explanation by general or specialized uplift only serves to pose an even more difficult problem, that of finding a cause for so tremendous an upheaval.

If emergence is ruled out there remains the alternative possibility, namely that of attributing the whole 8000 feet change in altitude to a lowering of sea level by that amount. This could come about either by foundering of the ocean-basin bottoms on a vast scale, or by the withdrawal of a tremendous volume of ocean water into the atmosphere. Neither the one nor the other of these occurrences is any more probable than those of continental uplift.

However Veatch and Smith (1939, pp. 30 and 41) insist that the geomorphic evidence at the mouth of the Congo River, Africa, warrants the conclusion that the Atlantic Ocean receded to a shore line 10,000 or more feet below the present sea level not longer than 25,000 years ago, and that the return to the present sea level was made only 5,000 years ago.

Even if it is held that such uplift of the lands or such lowering of sea level could take place there remains the difficulty of effecting a restoration to the conditions of the present, a problem no less awkward than that of providing suitable circumstances for the canyon erosion.

In view of the dilemma that results when a subaerial origin is postulated for the submarine canyons there has been eager casting about for an explanation of their occurrence that does not lead to such fantastic involvements. Appeal has been made to submarine currents, to emergence of submarine springs, to the erosion resulting from earthquake waves. Submarine currents or the flow of submarine springs with sufficient erosive effectiveness to excavate gorges rivaling that of the Grand Canyon of the Colorado in magnitude, and able to do such cutting within a very short interval of recent geologic time are not readily conceded by those competently informed in regard to such possibilities. These agencies seem quite inadequate for the task.

The earthquake-wave theory (Bucher, W. H., 1940) has in its favor the factors of universality of application and a magnitude corresponding to that of the phenomena produced. In brief it is that "earthquake waves" originate by sudden displacement of water on the ocean bottom from the breaks in the rocks that induce earthquakes or from submarine rock slides resulting from the earthquakes or from volcanic eruptions. Such displacement causes waves that are very long in comparison to the depth of the oceans. A wave 5 feet long in water 1 inch deep gives the idea. When such waves reach shallow water they take on a horizontal back and forth motion that enlarges and deepens depressions on the continental slope. Often repeated, the churning and sediment transport brought about by such wave motion are held to be competent to excavate those submarine valleys not directly linked up with large rivers.

SUMMARY

Sonic depth finding has made possible the rapid, accurate, detailed mapping of ocean-bottom topography. With only a fraction of the great task of surveying the vast oceanic areas done, enough is known to make clear that the old idea of monotonously uniform ocean-bottom plains is erroneous.

Islands are irregularities of the ocean floor high enough to project above the water surface. Islands have different origins, but in general, like the continental platforms, appear to be isostatically balanced. Deeps and troughs result from broad downwarps, downfoldings, and downsinkings between fault breaks.

Where the basement rocks of the continents, at the submerged margins of the continental platforms, are bent down toward the deep-sea bottoms sedimentary beds have accumulated to form underwater shelves, commonly many miles wide, extending outward to the depth of 600 feet. From the 600-foot depth there is a steeper descent, the continental slope, to oceanic depths.

The continental shelves and continental slopes are universally channeled and notched to great depths by submarine valleys. If it is sought to account for these valleys by subaerial erosion it is necessary to assume some sort of uplift of the continental platforms or a general lowering of sea level in the measure of 8000 feet or more in recent geologic time. As this is rather unthinkable there is much casting about for an explanation of the occurrence of the canyons in accord with existing knowledge of geo-morphic processes and geologic history.

BIBLIOGRAPHY

CLASSICAL

Sigsbee, C. D. (1880) *Deep-sea Sounding and Dredging,* United States Coast and Geodetic Survey, Washington.

Spencer, J. W. (1905) *The Submarine Great Canyon of the Hudson River,* Geographical Journal, Vol. 25, pp. 180–190.

RECENT

Daly, R. A. (1936) *Origin of Submarine Canyons,* American Journal of Science, 5th ser. Vol. 31, pp. 401–420.

Ewing, M., Crary, A. P., and Rutherford, H. M. (1937) *Geophysical Investigations in the Emerged and Submerged Atlantic Coastal Plain,* Bulletin Geological Society of America, Vol. 48, pp. 753–802.

Smith, P. A. (1937) *The Submarine Topography of Bogoslof,* Geographical Review, Vol. 27, 1937, pp. 630–636.

Stetson, H. C. (1937) *Current-measurements in the Georges Bank Canyons.* Transactions American Geophysical Union, Pt. 1, pp. 216–219.

Shephard, F. P. and Beard, C. N. (1938) *Submarine Canyons: Distribution and Longitudinal Profiles,* Geographical Review, Vol. 28, pp. 439–451.

Rude, G. T. (1938) *New Methods of Marine Surveying,* Proceedings American Philosophical Society, Vol. 79, pp. 9–25.

Colbert, L. O. (1939) *Charting Geomorphic Features of the Sea Bottom,* Journal of Geomorphology, Vol. 2, pp. 335–338.

Johnson, D. (1939) *The Origin of Submarine Canyons,* Columbia Geomorphic Studies No. 3, Columbia University Press, New York.

Veatch, A. C. and Smith, P. A. (1939) *Atlantic Submarine Valleys of the United States and the Congo Submarine Valley,* Special Paper No. 7, Geological Society of America.

Bucher, W. H. (1940) *Submarine Valleys and Related Geologic Problems of the North Atlantic,* Bulletin Geological Society of America, Vol. 51, pp. 489–512.

Murray, H. W. (1941) *Submarine Mountains in the Gulf of Alaska,* Bulletin Geological Society of America, Vol. 52, pp. 333–362.

Shepard, F. P. and Emery, K. O. (1941) *Submarine Topography off the California Coast,* Special Paper No. 31, Geological Society of America.

Jones, O. T. (1941) *Continental Slopes and Continental Shelves,* Geographical Journal, Vol. 97, pp. 80–96.

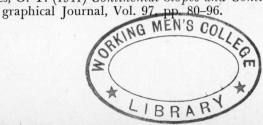

Chapter Four

GEOMORPHIC UNITS

Introduction. The geomorphology which is open to direct observation is that of the lands. Everything above sea level is in a subaerial environment; hence subject to subaerial processes. The American school of geomorphology, under the leadership of Davis, has devoted itself chiefly to a reading of the record made by these processes. This record gets expression mainly in relief features of the third order. Study of the origin of relief features of the second order on the lands has been more or less completely neglected. As is true of their development in the ocean basins, the relief features of the second order on lands are created, in general, by internal, that is, *endogenic,* forces. They are forms of structure. Their existence is independent of conditions due to subaerial exposure. But, unlike relief of the second order in the ocean basins, some of the relief features of the second order on the lands result from external, that is, *exogenic,* forces and processes. Davis recognized this fact by listing mountains and plateaus as *forms of structure,* and setting them off against till plains and alluvial fans, which he called *forms of process.* He implied, further, that forms of structure were to be regarded as finished, and to be differentiated between, geomorphically, on the basis of their stage (degradational) of dissection. On the other hand, accumulations of rock debris, such as alluvial fans, were to be considered in process of formation, and to be compared on the basis of their progress (constructional) toward completion.

If, with Davis, the point of departure for geomorphic inquiry is assumed to be fixed by the time when the degradational history of a relief form of the second order begins, a difficulty still remains. Some of his forms of process are completed, that is, are ready for, or, indeed, have been subjected to degradational processes. This is obviously true of till plains produced by the Pleistocene glaciation. Hence if geomorphic studies are to concern themselves with the degradational histories of items of relief of the second order, then forms of process, as well as forms of structure, will need to be included in a listing of such of these second-order units of relief, that are, so to say, ready at hand. In other words, the units on which subaerial geomorphic development takes place are in part the product of exogenic action, are not solely of endogenic origin. In this sense the exogenic as well as the endogenic units are forms of structure.

Structure. When geologic reference is made to the portion of the earth's crust underlying a particular area, the word "structure" is used primarily to denote the attitude of the rocks. In the same sense "structure" may also include designation of the constitution of the rock material; thus it may be called massive or thin-bedded structure; be said to have close or wide-spaced jointing, to be composed of competent or incompetent beds.

In geomorphology "structure" has a somewhat broader application. In addition to all the structural characteristics included in the narrower geologic meaning, structure, geomorphically, comprises every inherent quality of the rock substance that may influence the course of degradational dissection. Lithology is one such quality. The general nature and size of the unit involved is, geomorphically, a structural factor. Juxtaposition, that is, the factor of difference for geomorphic development that exists because of the close association of shale and limestone in one place, and of sandstone and limestone in another, is an item of geomorphic structure. In these relationships the function of attitude in structure may have its meaning extended to include the altitude of the rock exposure (Fenneman, N. M., 1936, p. 91).

Classes of Structure. If, then, an attempt is made to classify structures for the purposes of geomorphic study, the criterion for making distinctions should be the degree of divergence in erosional dissection that will result from a difference in structural conditions. On this basis two broad classes of structure are immediately recognizable, the *horizontal structures* and the *disordered structures*. The significant general characteristic of the horizontal class is the perfect simplicity of attitude and arrangement of the component parts; they are beds laid up horizontally to form a pile. There are, interestingly, wide areas that have such structure. For the class of disordered structures it is not possible to make so narrow and sure a definition. It requires no more than a high angle of dip to transfer a unit from the horizontal to the disordered class. So numerous are the possible complexities beyond this first departure that analysis of disordered structures based on their variety is impracticable.

Recognition of this difficulty has compelled the reference of geomorphic studies to physiographic provinces. A *physiographic province* is a region that has unit structure, any specified kind, and unit geomorphic history. It has, further, a particular climatic background. Each physiographic province is *sui generis*. A place name is needed to identify it, for example, the Great Plains, the Adirondack Mountains. From these circumstances it is evident that a physiographic province is really an *outcome* of geomorphic inquiry, not a point of departure for geomorphic studies. The place name asserts a particular structure but does not classify it, the locality of occurrence fixes the subaerial environment, and in each instance a particular stage of geomorphic development will have been attained. Physiographic provinces do not precede geomorphic study; rather they acquire reality by and from such inquiry. After geomorphic studies have been made physiographic provinces can be established. By ruling out physiographic provinces it becomes clear what it is that is sought, structurally, as a starting point for geomorphic investigation. It is a relief feature of the second order, of endogenic or exogenic origin on which the subaerial processes have or are acting to produce the third order of relief. By definition each such **geomorphic unit** will have uniformity of structure within its confines. The changes wrought by process will be the same or follow the same pattern within the limits of any given unit.

A geomorphic unit in its existing aspect will have been little, moderately, or greatly modified by the action of processes. It need not be encountered in its original structural state. By geomorphic analysis both its past and its future can be envisaged. Such reconstruction and prediction are the chief business of the geomorphologist who adopts the precepts of the American school. The first problem of such a program is to subdivide the primary classes of horizontal and disordered structures, particularly the latter, into geomorphic units that are distinctive, on the basis of the specifications set forth above.

Davis (1924, p. 143) made a tentative classification of structure as follows:

| Layered structures | Approximately horizontal
Moderately inclined
Steeply inclined and faulted
Moderately or greatly warped
Folded (moderately or strongly, regularly or complexly, etc.) | Each structure may be of varying resistance within its mass. |

| Massive structures | Crystalline or metamorphosed masses commonly of nearly uniform resistance, so that drainage is chiefly consequent or insequent; but in some instances of differing resistance so that a subsequent pattern of drainage may be developed. |

| Combined structures | Massive and layered structures associated in all possible relationships. |

| Volcanic structures | Cones, ash fields, lava fields of narrow area or widespread extension. |

Listing of Geomorphic Units. The listing and classification of geomorphic units that follows is admittedly imperfect. Some of the items proposed so completely fit the requirements that the student will immediately accept them as real and pertinent. In regard to others there will be doubt; in certain instances even strong objection. But each of the units proposed has at least the warrant that it has been singled out in the past by other workers in geomorphology for topical treatment. What may well be debated is the place to which each such unit is assigned in the classification here attempted.

The major divisions remain two classes, one of simple, the other of disordered structures. The class of simple structures differs from the original horizontal class in that it includes units in which the materials are simply but not necessarily horizontally disposed. Following the initial division into two classes each accepted geomorphic unit is put into one of five general groups. The larger group is defined; then a distinctive name and definition are given to each of the items included in that group. Finally the definition of each geomorphic unit is validated by citation of representative examples. Although these may usually best be identified by reference to specific physiographic provinces, it is to be remembered that the physiographic provinces, as such, have been established chiefly on the basis of geomorphic units. This was realized but not stated as a concept.

GEOMORPHIC UNITS

I. CLASS OF SIMPLE STRUCTURES

Group A

Geomorphic units composed of unconsolidated or weakly consolidated sediments, having generally horizontal, or simple, well or poorly defined, layered structure.

1. *Coastal Plains.* Regional emergence of marine or lacustrine sediments of geologically recent date. The parent water body comprises one margin; the other abuts an oldland. The original surface is approximately flat, and departs from a horizontal plane in that it characteristically slopes gently toward the shore line. This surface slope is repeated as to direction, but with slightly greater degree of inclination, by the dip of the beds of which the plain is composed. The stratification of the layers is well defined.

Atlantic Coastal Plain of the United States.

2. *Piedmont Plains.* This designation has not previously been widely used in the specific sense here applied. Piedmont plains have the general pattern of coastal plains in form and structure but differ from coastal plains in that their origin is by subaerial instead of underwater deposition of sediment. One margin is formed by the mountains from which the sediments were derived; the other may be indeterminate, involving a gradational merging with a different adjoining unit; or the plain rings about the playa or bolson of an arid basin. The surface slopes and dips of the beds are relatively steep near the mountains, decreasing with distance from the mountains. Stratification is irregular, may be obscure; beds vary greatly in texture, and units of superior resistance commonly have little continuity.

The Great Plains.

3. *Tundra Plain.* Mantle rock cover, commonly coastal and fluvial sediments or of glacial (northern Siberia) origin, consolidated to nearly complete imperviousness (Siberia) at shallow depths by ground ice. Difficult to classify in respect of composition because complete freezing of ground water may cause areas

underlain by consolidated rock to give somewhat the same responses to subaerial processes, and to have the same general aspect, as those made up of newly deposited sedimentary materials.

Bering Sea and Arctic Ocean coasts of Alaska; Arctic Ocean coast of Russia and Siberia.

4. *Fluvial, Lacustrine, and Deltaic Plains.* Brings together for listing as a single type of geomorphic unit items of slightly different origin. These are alike in (*a*) being made up, commonly, of sediments of fine texture, (*b*) having flat surfaces nearly horizontally disposed, (*c*) having comparatively low altitudes (1) in relation to the sea as a base level (2) in the sense that their expanse is sufficiently great to give them such a relation to neighboring geomorphic units. The following examples serve to validate the characterization: Nile Plain and Delta, Mississippi Flood Plain and Delta, Amazon Basin Plain, Glacial Lake Agassiz Plain, Lake Chad Plain, Africa.

5. *Erg.* The counterpart in desert basins of Fluvial, Lacustrine, and Deltaic Plains in humid lands. The Sahara term, *erg,* further implies sand-dune topography. The Sahara areas of erg were apparently water deposited and have not, despite wind modification of their surfaces, been reconstituted or transferred from the site of their original deposition. They fulfill, hence, all requirements for a geomorphic unit.

The Libyan Erg, Sahara.

6. *Glacial Plains.* Composed of morainic and outwash materials from Pleistocene or other extensive glaciation. Heterogeneous in composition; undulating, irregular surface of low relief; widespread in area. Require for their marked development a relatively low preglacial rock relief. Postglacially provide initial slopes over broad areas; hence inaugurate a new erosion cycle.

Till Plains of central, northern United States.

7. *Loessial Plains.* Made up of wind transported and deposited material of desert or proglacial origin. Differ from Glacial Plains in the homogeneity of texture of their substance, which is that of dust fineness, and its peculiar structure, which gives rise to high vertical walls. Akin to Glacial Plains in the undulating, low irregularity of the initial surface topography.

Loess regions of Turkestan.

Group B

Geomorphic units composed of more or less firmly consolidated rocks of sedimentary or igneous origin. The materials, like Group A, have some simple uniform arrangement.

8. *Interior Plateaus.* Sediments, commonly old, geologically, thoroughly consolidated, flat-lying or with a gentle monoclinal dip, initial or regional. The summit levels are sufficiently high, either in actual or relative altitude, to warrant the empirical designation "plateau."

Appalachian Plateau.

9. *Nested Saucer Basins.* Sediments or sheeted intrusives with centripetal dips. The igneous occurrences are designated geo-

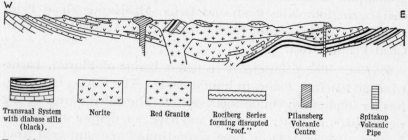

| Transvaal System with diabase sills (black). | Norite | Red Granite | Rociberg Series forming disrupted "roof." | Pilansberg Volcanic Centre | Spitzkop Volcanic Pipe |

FIG. 23. THE BUSHVELD LOPOLITH, AFRICA

Nearly 300 miles east to west. After a drawing by Alexander L. Du Toit, in *The Geology of South Africa.* By permission of the publishers, Oliver and Boyd, Edinburgh, Drawn by Walter Williams.

logically as **lopoliths,** and inferred to represent sags after intrusion. The Paris Basin. The Bushveldt Lopolith, Africa (Fig. 23).

10. *Lava Flow Plains and Plateaus.* The product of lava floods disposed horizontally in sufficient depth and sufficiently widespread to obliterate pre-eruption relief.

Columbia Lava Plateaus, Deccan of India.

11. *Volcanic Cones.* Composed of volcanic extrusions, lava and fragmented material, or a composite of the two in which case the materials are commonly bound together by interlacing intrusive dikes. The cones made up wholly or in part of fragmented stuff have high angle dips, lava cones have low angle dips, but both have simple radial structure. Areal extension narrow, but because of erection to high altitudes very effective in domi-

nating pattern of erosional development radiating from them as centers.

Aetna, Popocatepetl, Mauna Loa.

Group C

Geomorphic units made up wholly of calcareous rock; simple structures because of the homogeneity of the material.

12. *Karst Units.* Regions of considerable areal extent that have a massive limestone cover. The thickness of this cover is greater than the vertical measure of the third order of relief that develops on and in it. The ready yield of the calcareous substance to solution processes conditions all erosional development.

East coast of the Adriatic Sea, western interior Jamaica, B.W.I.

13. *Coral Islands.* Islands where one or more emerged coral reefs, in a terrace or a succession of terraces, constitute the structure subjected to subaerial topographic development.

Barbados, B.W.I.

II. Class of Disordered Structures

Group D

Folded and faulted units made up of consolidated rocks composed of sedimentaries, or including or involving sedimentaries.

14. *Dome Uplifts.* The general condition is that of lifting and warping a sedimentary cover so as to create a broadly circular or oval bulge. There are two types (*a*) laccolithic, (*b*) deepseated.

(*a*) Laccolithic. A conduit from a deep source is the route of an igneous intrusion which invades overlying sedimentary formations, themselves flat-lying. The intrusive mass is inferred to have a flat base resting on sedimentary layers, and to have lifted the formations above that level. The igneous mass is younger than the sedimentaries, and the upper surface of the igneous mass will not have experienced any erosional history.

The Henry Mountains, Utah.

(*b*) Deep-seated. An igneous mass of deep-seated batholithic type is subaerially eroded to low relief. It is then regionally depressed to permit marine submergence and the accumulation of a sedimentary cover. After this cover has been supplied the area in question is differentially warped upward to the general form of a dome. This uplift is presumed to result from the additions of igneous material from below. The sedimentaries are younger than the igneous mass and rest on its eroded surface. More extensive and lower domed upwarping is inferred to have had a similar origin and to have functioned in the same way though less conspicuously and less dominantly in conditioning geomorphic development.

The Black Hills, South Dakota, are representative of the sharply defined units of this type, the Nashville Dome of the broader upwarpings. Analysis by projected profiles and the seemingly antecedent courses of the upper branches of the Delaware River are considered by the author to be indicative of domed upwarping of the Catskill Mountains in New York.

15. *Fold Mountains. Type (a) Simple Folds; Type (b) Over-folded, Nappes, Thrusts.* Corrugations of sedimentary beds originally deposited in a geosynclinal trough. The attitudes and repeated sequences of the beds, resulting from their corrugation through horizontal compression, are the distinctive features of fold-mountain geomorphic units. Their summit altitudes, commonly of mountain height, may be the result of the folding or be due to regional upwarping of the folded sediments after more or less prolonged erosion. If the elevations are of a surface once worn to a monotonous low relief and then bowed up again, the course of the erosional cycle, conditioned by the re-elevated folded structure, will be accelerated and accentuated, but in other respects will not differ in its progress, or its expression, from that developed on the original folding. However, the structure resulting from original folding varies from simple symmetrical anticlines and synclines to nappes and overthrusts with corresponding differences in the pattern that results from erosion.

Type (*a*): Jura Mountains, Folded Appalachian Mountains; Type (*b*): The Alps.

16. *Fault-block Mountains.* These are geomorphic units by reason of the nature of their uplifting; hence are forms of process. Unlike the fold mountains they do not owe their significance solely to structure. Endogenic forces bring about the vertical or tilting uplift (relative) of notably thick, and, in some instances,

very extensive blocks of strongly consolidated rock. For the purpose of this classification the structure of the lifted blocks is to be regarded as complex. Then the surfaces and slopes acquired through the fault movement become the dominating factor in their erosional development. Actually a structure of almost any type may be involved in fault-block mountains. If such structure is sufficiently distinctive it will also be a factor in the erosional shaping of the block.

Sierra Nevada of California, Wasatch Mountains of Utah, Harz Mountains of Germany.

Group E

Geomorphic units best characterized in the group division as shields or ancient rigid masses. Topographically the Group E units have a plain, plateau, or dome expression. In general they are forms of process.

17. *Ancient Igneous and Metamorphic Shields.* Areas that have persisted as land masses through long geologic ages. If they have not been land areas uninterruptedly, they have been subjected to subaerial erosion so long and so continuously as to retain little or no trace of covering sediments. Such a history implies composition of ancient igneous and metamorphic rocks and maintenance of the areas at above sea-level altitudes of considerable height through most of the time of their existence. These elevations appear to be renewed from time to time as broad upwarpings.

Topographically represented by a plain in southern Finland; by a plateau in the Laurentian Shield of Canada; by a mountain mass in the Adirondacks.

18. *Peneplaned Sediments and Metamorphics.* The distinction between this type of unit and that of the ancient igneous and metamorphic shields is structural. The peneplaned sediments and metamorphics units comprise formations disposed more or less on edge (that is, having steep dips) uniformly cut across, truncated, by an erosion surface. They are, hence, a form of process and are distinctive geomorphic units in that they present areas that have experienced one complete cycle of erosion and are by this circumstance conditioned for their further geomorphic development.

Appalachian Piedmont, Upland of southeast New England.

19. *Continental Glaciers.* Ice domes of vast volume and continuity. "Rock" of completely uniform composition, igneous in the sense that it has originated by consolidation from the liquid or vapor phase of water by cooling or sublimation. Geomorphic units by virtue of their own relief expression and topographic forms. Despite their simple composition continental glaciers are put in the class of disordered structures because of contortions and faulting of their material and because they are agencies of process, owing to their movement, as well as geomorphic units.

The Greenland and the Antarctic icecaps.

The map, Geomorphic Units of South America, Plate I, serves to demonstrate the regional application of the geomorphic-units classification, and is authenticated by the appended bibliography. Although this list of works indicates that sufficient information is available to warrant the representation here made it will be appreciated that much of South America is still little known. Further studies will no doubt necessitate a shifting of the unit boundaries, or indeed disclose distinctive geomorphic units within the wide tracts here assigned to a single classification.

Bibliography Used in Constructing the map of

GEOMORPHIC UNITS OF SOUTH AMERICA

By George Berry

Anderson, F. M., Nonmarine Tertiary Deposits of Colombia: Geol. Soc. America, Bull., vol. 38, pp. 591–644, 1927.

Baker, C. L., The Lava Field of the Parana basin, South America: Jour. Geology, vol. 31, pp. 66–79, 1923.

Bosworth, T. O., Geology and Paleontology of Northwest Peru, London, The Macmillan Company, 1922.

Branner, J. C., Outlines of the Geology of Brazil: Geol. Soc. America, Bull., vol. 30, pp. 189–337, 1919.

Brown, C. B., On the Ancient River-deposit of the Amazon: Geol. Soc. London, Quart. Jour., vol. 35, pp. 763–777, 1879.

———, and Sawkins, J. G., Reports on the Geology of British Guiana, London, Longmans, Green & Company, 1875.

Bruggen, J., Grundzüge der Geologie und Lagerstättenkunde Chiles, Mathematisch-Natur-wissenschaftlichen Klasse der Heidelberger Akademie der Wissenschaften, 1934.

Douglas, J. A., Geological Sections through the Andes of Peru and Bolivia: Geol. Soc. London, Quart. Jour.; pt. 1, vol. 70, pp. 1–53, 1914; pt. 2, vol. 76, pp. 1–61, 1920.

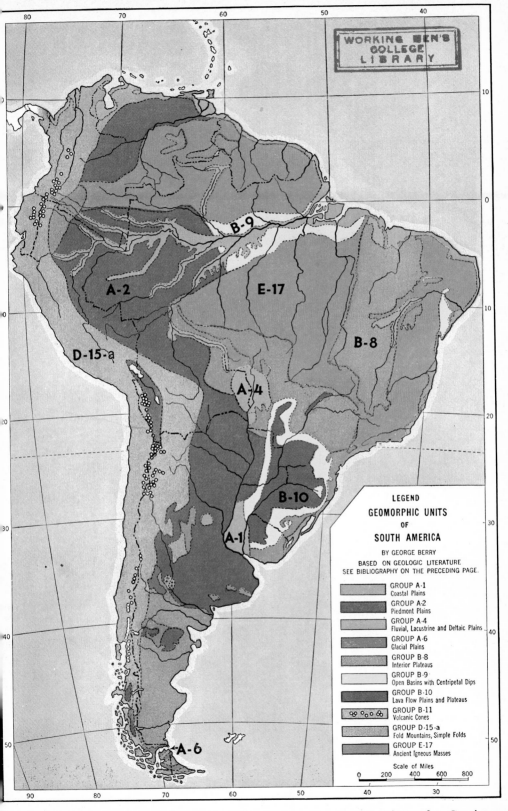

B-9

A-2

E-17

D-15-a

B-8

A-4

B-10

A-1

A-6

LEGEND

GEOMORPHIC UNITS

OF

SOUTH AMERICA

BY GEORGE BERRY

BASED ON GEOLOGIC LITERATURE
SEE BIBLIOGRAPHY ON THE PRECEDING PAGE.

GROUP A-1
Coastal Plains

GROUP A-2
Piedmont Plains

GROUP A-4
Fluvial, Lacustrine and Deltaic Plains

GROUP A-6
Glacial Plains

GROUP B-8
Interior Plateaus

GROUP B-9
Open Basins with Centripetal Dips

GROUP B-10
Lava Flow Plains and Plateaus

GROUP B-11
Volcanic Cones

GROUP D-15-a
Fold Mountains, Simple Folds

GROUP E-17
Ancient Igneous Masses

Scale of Miles

0   200   400   600   800

PLATE I.   Application of the Geomorphic Units Classification over the Area of a Continent.
Base map courtesy Denoyer-Geppert Company, Chicago.

Du Toit, A. L., and Reed, F. R. C., A Geological Comparison of South America with South Africa: Carnegie Inst., Washington, Pub. no. 381, 1927.

Engelman, Rolf, Geology of Venezuelan Andes: Am. Assoc. Petroleum Geologists, Bull., vol. 19, pp. 769–792, 1935.

Gerth, H., Geologie Südamerikas, Berlin, Gebrüder Borntraeger; erster Teil, 1932; zweiter Teil, 1935.

Harder, E. C., and Chamberlin, R. T., The Geology of Central Minas Geraes, Brazil: Jour. Geology, vol. 23; pt. 1, pp. 341–378; pt. 2, pp. 385–424; 1915.

Harrison, J. V., The Magdalena Valley, Colombia, South America: 15th Internat. Geol. Cong., South Africa, Compt. Rend., vol. 2, pp. 399–409, 1930.

Hauthal, R., Die Vulkangebiete in Chile und Argentinien: Petermanns Mitt., 49 Band, pp. 97–102, 1903.

Katzer, Friedrich, Grundzüge der Geologie des unteren Amazonasgebietes, Leipzig, Max Weg, 1903.

Kugler, H. G., Summary Digest of Geology of Trinidad: Am. Assoc. Petroleum Geologists, Bull., vol. 20, pp. 1439–1453, 1936.

Liddle, R. A., The Geology of Venezuela and Trinidad, Fort Worth, J. P. Mac-Gowan, 1928.

Lisson, C. L., Memoria sobre el mapa cronologico del levantamiento de los Andes Peruanos, Lima, 1924.

Little, J. M., The Geology and Metal Deposits of Chile, New York, Branwell Co., 1926.

Mather, K. F., Front Ranges of the Andes between Santa Cruz, Bolivia, and Embarcacion, Argentina: Geol. Soc. America, Bull., vol. 33, pp. 703–764, 1922.

Oliveira, E. P., Atlas geologico do Brasil, Rio de Janeiro, Servico Geologico e Mineralogico do Brasil, 1933–1934.

Oppenheim, Victor, Petroleum Geology of Central Sedimentary Basin of Uruguay: Am. Assoc. Petroleum Geologists, Bull., vol. 19, pp. 1205–1218, 1935.

———, Petroleum Geology of Gondwana Rocks of Southern Brazil: Am. Assoc. Petroleum Geologists, Bull., vol. 19, pp. 1725–1805, 1935.

———, Geology of Devonian Areas of Parana Basin in Brazil, Uruguay, and Paraguay: Am. Assoc. Petroleum Geologists, Bull., vol. 20, pp. 1208–1236, 1936

Reed, F. R. C., The Geology of the British Empire, London, Edward Arnold, 1921.

Sapper, Karl, Vulkankunde, Stuttgart, J. Engelhorn's Nachf., 1927.

Schaffer, F. X., Lehrbuch der Geologie, 3 Teil, Geologische Länderkunde (Regionale Geologie), 3 Lief., pp. 251–288; 4 Lief., pp. 289–315, 1932–1933.

Schuchert, Charles, Historical Geology of the Antillean-Caribbean region, New York, John Wiley & Sons, Inc., 1935.

Sheppard, George, The Geology of South-western Ecuador, London, Thomas Murby & Co., 1937.

Smith, Guy-Harold, Physiographic Diagram of South America, New York, The Geographical Press, 1925.

Steinmann, G., Geologie von Peru, Heidelberg, Carl Winters, 1929.

Sullivan, H. B., Catalogue of Geological Maps of South America: Am. Geog. Soc., research ser., no. 9, 1922.

Windhausen, Anselmo, Geologia Argentina; segunda parte, Geologia historica y regional del territorio Argentino; Buenos Aires, Jacobo Peuser, Ltda., 1931.

TABULAR SUMMARY OF THE CLASSIFICATION OF GEOMORPHIC UNITS

Group A

Simple structures
In general unconsolidated (?) sediments

1. Coastal plains
2. Piedmont plains
3. Tundra plains
4. Fluvial, lacustrine, and deltaic plains
5. Desert erg or Koum areas
6. Glacial plains (till and outwash)
7. Loessial plains

Group B

Simple structures
Consolidated rocks

8. Interior plateaus
9. Open basins with centripetal dips (nested saucers)
10. Lava flow plains and plateaus
11. Volcanic cones

Group C

Simple structures
Consolidated rocks
Limestone Composition

12. Karst units
13. Coral islands

Group D

Fold and Fault Structures
Consolidated rocks
Commonly composed of or involving sedimentaries

14. Dome uplifts
    Type (a) laccolithic
    Type (b) deep-seated
15. Fold mountains
    Type (a) Simple folds
    Type (b) Overfolded, nappes, thrusts
16. Fault-block mountains

Group E

Shield units—Ancient rigid masses
Metamorphic and igneous rocks
Plain, plateau, mountain topography
Long erosional history

17. Ancient igneous masses
18. Peneplaned sediments and metamorphics
19. Continental glaciers

The American School versus the German School of Geomorphology. In numerous instances the classification of geomorphic units outlined above depends on characterizations that themselves require elucidation. This is a defect that is remedied concurrently with progress in geomorphic study. In defense of the system it may be said that it is forward-looking and comprehensive. The units are so defined that their sequential development from an initial condition may be made the chief concern of geomorphic science. This formulation represents, if not perfectly, at least the essential aspect of the American approach and the American attitude in geomorphology as developed and sponsored by W. M. Davis. With one exception this American approach has been accorded acceptance by the geomorphologists of other nationalities. Foreign workers have, indeed, made notable contributions to geomorphic science through studies and papers based on the American concept.

The discordant note comes from Germany. It is rather important that the nature of the German objections to the American school be clearly appreciated in order to understand that different approaches to geomorphology are possible. The development of the controversy is described at length by O. Maull (1938, pp. 13–19) who is hostile to the American school. Davis (1924, pp. xiii–xxvi) has written in his own and its defense.

Before the Americans, Powell, Dutton, Gilbert, and Davis came on the scene the Germans had a number of eminent students of geography, including A. v. Humboldt, Ferdinand v. Richthofen, Karl Ritter, A. Supan, and A. Penck, who endeavored to classify land forms and to systematize study of these forms in accordance with various concepts. Their several schemes lacked a convincing, unifying principle. The evolutionary development proposed by Davis provided such a key. The Germans appear to have been resentful of its ready acceptance by other European scholars. They attacked the American formulation on two general grounds, oversimplification, and its divorcement from geology. They said the scheme was not valid because certain steps in the sequence of development postulated were not represented by actual occurrences. In part their objections were petty fault-finding based on inconsequential and wilful misconstructions of the American teaching. They argued that the course of change was not cyclic as Davis maintained; rather it was a continuous degradational sequence. They objected to a form of youth being on the one hand the result of only short-time application of process, and on the other an expression of marked structural resistance to degradational action. They accused Davis and the Americans of neglecting the study of processes as such. In particular they urged that geomorphic analysis as practiced by Davis rests on a false assumption; namely that a geomorphic unit has almost instantaneous endogenic creation and uplift and then stays put while degradational action takes its course. This, they said, is a special case and perhaps not even a common one. The uplift rather may be very slow, intermittent, accelerated at the start or at the close, or any conceivable combination of these variables. Not so clearly voiced, but nevertheless evident in German geomorphic writing, is unwillingness to recognize the importance of the role of structural difference in conditioning the course of development and giving rise to distinctive landscape features.

Davis combatted especially the misconstruing of his terms and the special case argument. In regard to the terms he made clear that the Germans were either very stupid or very captious. In answering the special case argument, he pointed out, first, that many of the other possibilities were actually incorporated in his scheme; second, that the prominence given the sequence of uplift, stillstand, and degradation was to insure simplicity and clarity in demonstration.

That Davis gave only cursory attention to process must be admitted. Also it is becoming more and more clear that exact knowledge of process is essential to true interpretation of many geomorphic forms. Such study is, however, the particular province of the dynamic geologist. The geomorphologist could, not unfairly, expect the dynamic geologist to provide him with adequate data. But if the dynamic geologist has not done the work it is necessary for the geomorphologist to undertake examination of process because the verity of a geomorphic interpretation will not uncommonly depend on a correct understanding of this factor.

It may be inferred that if the Germans were completely candid they would admit that for the most part the objections they have raised do not significantly invalidate the American position. The considerable attention later given to such criticism arose chiefly from the introduction of a novel concept of the field, forms, and functions of geomorphology originating in Germany with Walther Penck (1924), who died in 1923. Walther Penck proposed that the goal of geomorphic studies should be to trace the course of crustal movements. Instead of interpretation of the forms of the earth's surface being an end result, such knowledge, according to W. Penck, should serve rather to provide clues to an understanding of the manner and sequence of endogenic action. Indeed W. Penck anticipated that through geomorphic studies, so pursued, the ultimate problem of geology, the cause of crustal movements, could be solved. Thus the W. Penck program is, by contrast with the "forward looking" Davisian system, geologic in its attitudes, that is, "backward looking."

Aside from the difficulty of realizing an objective so ambitious as his, if the field of geomorphology were restricted to the area suggested by Penck's formulation it would be severely limited. The chief and almost sole concern of the science would be with land forms undergoing, or that had undergone uplift by warping, lateral thrust, or vertical heaving. Thus practically all geomorphic features due to glacial action would be omitted from consideration as of no significance. Geomorphology would become an analysis of slopes, and such study would be made to discover the nature, rate, and history of crustal movements.

It is interesting to note that while the Germans assailed Davis for making, as they asserted, uplift and stillstand, of units structurally varied, the normal condition for the initiation of a geomorphic cycle, W. Penck appears to have been obsessed with the conviction that geomorphic development is associated fundamentally with the slow, rapid, intermittent, accelerated, or decelerated rise of an expanding dome of uniform structure. This difference in approach perhaps arises from the fact that Davis was early impressed with the diversity of structure, as this is encountered in America, whereas W. Penck knew best the essential uniformity of attitude and composition characteristic of the mountain blocks of Central Europe.

By directing attention to the possible significance of slopes for the interpretation of crustal movement W. Penck made a significant contribution. This contribution, however, merely supplements, or perhaps enlarges, inferences and conclusions of the same purport to be gained from other geomorphic evidence. The American formulation is, on the other hand, comprehensive. The genesis, course of development, and explanatory, comparative evaluation of all land forms are its field. As already pointed out it acquaints itself with the structural unit, then looks forward through process to stage.

In the chapters that follow, the American approach is used but attention is given at appropriate points to the significant contributions in the W. Penck formulations.

SUMMARY

The forms of the third order of relief on lands result chiefly from subaerial processing. Units of the second order of relief provide the locale for this application of processes and set the conditions for its progress. To understand the development of the third-order forms it is necessary to know what second-order forms there are, and how they differ.

For geomorphic studies classification of the items of the second order of relief is most significantly based on structure, which, in turn, derives from the geologic history of the particular unit that is being scrutinized. Altitude and geographic position are other factors to be taken into consideration.

The broadest and simplest distinction that may be made between second-order units, for the stated purpose, is that between horizontal and disordered structures. Further classification is more difficult. Physiographic provinces will not serve the end in view. Physiographic provinces are identified by place names, and each one is unique because of the place relationship. The delineation of a physiographic province, further, is the outcome, not the antecedent of geomorphic analysis.

To meet the requirements indicated by this disqualification of physiographic provinces 19 different geomorphic units are defined and fitted into a classification. When it is known where an area fits in this classification a proper basis for the study of its third-order land forms is established.

The approach to geomorphology thus formulated is in accordance with the precepts of the American school and may be characterized as forward-looking. It is to be contrasted with the German attitude which is in effect backward-looking. The German objective is an elucidation of the geologic, that is, the past history of a geomorphic unit by study of its third-order relief forms, in particular its slopes. Although the German concept, in its broader aspects, has won little acceptance; the contentions it makes have greatly stimulated geomorphic study.

BIBLIOGRAPHY

CLASSICAL

Richthofen, F. v. (1886) *Führer für Forschungsreisende,* Jänecke, Hanover.

Penck, A. (1894) *Morphologie der Erdoberfläche,* J. Engelhorn, Stuttgart.

Davis, W. M. (1899) *The Geographical Cycle,* Geographical Journal, Vol. 14, pp. 481, 504.

Davis, W. M. (1909) *Complications of the Geographical Cycle.* In *Geographical Essays,* Ginn and Company, Boston, pp. 279–295.

RECENT

Penck, Walther (1924) *Die morphologische Analyse,* J. Engelhorn's Nachf., Stuttgart.

Davis, W. M. (1932) *Piedmont Benchlands and Primärrümpfe,* Bulletin Geological Society of America, Vol. 43, pp. 399–440.

Machatschek, F. (1938) *Das Relief der Erde,* Gebrüder Borntraeger, Berlin.

Symposium: Walther Penck's Contribution to Geomorphology. Reprint of the December 1940 number of the Annals of the Association of American Geographers, Vol. XXX, No. 4.

Howard, A. D. and Spock, L. E. (1940) *Classification of Land Forms,* Journal of Geomorphology, Vol. 3, pp. 332–345.

Chapter Five

PROCESS, STAGE, AND THE GEOMORPHIC CYCLE

Process. In books on general geology the discussion of processes is mainly devoted to the manner of their action. That is to
say, the physics and chemistry of their operation are considered
to be the significant matters. For geomorphic interpretation it is
sometimes necessary to demonstrate that certain processes are
competent to bring about a particular result, and even to describe
how they operate. But generally it suffices, in geomorphology,
to refer to a process by its accepted geologic name, under the
assumption that the manner and progress of its action are clearly
understood because they have been investigated by students in
the field of dynamic geology.

The geomorphologist's objective is to be able to recognize the
effect of each different process on the form of the land. Further
he wishes to discern how, and how vigorously, the process has
been applied, and to predict the result of the continuation of the
action. As each person's handwriting is different from that of
every other person so each process is found to leave its distinctive
mark on the landscape.

Although what is said above applies with equal force to destructive and constructive processes, it is with degradational changes
that the geomorphologist is usually concerned.

When rocks are being destroyed and removed the factor of
structure must be given consideration in attempting interpretations. Here an important principle applies. It is that structural
variations are most influential in determining the land forms to
be developed when the rock is subjected to a process that is delicate and discriminating in its attack. This principle is more
convincingly expressed when the emphasis is shifted. Consider
the force exerted by process to be so great that the complete
range of difference in resistance that rocks possess becomes a

74

FIG. 24.   BRYCE CANYON, UTAH

The delicate sculpture of beating rain and of solution processes; here given its pattern
by joints and stratification planes.   Photograph by courtesy of the Union Pacific Railroad Company.

FIG. 25.   DISENCHANTMENT BAY, ALASKA

A plane surface cut across rocks of varying resistance by wave erosion, later uplifted to appear as a wave-cut bench.

negligible factor. Under these circumstances differential yield will be minimized. The forms that result will reflect the dominance of the application of process (v. Engeln, O. D., 1937a; 1938a).

As examples of the two extremes of difference that may result, the intricate sculpture effected by rainwash and delicate solution

FIG. 26. TEXAS HOLLOW AND THE APPALACHIAN PLATEAU, CENTRAL NEW YORK
The great trough of Texas Hollow and the rounded modelling of the rock hills in the middle and far distance result from the mass erosion by continental glaciers. Airplane photograph by Cecil Robinson.

action at Bryce Canyon, Utah (Fig. 24), may be contrasted with the uniform plane made by the sea as it develops a wave-cut platform by smashing wave attack (Fig. 25). In the case of glaciers the agency is exceedingly massive and its erosional attack, in consequence, is apparently able to mold rock topography to aspects which are clearly a reflection of such action and have practically no relation to the structure or composition of the rock subjected to this glacial shaping (Fig. 26).

There are no clearly defined limits for the lower levels to

which the degradational effects of weathering, wind, and glacial
processes may be extended.   But wave action and the erosional
processes resulting from running water have the sea surface as
their *base level.*   In the case of waves, the depth of the base of
the greatest waves; in the case of rivers, the depth of the water
current where it enters the sea, actually fix the lowest base-level
altitudes.   In the broader sense it is proper to assert that when
the degradational processes of streams have succeeded in reducing
a region to the altitude of the ocean surface their action will stop.
An erosion cycle will then have been brought to its close.

The erosional processes of running water are peculiarly susceptible to the influence of structure.   While the geomorphic
forms that are produced by stream action will be only slightly
conditioned by rock and structural differences of a minor kind,
grosser variations of composition and structure are everywhere
reflected in the valley forms that result from stream erosion, and
the whole course of a stream may be adjusted to such differences.
Again, the action of running water is almost universally an agency
in the sculpture of the land.   These circumstances, together with
the clearly marked limitation imposed on the action of streams
by the sea-level base, permit the identification of steps in the
changes effected by streams with a certainty that is not (at least
not as yet) possible in respect to other agencies and processes.
These recognizable steps are appropriately referred to as stages.

Stage.   This term has occasioned much controversy in the
history of geomorphic study because often its true meaning has
not been grasped.   When a geomorphic feature, most commonly
a valley cross section, is said to be in a certain stage, it is meant
to indicate that its development by process has proceeded to a
given one of the characteristic points in the series of changes that
must ensue between a beginning and an end condition.   The
reference by such designation is to the form arrived at, and has
nothing to do with the measure of time required to bring about
that stage.   There are, further, and interestingly, rather clearly
recognizable transition points between any given stage and the
one that follows it.

The idea can be well expressed by turning to analogies.   Thus
when a primitive human set out to make an arrow head the work
proceeded by stages.   First there was the rough blocking out of the

piece of flint, then the stage of main shaping, finally the stage of giving finishing touches. An archaeologist coming upon the site of an arrow workshop could easily, without hesitation, classify his finds into these stages.

It will be readily understood that different arrow makers would require different lengths of time to fashion an arrow to any one of these stages. Also that some materials would require more time to work than others. Hence "stage" is not synonymous with "the measure of time." However there is some warrant for confusing time and stage. Stratigraphers have been known to use the words "age" and "stage" interchangeably with reference to rock beds; they denote by these words both specific time periods and sequence in time, and, recently, are actually able to date rock stages (ages) in the geologic history of the earth in terms of years since the present. In geomorphology it is the aspect of the terrain, not the length of time required to develop that aspect, that is significant.

Davis introduced three chief terms to designate stage: *youth, maturity* (Fig. 27), *old age.* These have found general acceptance. The comparison with life these terms imply makes another difficulty. However, in popular language years are discounted when an old person is said to display youthful vigor, to have a youthful skin. To make this distinction Davis compared willows and oaks. One may observe young willows and old willows. But a young oak may, in years, be as old as an old willow and still be a young oak.

One further complication arises from the fact that with very weak structures and very rapid processes the stage of youth, or even that of maturity, may be very transitory. A region may leap almost immediately into old age. Contrariwise, youth and, more commonly, maturity, may endure for a very long time. Again, with very slow uplift it is a possibility that neither the stage of youth nor that of maturity will ever be realized. If degradation keeps pace with uplift the relief forms of youth and maturity cannot come into existence. Davis recognized this combination and pointed out some of the consequences. He thought of it, however, as a very special case; whereas the German geomorphologists led by Walther Penck have made it a main point of departure. It is their *primärrmpf* concept, that is, a region which

FIG. 27. LATE MATURE STAGE IN THE FLUVIAL GEOMORPHIC CYCLE, SWEDEN VALLEY, APPALACHIAN PLATEAU, PENNSYLVANIA

Study the forms of the valley floor and of the slopes to note how well they conform to the analytical descriptions of this stage.

78

is at an end stage, vastly degraded, near base level in altitude, but which never had attained significant height nor had a large measure of relief.

By glorifying the primärrumpf these Germans sought to establish their broader contention; namely that the very numerous possibilities of difference in rate of uplift make the development of a succession of recognizable stages, due to the action of degradational processes during a period of stillstand, only feasible by improbable coincidence.

The answer to this argument is, first, the general body of geologic knowledge indicates that relatively rapid uplift, followed by long periods of stability, is the ordinary sequence (Bucher, W. H., 1939, p. 422). The uplifted areas do, in effect, wait for the degradational action to follow its appointed course. Second, with understanding of the forms resulting from such an ideal sequence, departures from it are discoverable, and constitute interruptions of the normal cycle. It is because each such variation does leave its distinguishing mark that interpretations of complex geomorphic histories can be made. These interpretations, in turn, may provide clues to an understanding of endogenic action, as the Penckians proclaim. Meanwhile, with reference to continents and islands, the province of geomorphology is the appreciation of the land forms as such.

The Geomorphic Cycle. Davis called the succession of stages, from an initial to an end condition, the geographic cycle. It may better be termed the *geomorphic cycle* (Lawson, A. C., 1894, p. 253).

If it be assumed that a region, once uplifted or created, does experience a period of stability, succinctly a stillstand during which degradation takes place, and if it be further assumed that this region is structurally a geomorphic unit of which there are counterparts elsewhere, then certain consequences should follow. The induced changes in relief and form should be progressive. They should have a beginning and an end. The forms produced at a given stage should have equivalent expression in each geomorphic unit of that type. They should, therefore, be identifiable, hence subject to comparison and classification. The classification, by virtue of the manner in which its categories are obtained, will be geomorphically explanatory of an area to which a particular classification is given. As the region experiences the successive stages, it goes through the geomorphic cycle.

The explanatory designations, by word or phrase, of the geomorphic cycle scheme serve several purposes. They are a short cut in description. They permit a visualization of what went before and what is to come. They imply numerous corollary phenomena. As Davis puts it, ability to apply the explanatory terms of the geomorphic cycle enables the observer "to see what he looks at and to say what he sees."

It is, however, ordinarily the practice to use three different types of terms. If a writer seeks to be noncommittal, or the item has no significance for the particular discussion, he will say cliff, gorge, lake, island, the so-called empirical terms. If structural relations are his chief concern such phrases as monoclinal ridge, transverse valley, serve the purpose. These are geologic designations. When, however, he writes mature dissection, monadnock, adjusted drainage, graded slopes, he is employing the explanatory terms to which the concept of the geomorphic cycle has given rise.

SUMMARY

The chief concern of geomorphology with geologic processes is to learn their role in modifying relief, and the rate at which they effect change in relief. Delicate processes search out and make manifest details of structure; grosser processes permit larger structural variations to get expression in the forms of the land. Broadly speaking the processing of the lands is limited to the base level fixed by the altitude of the surface of the sea. Of first importance for the geomorphology of the lands are the processes associated with the action of running water.

The changes in land forms resulting from the application of process are progressive and are marked by identifiable stages. The successive emergences of these stages are not governed merely by the lapse of time. The more resistant the structure and the feebler the process, the longer the time required to achieve a given stage in the geomorphic cycle. Under certain conditions a given stage or stages will have a very transitory existence or will be missing from the sequence normally followed. These variations do not invalidate the concept of the geomorphic cycle.

The fact that the features and phenomena of a given form stage on a given type of geomorphic unit will be duplicated if similar processes act on similar structures for a similar time at some other location makes possible concise explanatory descriptions of land forms. The conciseness then achieved depends greatly on the utilization of an extensive vocabulary of geomorphic terms.

BIBLIOGRAPHY

CLASSICAL

Greenwood, G. (1857) *Rain and Rivers,* Longmans, Green & Company, London.

Davis, W. M. (1909) *Base-Level, Grade, and Peneplain,* in *Geographical Essays,* Ginn and Company, Boston, pp. 381–412.

RECENT

Fenneman, N. M. (1936) *Cyclic and Non-Cyclic Aspects of Erosion,* Science, Vol. 83, pp. 87–94.

v. Engeln, O. D. (1938) *Glacial Geomorphology and Glacier Motion,* American Journal of Science, Vol. XXXV, pp. 426–440.

Chapter Six

THE PENEPLAIN CONCEPT

The Doctrine of Uniformitarianism. Throughout the medieval period of European history it was thought that the earth had acquired its surface configuration by catastrophic action. Sudden, violent change in the era of creation was held to be responsible for the relief of the lands. Once made, mountain and plain were considered to have endured unchanged and to be unchanging. Eventually, however, better understanding was gained, and it came to be perceived that land forms result from noncatastrophic upheavals and from slow degradation of the elevated areas. The greatest single contribution to this new knowledge was made by Hutton and Playfair. At a later date Lyell asserted that the same processes, and no others, acting in the present, have acted in the past and will act in the future and at the same rate under similar climatic conditions to make and modify land forms. This represents a complete reversal in thought from the medieval view. In the extreme form Lyell gave to it, the modern approach is referred to as the doctrine of uniformitarianism.

Since Lyell's time the pendulum has swung back from the completely uniformitarian interpretations he advocated. It is realized that there have been geologic periods of much greater intensity of change than now, also times when the pace of landscape alteration was much slower than at present. Further, certain agencies, no longer in action, notably continental glaciers in the middle latitudes, were once completely dominant over wide regions.

The doctrine of uniformitarianism, with its motto, "the present is the key to the past," applies only if numerous qualifications and exceptions are kept in mind.

Nevertheless it is the general applicability of the uniformitarianism dictum that gives validity to the concept of the geomorphic cycle. If uniformitarianism prevails there will be time for a geomorphic cycle to run its course. The cycle idea, to be sure, was not in the minds of the proposers of the doctrine of uniformitarianism. But it is this outcome of their proposals which has first significance for geomorphology.

For if an indefinitely long period is at the disposal of the normal degradational processes and agencies, namely weathering processes and streams flowing down to the sea, it is obvious that such activity will eventually bring about the reduction of the highest and broadest of uplifted regions to an ultimately lowest level. Powell pointed out that the surface of the sea would be the grand base level of such erosion; Davis called the land form, which had been reduced in altitude until it approximated this lowest ultimate level, a peneplain.

It has been suggested that the term should be *peneplane,* because the area is planed down to a nearly level condition. However the word "plane" suggests a geometrical surface, which the peneplain is not, and divorces the term from its geographic connotation. On the other hand it seems desirable to make the verb for the process be "peneplane." Thus: "The region was peneplaned in Tertiary time. Only very small remnants of this peneplain persist in the present."

Davis (1902, *Essays,* 1909, p. 408) sought to establish a distinction between "denudation" and "degradation." "Denudation" should apply to processes by which rock structures are laid bare because waste is removed as fast as it is formed, effective early in the cycle, "degradation" to the slower removal of the continuous waste cover characteristic of the later stages of the cycle. But as there is need for one term to express general reduction of elevation, *degradation* is chosen for use in this book in the sense that it will contrast with *aggradation,* the building up of a surface by deposition.

Occurrence and Characteristics of Peneplains. Few, if any, peneplains now exist at the near sea-level altitude of their development. The nearest known approach to that condition is southern Finland (Machatschek, F., 1938, p. 182). The Finnish area has the appropriate low altitude and there is evidence of its having experienced the long history of subaerial degradation necessary for peneplain development, but the rock surface of the Finnish region, if it was a true peneplain, has since been greatly modified by glacial action. As unchanged peneplains *in situ* are not avail-

able for observational study many of the characteristics of peneplains must be deductively inferred. The uplifted, more or less
dissected, peneplain surface is a marker of the same kind, but
of even greater significance, to the geomorphologist that the stratification plane is to the stratigrapher.

It is assumed that a widespread peneplanation will extend
across rocks and structures differing greatly in their resistance to

FIG. 28.   PENEPLAIN, SURFACE OF THE APPALACHIAN PIEDMONT NEAR SPROUSE,
VIRGINIA

View looks west toward the Blue Ridge Mountains. Metamorphic and
igneous rocks varying greatly in resistance to degradation underlie this
widespread plain. The monadnock, Willis Mountain, Fig. 32, is directly east
from this site.

the degradational action of weathering processes and to those of
running water (Fig. 28). If these unlike materials have all been
reduced to the essentially uniform level of the peneplain, the
surface so developed must truncate the varying beds and structures indifferently. Throughout the history of the degradation,
weathering processes were disintegrating and decomposing the
rock, preparing it for removal. At the surface of the peneplain
there should be a deep mantle of rock waste (Fig. 29). This

mantle will be composed of weathering products on the divide areas, of extensive alluvial deposits on the valley floors. Streams flowing across a peneplain may be assumed to have lost all contact with the underlying bedrock. Near the sea the larger rivers will wander in slow meandering courses over broad flats of stream-deposited sediment.

FIG. 29.   RESIDUAL SOIL AND BOULDERS OF DECOMPOSITION
Below peneplain surface. Road cut near Athens, Georgia.

Inland some measure of relief will persist. The slope of the peneplain surface must reach back to, and terminate in an upland divide region (Fig. 30) of sufficient altitude to permit the flow of drainage from its hilly environs to the sea. It is also improbable that peneplain development is ordinarily so perfect as to afford the monotonously level, lowland reaches that some have imagined should be present near the sea borders (Fig. 31). Valleys and divides will even there continue to be differentiated by low undulations. The sites underlain by the stronger rocks and structures will still be represented by areas of higher-than-average altitudes. Surmounting the uneven, but generally low plain, isolated

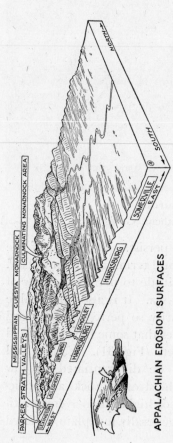

APPALACHIAN EROSION SURFACES

Fig. 30. APPALACHIAN EROSION SURFACES, ACCORDING TO W. STORRS COLE

Note the upland divide area, with culminating monadnocks, from which the earlier peneplain surfaces, Schooley, Allegheny, Harrisburg, Lexington, since uplifted and dissected, sloped east and west. Drawing by Steve Barker.

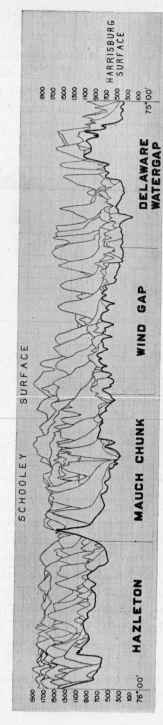

Fig. 31. PROJECTED PROFILES ON EAST TO WEST LINE ACROSS THE TOPOGRAPHIC SHEETS NAMED

Illustrates the analysis of contoured maps for uplifted and dissected erosion surfaces by the method of projected profiles. The vertical scale is a twenty-six times exaggeration of the horizontal scale. Analysis by W. Storrs Cole.

86

FIG. 32. WILLIS MOUNTAIN, VIRGINIA

A monadnock of quartzite and kyanite rock rising abruptly from the pene-planed surface of the Appalachian Piedmont. Southeast of Charlottesville, Virginia.

FIG. 33. MT. MONADNOCK, NEW HAMPSHIRE

The mountain from which the generic name, "monadnock," is derived. Rises above the dissected peneplain constituting the New England upland. Photograph by Charles Keene.

87

summits rising to considerable heights may be present (Fig. 32). Such summits are *monadnocks,* named for the type example, Mt. Monadnock in New Hampshire (Fig. 33). Monadnocks standing above the peneplain level at points near the sea are held to have survived the general downwearing because they are composed of rock of exceptional durability. These are *härtlinge* (hard ones) in the German terminology. Monadnocks that are part of the more remote unreduced divide areas are *restberge* (remainder mountains), also called *fernlinge* (distant ones), and, in karst lands (Maull, O., 1938, p. 272), *mosore.*

German Terminology. Here, and in succeeding chapters, numerous German geomorphic terms are introduced and defined. The Germans have earnestly endeavored to establish a system of geomorphic interpretation wholly independent of the American formulation. Their concepts and criticisms afford a valuable, and the only check on, accepted doctrine. The German approaches cannot be appreciated except as the German terms are understood. While the German system has little prospect of supplanting the American tenets many of the ideas it includes have won respectful hearing, and are much debated by American geomorphologists.

German Terms for Degradational Surfaces. The Germans use "peneplain" or its literal translation, *fastebene,* to designate a degradational surface that has resulted from the conventional Davis cycle, namely rapid uplift, followed by stillstand and downwearing. If the Germans wish to be noncommittal in regard to the genesis of such a surface they call it a *rumpffläche,* which translates "torso-plain," and means in effect a plain extending across a region underlain by massive or undifferentiated rocks. When it is sought to distinguish between different rumpfflächen with regard to origins they are divided into two classes, those of primärrümpfe and of endrümpfe. The term *endrumpf* (terminal-torso), like the word "fastebene," means "peneplain," but when "endrumpf" is used a German writer means that he considers the surface in question to be the end stage of a land mass that originally had high relief but has been leveled down by degradation. But the word "endrumpf" does not imply a particular sequence of development leading up to the terminal plain.

Primärrumpf, as already noted, is the special concept of W.

Penck. It was Penck's idea that when a portion of the sea floor is lifted above sea level, or when any block of the earth's crust, with an originally featureless surface, is upheaved, the uplift begins so slowly that degradation is of equal measure over all the region affected. That is to say, no relief resulting from the presence of valleys and divides develops on the rising dome. In other words valley erosion proceeds so slowly that divides are concurrently erased; the sole topographic development is that of the torso emergent because of the uplift (Fenneman, 1936, p. 92, gave independent expression to this idea, and referred to it as *noncyclic erosion*). Penck argued further that such would be the initial circumstances of all new land units resulting from uplift. The featureless degradational plain thus brought into being is a primärrumpf, that is, an initial torso. When the rate of uplift becomes sufficiently accelerated to permit valley development in the rising dome the unit is still to be regarded as a primärrumpf because it had the rumpffläche-surface to start with. The sides of valleys developed in a primärrumpf that is undergoing active dissection will exhibit convex slopes, whereas those of an endrumpf will be concave. The reason for this difference in form of the slope-curves is asserted to be the fact of acceleration of the rate of uplift in the case of the primärrumpf; declining rate of uplift, or stillstand, in the case of the endrumpf. A primärrumpf-surface, like that of an endrumpf, may extend across the edges of inclined beds. Thus level surfaces in the summit areas of young, lofty, fold mountains, specifically such surfaces observed in the Argentinean Andes, are interpreted to be remnants of primärrümpfe, not endrümpfe. The line of thought here followed is that neither the geologic circumstances nor the time available would have permitted these territories to have been reduced to the fastebene, peneplain, endrumpf, or terminal type of erosional plain. To indicate the deceptive resemblance of such high mountain flats to peneplains the Germans proposed that they should be designated *trugrümpfe* (pseudo-torsos) (Machatschek, F., 1934, p. 58).

Where a rumpffläche is encountered the existence of a torso, or massive body of rock is inferred. To specify a degradational surface of low relief that extends across inclined but nearly horizontal beds, a plain which bevels the edges of such layers at a

FIG. 34. STRIPPED PLAIN, CANYON DE CHELLY NATIONAL MONUMENT

The strong bed whose top surface governs the level of the plain shows clearly in the middle distance at the upper edge of Monument Canyon. The plain was stripped at a low altitude and has been uplifted in recent geologic times. Photograph, Copyright, from Spence Air Photos.

very low angle, the term *schnittfläche* is used. Like the primär-rümpfe, the schnittflächen are thought to result from uplift so slow that the reduction by degradation can keep pace with it over all the area of gently inclined strata constituting the unit. It is conceded that this development is impossible if the beds differ greatly in their resistance to degradational processes.

Peneplains versus Structural Plains. The work of the Germans has made it clear that not every nearly level surface that extends uninterruptedly across diverse rock beds and structures is to be assigned offhand to the peneplain classification. On the other hand, in the same manner that the sedimentary record is the chief content of stratigraphy, so degradational surfaces are the principal indexes of geomorphology. It follows that a nice discrimination must be exercised in the identification and differentiation of such surfaces and in distinguishing between them and surfaces of other origins which simulate them.

The *structural,* or *stripped plain,* deserves first attention in this connection (Fig. 34). If a very durable, horizontal stratum is present immediately below an extensive level surface that exists at a considerable altitude above the ultimate base level of the sea, or, indeed, above adjoining lower lands, it is a warranted first inference that the elevated surface is governed by the top side of the flat-lying, resistant rock bed. The Appalachian Plateau, as an interior plateau geomorphic unit, has the durable Pocono and Pottsville sandstones, and these appear to be important factors in the control of its summit altitudes. Weaker beds originally overlying these resistant layers have been disintegrated and removed. Thus "stripped plain" is applicable to the summit levels of this plateau. But as Fenneman (1936, p. 91) argues, to do a clean job of stripping a resistant horizontal bed of its weak cover materials over wide areas is just as difficult as to make a perfect peneplain. Both structural and topographic plains tend to take horizontal attitudes. The coincidence of the structural and topographic surfaces is therefore expectable and does not in itself imply that they are genetically related. If a stripped, structural plain stands high above the surrounding territory its margins will be subject to very active erosional dissection (Fig. 35). The question is: Can these edges be maintained in a given position long enough to permit a widespread area of the upper surface of a resistant bed to be stripped at high altitudes? Plains of narrow area, unquestionably of the structural type, are common; concerning the origin of plains of larger dimensions that appear to be so conditioned there is considerable dispute.

The Edwards Plateau in Texas and the Great Sage Plain of southeastern Utah and southwestern Colorado are cited as examples in point. The Edwards Plateau has a surface 1000 to 3000 feet above sea level (400 to 1200 feet above its surroundings), governed

FIG. 35. DISSECTED EDGE OF STRIPPED PLAIN, PAINTED DESERT, ARIZONA

Illustrates clearly how the margins of a stripped plain are rapidly dissected by erosional attack following uplift. Photograph, Copyright, from Spence Air Photos.

by the Edwards limestone beds. These beds constitute resistant strata in the Texas climate but their edges are nevertheless being very rapidly indented. The rate at which the borders of the Edwards Plateau are now being made to retreat would not allow time for the development of a widespread upland structural plain by stripping. In view of these circumstances it is a warranted inference that the stripping was accomplished at a much lower altitude, perhaps near base level. This interpretation is confirmed by the finding that the surface bevels across the edges of the several beds.

The upland surface of the Great Sage Plain coincides with that of the top of the Dakota sandstone at altitudes of 6000 or 7000 feet above the sea. It appears to be a perfect stripped plain. But it is being very rapidly invaded from the sides by deep branching canyons. It is very improbable that a plain so extensive as this one is could have been maintained on the upper surface of the Dakota bed while the shale which once covered the Dakota was disintegrated and washed away, if the plain was subject to such attack by canyon streams at its edges. The stripping very obviously must have taken place at a much lower altitude. In that event the process of the reduction was in effect a peneplanation.

The Treppen Concept. The presence of remnants of numerous erosion surfaces at different levels, inferred to be remainders of earlier peneplains, has been explained (Meyerhoff, H. A., and Hubbell, M., 1927–28) as a response to intermittent, *per saltum,* vertical uplifts of the region where they occur. According to this *treppen* (stair steps) *concept* of multiple erosion surfaces each uplift introduces a **knickpunkt** (Fig. 106) in the course of the trunk stream of the region, that is, a waterfall or rapids site which tends to migrate upstream. Below the knickpunkt the stream proceeds to erode its bed toward the new base level afforded by the uplift. In doing this it first cuts a gorge which has steep walls. The gradient of the bottom of the stream below the knickpunkt is, however, relatively gentle. Under the attack of weathering the walls of the gorge retreat from either side of the stream but are maintained as steep declivities. Their angle of slope may be less steep than that of the gorge walls in which they have their origin, but, once established, remains constant as the walls are wasted back by weathering. The result of their retreat is to develop a triangular plain at the level of the stream gradient, with its apex at the knickpunkt, but wider, progressively, downstream. A succeeding uplift introduces a new knickpunkt at the lower end of the plain first formed and the sequence is repeated. The same effect follows with each further uplift. Meanwhile expansion of the highest level plain proceeds, and is, indeed, facilitated because the knickpunkt reaches tributary streams and retreats up their courses. Thus there is an adequate area of upper level plain always available for consumption in the development of the plain next below it.

It is argued (Rich, J. L., 1938) that such a sequence is impossible except, perhaps, under special structural conditions. In homogeneous rock, Rich contends, the knickpunkte would be transient features and the bordering cliffs would be rapidly flattened out by erosional attack at their top edges and aggradation at their bases. It is conceded that in warm, moist climates some varieties of crystalline rock, resistant to mechanical erosion but yielding readily to chemical processes might permit the retreat of the valley walls at an unvarying declivity. The Asheville Basin area in North Carolina is cited as an instance of such development.

It is also suggested that if the structure consists of strong, flat-lying beds, separated by considerable vertical thicknesses of extremely weak layers, the steep, bounding declivities initiated by the erosion of a gorge might persist indefinitely. In this case, however, the resulting flats would only be a particular variety of stripped plain.

Accordance of Ridge Levels. The most disputed topic in the concept of peneplains is that of the correct interpretation of a series of accordant levels occurring at different altitudes within a single geomorphic unit or extending without interruption across unlike, but adjoining, units. This problem is encountered when the phenomena of stripped plains are under consideration; it becomes more difficult when such accordances of summit level are observed in the geomorphic unit of fold mountains where beds of greatly varying resistance are steeply inclined. If a fold mountain unit is deeply dissected the summits of the ridges are observed to be located on the edges of the upturned resistant beds. Such ridges may be found to exhibit accordance in altitude at a number of levels. Is each such accordance in altitude to be interpreted as a whole or partial peneplanation developed in conformance with base level, and later raised and partly dissected, or are the several accordances to be otherwise explained?

It may be assumed that where the narrow ridge crests result from the outcropping of durable beds in fold structures that have been laterally truncated, and are observed to have a single culminating altitude level, there once existed a widespread low-elevation peneplain or, note, a primärrumpf. Uplift of the peneplain or acceleration in rate of uplift of the primärrumpf brought about dissection and degradation of the fold structures. The exposed edges of belts of weak rock then experienced rapid lowering through weathering and stream erosion. The tops of resistant beds were made to stand up in relief by the excess of material removed from the weaker layers bordering them, and, once this relation was established, the summits were themselves little affected by stream action. Instead they were only slowly crumbled down by weathering and wash, so that their individual horizontality of summit, and collective uniformity of altitude were preserved, but at progressively lower levels.

However ridges owing to different beds would be reduced at different rates, according to the compositional durability and width of the particular rock responsible for their existence. A given stratum with the same width of outcrop would have the same height at widely separated places but this altitude would not be the same as that of another bed. The highest set of accordances should represent the original peneplain or primär-rumpf surface but not at the altitude to which it was uplifted. It has been estimated (Ashley, G. H., 1935) that the minimal lowering of the original surface of a peneplain thus uplifted and dissected is 100 feet in a million years. However a weak belt may be reduced in level by 500 feet in the same time that a strong, ridge-forming layer is lowered only 50 feet. Between such extremes, beds of many other degrees of resistance may occur. It is then a question whether each of the accordances of level to be observed, at different altitudes, in a unit of fold mountains once peneplaned, then uplifted and dissected, is to be referred to equivalence in downwasting of beds of like durability. Or does each accordance represent a partial peneplanation interrupted by renewed uplift (Fig. 30)?

It is necessary to make careful field studies if a landscape so constituted is to be correctly interpreted. The presence of a remnant of a weak bed (Fig. 36), associated with and at approximately the same height as that of a ridge composed of a durable bed whose summit marks a particular accordance of level, would be indicative of peneplanation. So, also, would the development of distinctly different levels, separated by sharp declivities, across one or more durable beds, be evidence of an equal number of base levels (Fig. 37, Plate II).

Stream Planation. The perfectionist conception of a peneplain is a level, nearly featureless expanse of country. Perhaps so complete reduction of land surfaces of diverse structure and composition to low plains has been in the geologic past at times and in places attained. The other extreme is to regard any degradational surface of subaerial origin that has a generally uniform

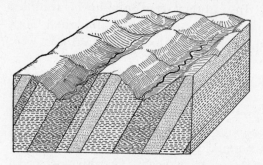

FIG. 36. ACCORDANT LEVEL OF RIDGES ON STRONG AND WEAK BEDS

Indicative of a former erosion surface at the level of the summits. Drawing by Elizabeth Burckmyer.

level of divides and a moderate measure of relief as a peneplain. It has been affirmed that major valley axes persist from one geomorphic cycle, carried through to complete peneplanation, to the same end stage in the following cycle. That is to say, it is doubted

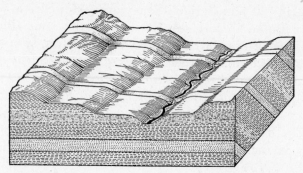

FIG. 37. DIFFERENT LEVELS IN WIDE TERRACES INTERSECTING STRONG BEDS

Each level is indicative of an erosional development with reference to a particular base level because weak and strong beds appear at the same altitude in each level. The steeper slopes of the upper terraces result from the successive uplifts. Drawing by Elizabeth Burckmyer.

whether slow wasting down can ever finally eliminate low hills from the divides between major streams.

In support of the visualization of the end stage of subaerial degradation as a level surface Crickmay (1933) has urged that this result will be achieved by the lateral corrasion of streams. As soon as a river ceases active downcutting its swinging from side

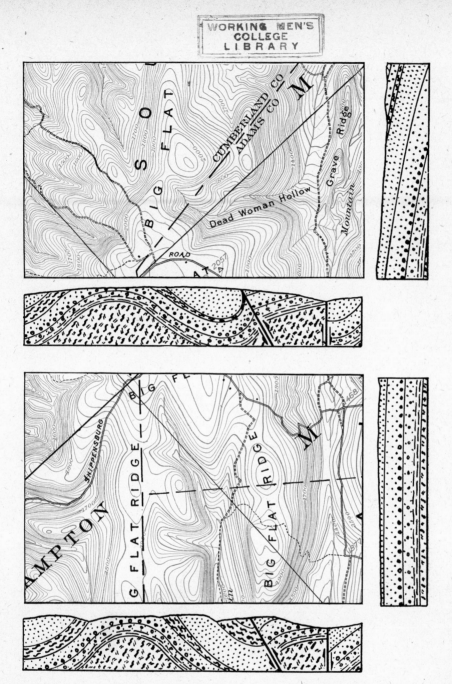

PLATE II. Verity of the Schooley, Appalachian, Peneplain. Parts of the Newville and Fairfield, Pennsylvania, quadrangle maps of the United States Geological Survey. Horizontal scale of the map and vertical scale of the cross sections are the same, one inch = one mile. It will be noted that the level summits truncate rocks and structures of varying resistance indifferently. Described by G. W. Stose in the *American Journal of Science*, July 1940. Arranged by Laurence Nugent.

to side on its valley floor effects a persistent, alternate trimming of the base of the valley slopes. By this means a low cliffing of the foot of the valley sides (Fig. 60) is maintained throughout the latter part of the erosion cycle. Eventually the level surfaces of adjacent stream floors, concurrently developed by such planation, become confluent and a *panplane,* a very level plain with a general seaward inclination, is produced. Although the potentialities of lateral planation by streams had been appreciated before Crickmay published, his exposition served to call attention to the possible importance of the process in the end stages of a geomorphic cycle. It has been objected that a panplane is not a peneplain; also that lateral corrasion by streams is probably of greater consequence in semiarid than in humid regions. It remains, however, that panplanation is a phenomenon of subaerial degradation, and is conditioned by the grand base level of the sea.

Summit Concordances. The several levels of accordant ridge summits, observed to occur in dissected fold mountain units, as previously described, is one expression of a class of phenomena here designated *summit concordances.* In the case of the fold-structure ridges there is uncertainty whether the levels should be attributed to successive partial cycles of erosion, or to differences in the rate of degradation, by wasting, of different particular beds, each of which outcrops repeatedly, and all of which were once at a common peneplain or primärrumpf level. It is clear that one or the other of these explanations will fit. The problem of which one may be solved by reference to associated phenomena.

A similar development commonly noted in elevated geomorphic units of horizontal structure has a different origin. When the originally level summit surface of such a horizontal-structure unit has been dissected to the stage where it is represented only by sharp, even-crested ridges, reduction of the summit plane to levels below the altitude of the initial surface will take place at a uniform rate along the ridge summits. If there is no further uplift the slopes descending from the ridge crests will flatten as the crests are lowered. If there is further uplift, continuous or intermittent, it may be that the steepness of the slopes and the depth of valleys will remain unchanged while the divides are greatly lowered. But in a contiguous area, where the rock is more durable, the lowering of the ridges by erosion may not have kept pace

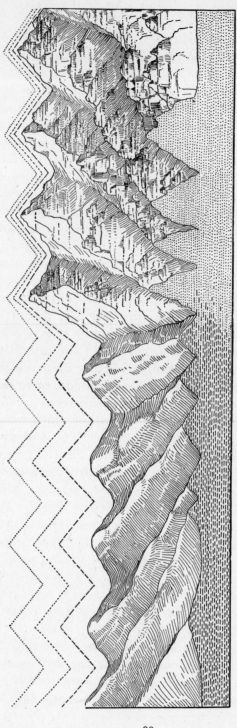

FIG. 38. SUMMIT CONCORDANCE AT TWO LEVELS, A STOCKWERK

Concurrent reduction of divide ridges and valley floors on rocks of unlike resistance to degradation. The ridge summits decline in altitude in the direction of the drainage. The distinguishing characteristics are much exaggerated. Drawing by Elizabeth Burckmyer.

98

with the increase in altitude owing to the uplift. Then there would be different levels of ridge summit accordance, simulating but not representing two erosion cycles (Fig. 38). This type of two-level accordance is called a **stockwerk** (building-story) in the German terminology, and the upper level would be referred to as the *scheitelflur* (crowning level).

The distinguishing mark of the ridge accordances in horizontal structures is that the ridge levels decline in the downstream direc-

Fig. 39. GIPFELFLUR, STARNBERG, NORTH TYROL, SWITZERLAND
Subequality of level of numerous lofty summits inferred to result from one-cycle, orogenic development. Photograph by John Jackson.

tion of the drainage. The steeper the stream gradients, the more perceptible this decline of ridge altitudes should be.

Gipfelflur. Another type of summit concordance is that called *gipfelflur* (peak-plain) by the Germans. It is the crowning level (scheitelflur) of lofty mountains. The summit peaks and ridges of the Alps (Fig. 39), Pyrenees, Alaska Ranges, and Canadian Selkirks, among others, are observed to rise to a subequality of altitude. An observer who stands on a peak in any one of these mountain districts and looks out to the horizon will see that all summits rise up to approximately the same level. If the valleys between the peaks were to be filled in up to this general level, a broad plain with an undulating topography of low relief would result. The questions then arise: Is the inferential summit surface of such a restoration that of an earlier peneplain, produced at base-level altitude, later uplifted and dissected, hence of two-cycle development, or is it of one-cycle origin, that is, the appropriate result of orogenic processes?

If broad plateau expanses are a part of the gipfelflur, and these tracts are underlain by rocks and structures clearly of different degrees of resistance to degradational processes, the peneplain (or perhaps primärrumpf) interpretation is warranted.

In the absence of extensive undissected level tracts, of the kind described above, the view opposed to peneplanation, namely that the gipfelflur accordance is inherently orogenic, should have preference. R. A. Daly (1905) points out that geomorphic science tends to be dominated by the "lowland view of erosion," that is, by observation and deduction conducted at and fitted to low altitudes. The "highland view of erosion," perhaps the other half of geomorphology, is much less commonly part of human experience, even that of competent geomorphologists.

> If the highland view is taken it is evident at once that the tremendous mountain elevations indicated by reconstruction of great anticlinal folds are highly improbable. Altitudes 40,000 to 50,000 feet above sea level would result. Instead, after some critical level was attained by tangential thrust the center of the mountain mass presumably settled isostatically by underflow or faulting. Thus the higher summits would begin existence at a somewhat uniform level. A further isostatic leveling tendency is introduced when valley excavation has attained significant dimensions; the high areas then tend to sink and the valley bottoms to rise.
>
> The summit rocks of lofty ranges are commonly of metamorphic kinds, very different petrographically but very similar in their degree of resistance to degradation. The original upper surface of metamorphism was probably much less uneven than the outer surface of a range. The unmetamorphosed cover could rapidly succumb to subaerial degradation leaving the altered underrock to be the outer surface at a fairly uniform height.

The original gipfelflur idea was that there is a limiting altitude above which uplift is incapable of lifting peaks or ranges because the degrading agencies above that level are of such extreme effectiveness that the crests are reduced as fast as they rise to that height. An upper horizon is thus fixed by an abrupt, great enhancement in degradation rate at a specific, critical level. A corollary to this concept is that there is a direct ratio between rate of degradation and height; the higher summits are reduced while the lower ones can still grow. That is to say, the rate of degradation in the first case tends to match rate of uplift, in the second is much inferior to it. Independent of other factors, this varying ratio between uplift rate and degradation rate would appear to provide an entirely adequate mechanism for bringing about the subequality of high mountain peak and ridge altitudes which constitutes the phenomenon of the gipfelflur.

Plains of Marine Abrasion. The degradational surfaces previously considered are all attributed to the action of weathering and stream processes. In the early history of geomorphology the production of level surfaces truncating diverse rock strata and structures was thought to result from altogether different circumstances.

If an uplifted block of the earth's crust is exposed to strong wave attack at its borders and stays unchanged in altitude (or, better, slowly sinks) over a considerable period of time, the wave-cut terrace, which develops along coasts undergoing vigorous marine erosion, may be extended inland to become a wide *plain of marine abrasion.* Such a plain could be expected to acquire a cover of marine deposits before a succeeding uplift brought about its emergence above sea level. Where undisturbed sedimentary beds are found resting on a plain that truncates the beds and structures of older rocks the geologist notes an angular unconformity when he has access to a vertical section of the formations (Fig. 40). It does not, however, follow that the buried rock plain is necessarily a plain of marine erosion. It may be a peneplain in origin, sliced across and leveled off by the wave attack. It is conjectured that much longer time is required for truncation of any wide area by wave action, than for its reduction by weathering and stream processes, (especially as any slight uplift will vastly increase the amount of action required of the sea, and only little that required of subaerial agencies, whose activities, further, will be accelerated by the uplift). Hence peneplains are thought to be more commonly produced than are plains of marine erosion. This expectancy would hold whether the developed rock plain was manifest as an unconformity, that is, under beds of sediment, or barren of a cover. The only criterion for discrimination between peneplains and plains of marine ero-

Fig. 40. PLAIN OF MARINE EROSION, GRAND CANYON OF THE COLORADO, ARIZONA

Horizontal, undisturbed, Tonto sandstone resting unconformably on the truncated surface of the Vishnu schist, presumed to have been developed as a plain of marine erosion. Photograph from United States Geological Survey.

sion is a possible greater perfection of truncation of formations of varying resistance in the case of the plain of marine abrasion. But as a peneplain might have its top pared off by a transgressing sea, this criterion has only secondary significance.

Desert Leveling. Deserts are characteristically regions of interior drainage. Their degradational development, hence, is unrelated to the sea as a base level. From observation and deduction, it has, however, been learned that plains of very low relief, truncating formations of greatly varied resistance are developed by the processes of weathering and erosion operative in arid regions. This result is referred to as *desert leveling without base-leveling.* A plain of desert leveling may occur at any altitude above sea level; and may, after its origin in an arid climate, be subjected to dissection in a humid climate. In consequence of these circumstances the desert plain intact, or partially destroyed, is still another possibility that must be considered when accordance of summit level is discovered, or when it is sought to interpret an ancient erosion surface extending across rocks of varying resistance.

SUMMARY

Formulation of the uniformitarianism principle provided a sound basis for geomorphic science. Time was made available for geomorphic cycles to run their courses. Lands originally at high altitudes are progressively dissected and degraded by stream erosion and weathering to regions of low relief, that is, to peneplains, and such plains will have only slight elevation above the grand base level of the sea.

A peneplain surface truncates rocks of varying durability, and at the altitude of its development should have a thick mantle of alluvial and weathering waste.

According to the Germans, there are surfaces that simulate peneplains, but which never had a high measure of relief, that is, were not developed by reduction in stages from an original high altitude. Such are primärrümpfe.

When peneplains or primärrümpfe are rapidly uplifted, then experience stillstand and dissection, accordant remnants of the earlier degradation surfaces appear at high altitudes. Summit level accordances are not, however, always indicative of peneplain surfaces. Various combinations of structural conditions and process-application may suffice to develop equality of summit levels over wide areas independent of the sea as a base level. Where the accordant levels appear at different altitudes, in series, many possibilities must be carefully considered before attributing the levels to successive erosion cycles. The gipfelflur characteristic of lofty mountain summits is commonly unrelated to base level.

Other erosion surfaces that may be wrongly interpreted as of peneplain origin are plains of marine abrasion and plains resulting from desert leveling without base-leveling.

BIBLIOGRAPHY

CLASSICAL

Davis, W. M. (1896) *Plains of Marine and Sub-Aërial Denudation,* Bulletin Geological Society of America, Vol. VII, pp. 377–398. In *Geographical Essays,* Ginn and Company, Boston, pp. 323–349.

Davis, W. M. (1898—revised, 1909) *The Peneplain,* in *Geographical Essays,* Ginn and Company, Boston, pp. 350–380.

Tarr, R. S. (1898) *The Peneplain,* American Geologist, Vol. 21, pp. 351–370.

Davis, W. M. (1922) *Peneplains and the Geographical Cycle,* Bulletin Geological Society of America, Vol. 33, pp. 587–598.

Davis, W. M. (1923) *The Cycle of Erosion and the Summit Level of the Alps,* Journal of Geology, Vol. 31, pp. 1–41.

Chamberlin, R. T. (1930) *The Level of Base Level,* Journal of Geology, Vol. 38, pp. 166–173.

Bowman, I. (1934) *William Morris Davis,* Geographical Review, Vol. 24, pp. 177–181.

RECENT

Bryan, K. (1934) *Geomorphic Processes at High Altitudes,* Geographical Review, Vol. 24, pp. 655–656.

Cole, W. S. (1935) *Rock Resistance and Peneplain Expression,* Journal of Geology, Vol. 43, pp. 1049–1062.

Wooldridge, S. W. (1935) *Erosion Surfaces,* Nature, Vol. 136, pp. 897–898.

Glock, W. S. (1936) *Desert Cliff Recession and Lateral Regional Planation,* Pan American Geologist, Vol. 66, pp. 81–86.

Tanner, V. (1938) *Die Oberflächengestaltung Finnlands,* Centraltrycheri och Bokbinderi a. b. Helsinfors.

Rich, J. L. (1938) *Recognition and Significance of Multiple Erosion Surfaces*, Bulletin Geological Society of America, Vol. 49, pp. 1695–1722.

Peel, R. F. (1941) *Denudational Landforms of the Central Libyan Desert*, Journal of Geomorphology, Vol. 4, pp. 3–23.

Chapter Seven

THE NORMAL OR FLUVIAL GEOMORPHIC CYCLE ON A COASTAL PLAIN

A. STREAM AND VALLEY DEVELOPMENT

Introduction. In the preceding chapter an attempt is made to
explore the different ways in which a plain that is the surface
expression of consolidated rock, whether the plain is continuous
at low or high altitudes, or is tangential to isolated summits, may
be developed by one, or by a combination of degradational processes. It appears that a variety of possibilities must be given
consideration when it is sought to interpret such plains and that,
with regard to particular instances, it is often difficult to be certain
of the origin. But it is found that the peneplain, the end stage
of a cycle of fluvial erosion directed toward the reduction of an
elevated region to the level of the sea as a final base, either intact,
at its altitude of development, or uplifted and partially dissected,
may be regarded as the regular outcome. If too great enthusiasm
for this concept caused peneplain surfaces to be postulated where
they do not exist the fault is not with the idea but with the
observers.

Running water is the most potent and most nearly universal
agency for the shaping of relief by subaerial processes. Over
the major part of the land surface, drainage runs down to the
sea. Streams transport the rock waste of weathering and erosion
to the place of its final deposition on the sea floor. The normal
history of landscape is, therefore, one of progressive dissection and
degradation of uplands by fluviatile action. Such action leads to
the development of a lowest relief and lowest level, the peneplain,
whose ultimate altitude is governed by the base level of the sea.

It is, therefore, appropriate to refer to the *fluvial geomorphic
cycle* as the **normal cycle**. For competent understanding of geo-

morphic development, it is necessary to become fully informed in regard to the progress of the fluvial cycle.

There are good reasons for beginning the study of the fluvial cycle by examining its course on the geomorphic unit of a coastal plain. A coastal plain has simple structure, but the elements of this structure are well defined, hence effectual in guiding geomorphic development. The simplicity and clear expression of the structure permit the sequence of changes on coastal plains, and the pattern of the forms that result, to attain ideal and diagrammatic development. In other geomorphic units the succession and the ordering of the results are much less obvious, that is, more difficult to follow and to interpret. A very large number of the genetic terms that Davis introduced, terms which are key words for extension of the cycle analysis to other geomorphic units, have their easiest and most direct application in coastal-plain features.

Davis's own estimate of his contribution to geomorphology ascribed great importance to this terminology. He wrote, (Bowman, I., 1934, p. 180) when asked to revise an appraisal of his work that some one had made: "Powell's work was noteworthy for the forceful ideas it conveyed of base-leveled surfaces; Gilbert and Dutton excelled in their analysis of individual features; Davis systematized the sequence of forms through an ideal cycle and provided a terminology."

Structure of a Coastal Plain. A coastal plain is an emerged portion of the continental shelf. The emergence is usually owing to uplift but it could also result from a general lowering of sea level. Previous to its uplift the area of a coastal plain will have been a site where layers of sediment, sand, clay, calcareous muds, were deposited. The material of the sediments is debris, transported thence by streams, or debris got by marine erosion of shores near and remote. The sediments were distributed in widespread beds by marine currents. Investigation of the sea bottom off the Massachusetts coast (Raymond, E., and Stetson, H. C., 1931) indicated that the surprisingly broad extension of such beds results in part from the flotational action of an organic jelly that develops in the sea and comprises part of the sedimentation. A sluggish marine current is enabled to transport sedimentary particles of sand-grain coarseness by virtue of the buoyancy furnished

FIG. 41. TERRACE LEVEL, COASTAL PLAIN, NEAR GREENHEAD, FLORIDA

Perfection of level surface. Sand of a Pleistocene beach, the "Second Terrace" level. Representative of the younger parts of a coastal plain.

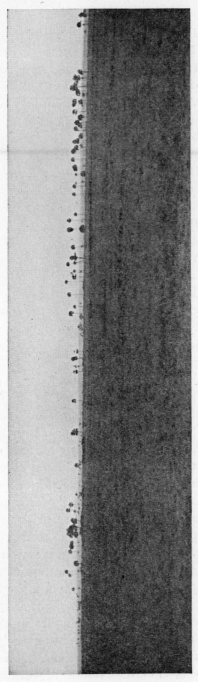

Fig. 42. UNDISSECTED, NEWLY UPLIFTED COASTAL PLAIN AREA NORTH OF LAKE OKEECHOBEE, NEAR BRIGHTON, FLORIDA Flatness of the region induces a mirage-like looming of the palm trees.

them by this jelly. Thus beds of sand are made to extend far out from shore. When the movement of the water is even less active, or when sand is not supplied to it, clays and oozes are laid down. The sorting action of the water, while the sedimentation is in progress, is remarkably delicate in its discriminations. The beds commonly show great perfection of stratification.

As deposited, the beds have a gentle slope seaward corresponding to the inclination of the bottom. In the Atlantic Coastal Plain of the United States the deeper beds have progressively steeper dips. The bottom appears to have bent down as the layers were deposited. This depositional inclination is the *initial dip.* Uplift (unless directly vertical, which is seldom if ever realized) involves an increase in the steepness of the dip. That is to say, the layers emerge slantingly. The new, steeper dip is the *regional dip.* On the Atlantic Coastal Plain the topmost bed of the uplifted belt is almost horizontal near the coast, and north of the James River is largely of fluviatile origin, but the surface gradient steepens inland. There uptilt has increased the dip and exceeded the rate of degradation in measure.

As indicated by stratigraphic and geomorphic evidence, uplift is not single and sudden, nor even continuous. Normally it is intermittent. It may even be interrupted by slight resubmergences. Because of these facts there is offlap and onlap of layers. Specific beds have a landward termination along lines parallel to the shore. In fact, a series of wide, low terraces comprise the younger portions of the Atlantic Coastal Plain (Fig. 41).

Surface of a Coastal Plain. The emergence of a coastal plain is usually referred to as an "upwarping." This word is noncommittal with regard to the exact nature of the uplift or the kind of slopes developed. It is, however, clear from observation that the general slope, like the regional dip, is seaward. A newly uplifted, undissected, area of coastal plain appears to be nearly flat over as wide prospect as can be had from a single viewpoint (Fig. 42). The surface inclination is very slight and the original relief, that is, difference in altitude of the higher and lower points, very small except for the declivities between terrace levels.

Consequent Lakes and Consequent Streams. Nevertheless significant inequalities of level exist. Neither deposition, nor uplift is completely uniform. As rain falls and drainage collects, runoff is concentrated in the minor hollows. Thus *consequent lakes* and *consequent streams* come into being. They are called consequent lakes and consequent streams because they exist and flow in consequence of the original inequalities of the surface. Use of these terms is not limited to occurrences on coastal plains. They have general application. That is to say, wherever a new land form is created: uplift of mountains, deposition of a till plain by a con-

FIG. 43. SHORE LINE OF LAKE OKEECHOBEE, NEAR PORT MACAYA, FLORIDA, A CONSEQUENT LAKE
Derelict Indian skiff in the foreground.

tinental glacier, drainage which follows the new regional slopes, or collects in the new regional hollows, is consequent.

Lake Okeechobee (Fig. 43) at the north side of the Everglades district in southern Florida is an uncommonly extensive development of a consequent lake. It occupies a shallow depression of what was geologically recently a shallow sea floor, and is surrounded by wide level expanses of sands laid down in Pleistocene time over the flat limestone beds of that area.

Consequent lakes on a coastal plain are sometimes merely swamps. Consequent streams flow into and out of such broad low areas along the original linear depressions of the coastal-plain surface. The courses of consequent streams on a coastal plain are generally parallel (*parallel drainage pattern,* Fig. 44a), for

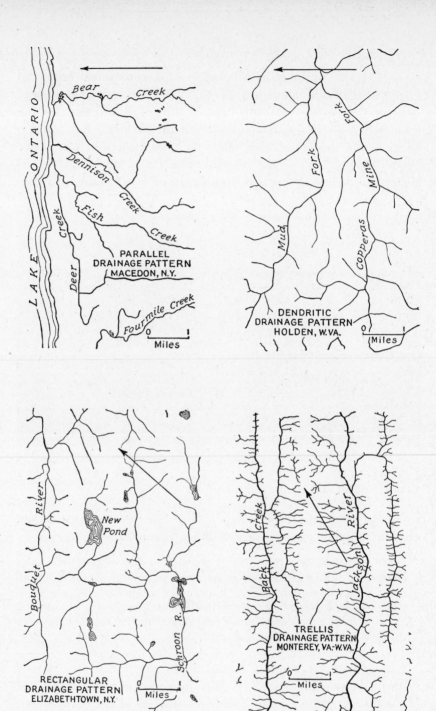

FIG. 44a. DRAINAGE PATTERNS

112

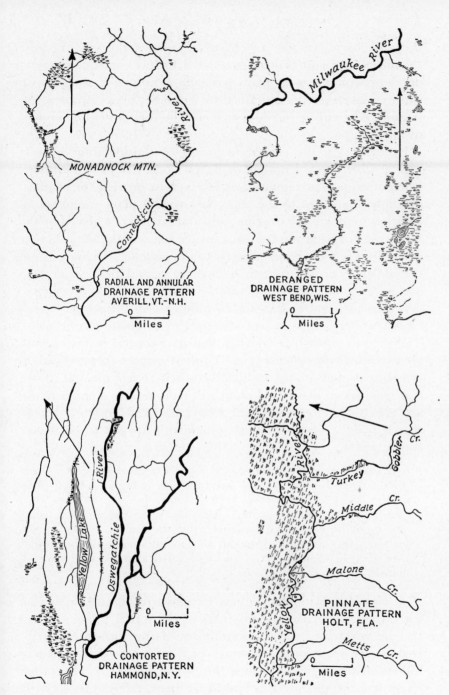

RADIAL AND ANNULAR
DRAINAGE PATTERN
AVERILL, VT.-N.H.

0   1
Miles

MONADNOCK MTN.

DERANGED
DRAINAGE PATTERN
WEST BEND, WIS.

0   1
Miles

Milwaukee River

CONTORTED
DRAINAGE PATTERN
HAMMOND, N.Y.

Yellow Lake

Oswegatchie River

0   1
Miles

PINNATE
DRAINAGE PATTERN
HOLT, FLA.

Gobbler Cr.

Turkey

Middle Cr.

Malone Cr.

Metts Cr.

Yellow River

0   1
Miles

FIG. 44b. DRAINAGE PATTERNS

113

they all flow down the regional slope toward the sea. Because the initial inequalities of surface are slight, any consequent stream developed on a coastal plain has only a limited drainage area. But in a given territory, drained by a number of such consequent streams, one will be the largest; it will be the *master consequent* of that section.

By definition the coastal plain under consideration is in a region subject to the normal or fluvial cycle, that is, one situated where adequate precipitation is received to provide for continuous flow of streams to the sea. As a coastal plain comprises an addition to previously existing subaerial territory, achieved by the upwarping of what was the adjacent sea bottom, the inner border of a coastal plain is joined directly to the *oldland.* Drainage from the oldland reached the sea before the coastal plain came into existence. Oldland streams would, as the coastal plain emerged, flow across it; that is, they would follow down the regional slope exactly as do the consequent streams that originate on the plain. The streams on the coastal plain that have sources in the oldland are *extended consequents* (Fig. 47); their courses are extended, as consequents, beyond their oldland courses. Every oldland stream that emerges on the coastal plain will tend to have a larger drainage area than any consequent whose course is confined to the coastal plain. Thus extended consequents are apt to be master consequents.

It should be clearly understood that "extended consequent" applies only to the part of the stream which is on the coastal plain itself. The oldland part of such drainage may be any one of a number of kinds of streams. Ordinarily, extended consequents will occur only on coastal plains. But the same possibility exists for drainage emerging from an old mountain region on a new lava flow, or drainage from an unglaciated area crossing a region mantled with glacial deposits.

The spacing of the consequent streams will depend in part on the disposition of the irregularities of the initial relief. It will also be governed by the permeability of the surface materials. If these are very permeable much of the total precipitation will follow an underground course for some distance. The consequent streams, then, will be spaced far apart, referred to as *coarse texture of drainage,* and have few tributaries.

Valley of the Young Consequent Stream on a Coastal Plain.
In its initial development the consequent stream on a coastal
plain will occupy without modification a series of original depressions leading down to the sea. Where such depressions are
wide and shallow the drainage expands into consequent swamps
and lakes. Concentrated flow in narrow depressions brings about
the removal of particles from their bottoms by current sweep.
The weakly consolidated upper layers of the coastal plain sediments are readily softened and dissolved by the constant wetting,
so that fragments are continuously being loosened and carried
away. As a result of such removal the channels are deepened.
Where the streams flow into consequent swamps, or lakes, sediment is deposited. By overflow from such expansions of the
drainage, outlet sites are cut down. The combination of filling
and downcutting operates effectually to eliminate consequent
swamps and lakes from a drainage course so that shortly the stream
has a narrow, well-defined channel extending to its headwaters.

After it has become established in a particular groove the downcutting activity of the consequent, coastal-plain stream is greatly
enhanced. In its confined course it flows with greater velocity.
Current sweep is supplemented by scour resulting from the abrasion of the bottom by particles of debris in transport. Like a rain
gully of conspicuous development on a newly graded surface, the
consequent stream cuts a vertical-sided channel with a bottom
width equal to that of the current. It is a gorge in miniature
(Ireland, H. A., Sharpe, C. F. S., and Eargle, D. H., 1939).

As the stream cuts down it encounters layers of different degrees
of resistance to erosion. In view of the onlap or offlap circumstances of deposition of the coastal-plain beds, as outlined above,
these layers may have a very definite line of termination at their
inland edges. This line will be roughly parallel to the coast.
Where a bed of superior strength is encountered it will not be
cut into at its inner edge, nor cut through on its upper surface
downstream from the inner edge, as fast as the weaker layers
stratigraphically above and below the resistant bed are eroded
away. Where the stream crosses the outcrop of the resistant bed a
rapids develops. The steepness of such rapids is determined by
the angle of the regional dip. The resistant stratum will also
determine the altitude of a *local base level* upstream from its

outcrop. No part of the valley above that point can be cut down below the level at which the resistant bed is encountered. The longitudinal profile of an ideally developed, young, consequent, coastal-plain valley will, accordingly, consist of nearly flat reaches separated by steeper, shorter descents.

Tributaries to Young Consequent Streams on a Coastal Plain. The consequent streams of a coastal plain are, from the start, entered by small tributaries. These may be *secondary consequents,* that is, drainage that follows initial hollows with trends at a marked angle to that of the course of a main consequent. Such secondary consequents do not, however, ordinarily attain any greater development than that of the rain gullies which shortly gash the lateral slopes of the consequent courses at random sites. In fact, minor initial hollows, extending to the right or left of a main consequent course, may serve as the starting points for rain gullies. Or a gully may develop because exceptionally heavy rainfall is concentrated at one point. Because it is ordinarily difficult to discern the circumstances which led to the establishment of much of this minor lateral drainage where it actually occurs, it is customary to speak of it as insequent. In other words, an *insequent stream* is one that follows a course governed by obscure and random factors.

> The designation "insequent" is regularly used for the occurrence, on any geomorphic unit, of a stream or valley whose course is not related to any recognizable set of circumstances. It has been suggested that the use of "insequent" is simply a confession of inability to determine the conditions of the occurrence. The criticism is in some degree valid. But in defense it may be urged that the governing factors of insequent drainage are either so delicate or remote that they have no significant bearing on the course of geomorphic development.

Although tributaries of coastal-plain, consequent streams are indicated above to have, in general, an insequent origin, the insequent relationship proves to be very short-lived. Where an insequent chances to develop over weak beds it readily deepens its channel, and it also rapidly lengthens (Fig. 45) its course by *headwater* or *retrogressive erosion.* Contrariwise, an insequent started on a strongly indurated stratum makes practically no erosive impress. On such beds sweep erosion is little, if at all, effective, and as, by definition, the volume of current is initially slight and unconcentrated, it will have little potence in the scour erosion of a resistant bed. The insequent that starts on a strong

FIG. 45. HEADWATER EROSION IN UNCONSOLIDATED BEDS, BEACH RIVER FALLS, WISCONSIN

This is representative of such erosion in coastal-plain materials. The beds are sandy; the development of the gullies is insequent. As the extension of the gullies progresses the downstream sections of the axial channels will merge laterally by abstraction to form one main valley. Photograph from United States Department of Agriculture, Soil Conservation Service.

bed experiences little development and may be entirely eliminated in the further progress of the fluvial cycle.

Induration of coastal-plain strata results primarily from cementation. Cementation acts chiefly to consolidate sandy or calcareous sediments. Silica, iron, and lime bind sand grains together; lime muds develop a continuous crystalline coherence of their own substance to become limestones. Clayey layers, however, consolidate almost solely from pressure, hence seldom attain any considerable degree of cohesion. Under a heavy load of overlying beds they are converted to shale, by compaction, but even in this final degree of consolidation the yield of the clayey materials to all disintegrating processes is easy and rapid. Far greater quantities of clay, in thickness and extent, are laid down as sediments than of sand or of calcareous substance. Thus clay, or shale belts, are, in general, broad; sandy and calcareous strata thin and widely separated. Lowland areas, therefore, tend to be wider than hilly belts.

The weakness and extent of clay beds greatly facilitate the erosive activities of the insequent tributaries that have their beginnings on such strata. Torrent flow, at a time of heavy precipitation, permits an insequent rain gully in clay beds or shale to be cut down almost at once to the level of the consequent to which it is tributary, and to develop insequent tributaries of its own. Big and little the streams on the clay beds elongate their courses by headward erosion, and gain in volume and erosive power. It may be assumed that a clayey belt will have indefinite extension along the line of strike; and that the farthest elongation and greatest valley development will, accordingly, be in that direction.

This longest stream becomes a dominant line of drainage and is referred to as a *subsequent stream* and the valley it erodes is called a *subsequent valley.* These terms indicate that the subsequent stream and valley "follow after" the consequent stream and valley in development, and such is indeed the case. But the terminology is faulty in that it does not suggest that the subsequent stream starts as an insequent and that subsequent streams and subsequent valleys owe their differential enlargement to the circumstance that river erosion of weak beds and weak structures is achieved much more rapidly than that of distinctly durable rock. This relation cannot be too much emphasized. Complete understanding of its application is fundamental to full appreciation of geomorphic development under the normal or fluvial geomorphic cycle. Subsequent streams and subsequent valleys are a response to the presence of weak rocks and weak structures and are the product of the comparably very rapid erosion of the little resistant materials.

On a coastal plain subsequent streams develop along the line of strike and will normally enter the consequents to which they are tributary at right angles. But there is no requirement that subsequent streams and valleys must adhere to this particular pattern. On other geomorphic units it may be very different. Any belt of rock on which erosion of running water operates more effectively than on adjacent more resistant materials, whether the weakness is owing to composition, close-spaced jointing, anticlinal structure, the shatter zone of a fault, or any other factor, affords, by reason of such weakness, the appropriate locale for the development of a subsequent stream course and a subsequent valley.

The Inner Vale and Outer Vales and the Cuesta. As has been noted, the strong bed situated stratigraphically above the weak belt on which a subsequent valley is opened up, occasions rapids where the consequent stream cuts it transversely. The downward erosion of the subsequent tributary keeps pace with that of the consequent as it makes progress in reducing the strong formation. But the course of the subsequent does not remain exactly on the line along which it started. As the subsequent stream cuts down it encounters beds of varying resistance within the generally weak,

FIG. 46. DOWN-DIP LATERAL MIGRATION OF A SUBSEQUENT STREAM, LAUREL RUN, WILKES-BARRE, PENNSYLVANIA

The development is especially conspicuous here because a coal bed is experiencing the lateral erosion. Drawing, from a photograph, by Elizabeth Burckmyer.

presumably clayey, belt. These differences in durability may not be pronounced, but they suffice, always, to facilitate erosion on the downdip side of the subsequent's course. The reason is simple. If, at a given instant, erosion is taking place in a peculiarly weak stratum, that bed will be cut through and the stronger bed next below will first be encountered on the updip side of the width of the current. Erosion will be handicapped there from then on. On the other side of the current downward erosion will continue unchecked. On that side the water will become deeper and deeper so that eventually all the flow will be concentrated in a very narrow line on the downdip side. Cutting through, by downward erosion to the next, lower, strong bed is facilitated by such concentration of the current. Meanwhile, lateral erosion of the weak bed is promoted by the downdip direction of the current against its exposed edge. As a result the whole course of the subsequent stream tends to be shifted in the downdip direction (Fig. 46). Its valley will show a long gentle slope on the updip side, a steep undercut slope on the downdip side. Divides, for tributaries to subsequent streams will migrate down the dip.

This particular case exemplifies a general law; namely, that where inclined sedimentary formations are undergoing degradation in the fluvial geomorphic cycle *divides will migrate in the direction of the dip.* It is shown, here, to apply with reference to a stream whose course is parallel to the strike; the law is similarly in effect with regard to streams with courses at right angles to the line of strike. The larger geomorphic significance of the law is that where regions of such structure have experienced a long history of degradation it may be inferred that all divide lines have been shifted appreciable distances laterally in the direction of the regional dip.

The development of subsequent tributaries and valleys takes place on each side of a consequent stream (Fig. 47). As the belt of weak beds may be assumed to be continuous across the courses of a number of adjacent consequent streams, the floors of subsequent valleys which develop in the weak belt will line up to form a lowland. In transverse profile this lowland will have a gentle slope up toward the oldland, the *dip slope,* and be terminated by a steep slope, the *escarpment slope* (Fig. 48), also called the *inface,* on its other margin. The lowland comprising the dip slope extending from the oldland to the base of the escarpment slope, considered as a unit, is termed the *inner vale,* or *inner lowland.* Similar lowlands developed in successive parallel belts farther seaward, by other subsequent streams, are called *outer vales,* or *outer lowlands.* If the ridge, consisting of the escarpment slope of one subsequent valley, and the dip slope of the parallel subsequent valley next seaward, is regarded as a unit, it is termed a *cuesta.* "Cuesta" is a Spanish word adopted in geomorphology to mean a hill with one gentle slope, in general 30 degrees or less, and one steep slope. Hills of that form may have various origins; in geomorphic usage the word "cuesta" should be reserved to designate only those hills which have the structure and erosional history set forth above. The presence of cuestas, then, implies the structure of a coastal-plain geomorphic unit, but the occurrence may be a second cycle development. That is to say, the whole of a first cycle development of cuestas may be eliminated, by reduction of the area to a peneplain, but with renewed uplift, the structure remaining unaltered, the cuesta development will be repeated, and, commonly, with greater conspicuousness than in the first cycle (Frontispiece)

Belted Coastal Plain. It is conceivable that a coastal plain many miles wide could be created by a single rapid uplift. From the stratigraphic succession which coastal plains exhibit it appears, instead, that their emergence usually occupies a considerable interval of geologic time; also that the uplift is ordinarily intermittent. It may be inferred from these circumstances that the inner portions of coastal plains have been exposed to subaerial processes much longer than those nearer the sea. As the inner parts participate in all the uplifts they will, of necessity, attain the greatest altitudes. Thus the inner belts of a coastal plain will regularly have experienced a large measure of dissection while the near-sea tracts retain their initial topography almost unmodified,

As the dissection of the older, higher parts proceeds, successive parallel bands of vales and cuesta scarps become the dominant topographic features of such areas. The inner vale at the base of the oldland may be opened out to a great width and is then called a *terre plaine.* The strong formations of the cuesta ridges attain considerable relief, the lowlands become well defined. The patterning of the landscape that results is conspicuous; the phenomenon is referred to as a *belted coastal plain.* A noteworthy development of this sort is present in northern Alabama (Fig. 49); the coastal plain of Mexico at the foot of the Sierra Madre Oriental west of Vera Cruz also shows these characteristics. The pattern of the belted coastal plains is commonly too gross to be impressive in the near view. The cuestas usually appear as a strip of hilly country, not as sharp ridges.

Water Gaps. Where a consequent stream cuts across a cuesta ridge its valley long retains the gorge form that results from active downcutting. Such narrow passages through the strong rock beds are *water gaps* on a small scale.

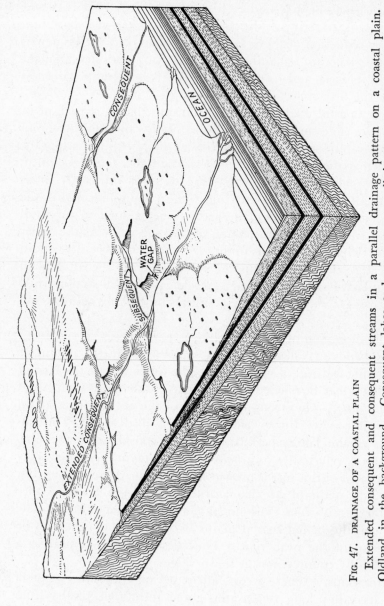

FIG. 47. DRAINAGE OF A COASTAL PLAIN

Extended consequent and consequent streams in a parallel drainage pattern on a coastal plain. Oldland in the background. Consequent lakes and swamps; a small insequent valley downstream from the water gap. A low, nipped, terrace declivity at the former coast line. A subsequent stream and the development of a subsequent valley. Drawing by Elizabeth Burckmyer.

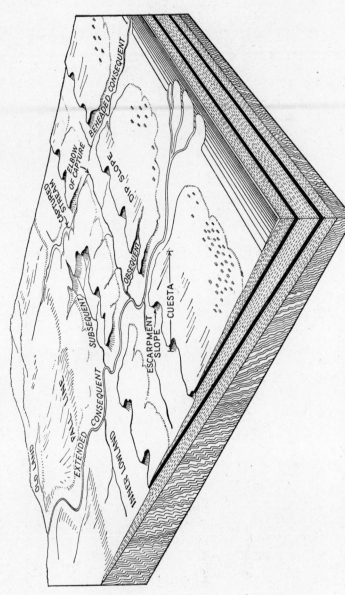

FIG. 48. DRAINAGE OF A COASTAL PLAIN, ADVANCED STAGE

Compare with the preceding figure. Erosion has brought cuestas into sharp relief, and the drainage is being linked up to present a rectangular pattern. A broad inner lowland, or inner vale, has been opened up. The subsequent stream in the outer vale has captured a parallel consequent; another capture, by the subsequent in the inner vale, is imminent. Obsequent streams are developing valleys on and across the escarpment slopes of the cuestas. Drawing by Elizabeth Burckmyer.

123

Fig. 49. Cuesta section of belted coastal plain in northern Alabama

Six miles north of Livingston, Alabama. The line of hill summit swinging to the right across the picture is the crest and inface of the cuesta above the Selma Chalk. The scale of cuestas and lowlands in nature is too large to show photographically in the manner of the diagrammatic representations of these features.

a

b

Fig. 50. RIVER CAPTURE BY A SUBSEQUENT THAT IS TRIBUTARY TO A MASTER CONSEQUENT

Drawings by Elizabeth Burckmyer.

River Piracy. It was previously noted that in a given district one of the consequents crossing the coastal plain is larger than any of its competitors and becomes the master consequent. This distinction is not attained by greater volume alone. Greater volume, it is true, may be assumed to insure more rapid downward erosion. But the master consequent may also owe its superior rank to a steeper course or a shorter course down to the sea, or to a course across fewer resistant beds.

The subsequent tributaries to a master consequent have a lower local base level than those of tributaries to neighboring, competitor consequents. The headward erosion of a subsequent that is tributary to a master consequent will be facilitated by a steeper

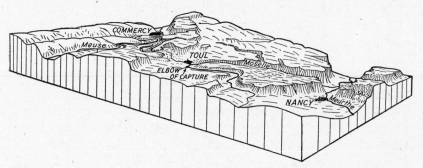

FIG. 51. CAPTURE, BY THE MOSELLE, OF THE FORMER HEADWATERS OF THE MEUSE, IN FRANCE

The col to the left of Toul is the site of the former flow toward the Meuse. After de Martonne. Drawing by Walter Williams.

gradient than that of its duplicate flowing in the opposite direction on the same weak beds to join a consequent whose channel is at a higher level (Fig. 50a). The divide between the headwaters of the rival subsequents will constantly be moved toward the lesser consequent. It is to be noted that as this action proceeds the lesser subsequent is progressively deprived of drainage area, hence dwindles in volume and power. At sites where the disproportion in effectiveness of the opposed subsequents is great the contest will ultimately result in the complete elimination of the weaker subsequent. Then the headwaters of the conquering stream reach the lesser consequent and divert its upper waters into the newly established subsequent course leading to the master consequent (Fig. 50b).

Such diversion is *river capture,* or *river piracy.* The point at which the capture takes place is called the **elbow of capture** (Fig. 51); the term is indicative of the sharp right angle turn that the combined stream course makes there. While the competition between the two consequents was in progress the divide was *creeping* toward the lesser consequent; at the time of the capture the divide *leaps* to the headwaters of the lesser consequent. Below the point of capture, that is, beyond the crest of the cuesta escarpment, the lesser consequent continues in diminished volume; it is now a **beheaded consequent.** The large access of volume, available both to the capturing subsequent and to the master consequent, suddenly enhances their powers of erosion and so enables them to develop and to flow over a lower gradient. By successive captures the inner- or outer-vale lowland of a dominant subsequent is gradually converted to a continuous, level plain.

As is true of other features, it is easy to recognize and describe these sequences on coastal plains, because of the simple structure in which they are developed. But river captures may occur in other kinds of geomorphic units. The sharp turn developed at the elbow of capture is a conspicuous earmark. Where such a change is noted in a stream course it may be suspected to indicate a capture. It should be understood, however, that not all right-angle turns in stream courses are elbows of capture.

The development of subsequent valleys and the incidence of stream captures are phenomena associated with progressive **adjustment to structure.** If the master consequent owes its superiority to the fact that it had fewer or less resistant beds to cut through, its course also represents an adjustment to structure. As the normal, or fluvial geographic cycle advances in stage toward maturity this adjustment to structure becomes more and more complete.

Obsequent Streams. A short reach of the captured consequent, extending down the escarpment slope to the site of the elbow of capture may be referred to as a *reversed consequent.* At its head, in the gorge through which the lesser consequent formerly traversed the strong beds of the cuesta ridge, a new divide is established. The former gorge channel is then left dry and becomes a *wind gap.* As is true of water gaps, wind gaps on a coastal plain are small, obscure features. The same sequence carried through in regions of high altitude, plateaus, or mountains, results in wind gaps of such magnitude that they are conspicuous elements of the landscape (Fig. 52).

In its later development the reversed consequent becomes a special case in the general class of **obsequent streams.** Obsequents are sometimes referred to, also, as "against the dip" streams. It would be remarkable if the strong bed that gives rise to a cuesta

FIG. 52. A WIND GAP (DOLL'S GAP) ON NEW CREEK MOUNTAIN, WEST VIRGINIA. View from the Allegheny Front, West Virginia.

ridge were uniform in structure and composition at all points of its outcrop along the line of strike. Instead it will normally be less indurated, less thick, more closely jointed, or in other respects weaker in some places than in others. The small volume of drainage that collects on the escarpment slope of a cuesta will enlarge its channels at these weak places much more rapidly than elsewhere. These channels are the beginnings of obsequent valleys.

Though small at the start, obsequent streams (Fig. 53) once established are exceptionally competent as erosive agencies. In second cycle cuestas developed by differential erosion of strongly consolidated beds obsequent streams may have, initially, gradients approaching 90 degrees in steepness. At their heads obsequent streams operate, through erosion of the underlying weak beds by undermining, to deprive the strong capping layer of the cuesta

FIG. 53.   EROSIVE ACTION OF AN OBSEQUENT STREAM
   The stream is descending across the outcropping edges of shale and sandstone beds. The current tends to undermine the stronger sandstone beds. Central New York. (This stream is obsequent in pattern but has a consequent course down a slope created by glacial erosion.)

ridge of support. Differential weathering facilitates this sapping process. The tendency of the subsequent stream to keep close to the base of the escarpment insures rapid removal of waste brought to the foot of the slope by the obsequent. These circumstances, and the simultaneous functioning of the processes they condition, permit the retrogressive erosion of obsequents to proceed rapidly. Once a master-consequent and subsequent adjustment-to-structure has been achieved, obsequents become the most active streams in the further regional dissection of an area. An obsequent may achieve significant river capture.

From the previous discussion it could be inferred that all subsequent valleys are of equal magnitude, and are eroded downward to the same depth. Actually they are of various sizes and flow at various altitudes. It is therefore entirely feasible for an obsequent that is tributary to a major subsequent to extend its course by headwater erosion until it reaches and diverts a higher level subsequent. At the point of capture the stream courses will have the pattern of the head of a capital T. The stem of the T is the obsequent stream, the cross bar of the letter represents the parts of the dismembered subsequent that join the obsequent from the right and left.

Rectangular Drainage Pattern. It should be clear that the linking up of drainage courses, described with reference to specific circumstances in the preceding paragraphs, can and will be repeated many times in the course of the dissection of a coastal plain by consequent, subsequent, and obsequent streams. Eventually one master consequent will be the trunk drainage course for a wide district. Numerous successful subsequents will flow into it, and these subsequents, in turn, will each command wide drainage areas (*a*) by beheading lesser consequents and (*b*) through captures effected by their obsequent branches. The straight reaches of the several types of streams, together with the sharp elbows and T heads of the capture sites, will comprise a right-angle system called a *rectangular drainage pattern* (Fig. 44a, Plate III).

SUMMARY

Moving water is the ubiquitous agency of land degradation. The phrase, "fluvial geomorphic cycle," designates the normal, sequential development of relief through degradation by wash and streams. Its evolution on a coastal plain is conditioned by a simple, but significantly patterned structure. The generally seaward slope of the surface gives rise to parallel consequent streams. The outcrop of weaker belts governs the development of subsequent drainage. The subsequent tributaries to a master consequent (commonly an extended consequent, one that derives part of its volume from an oldland river) capture and divert the head-

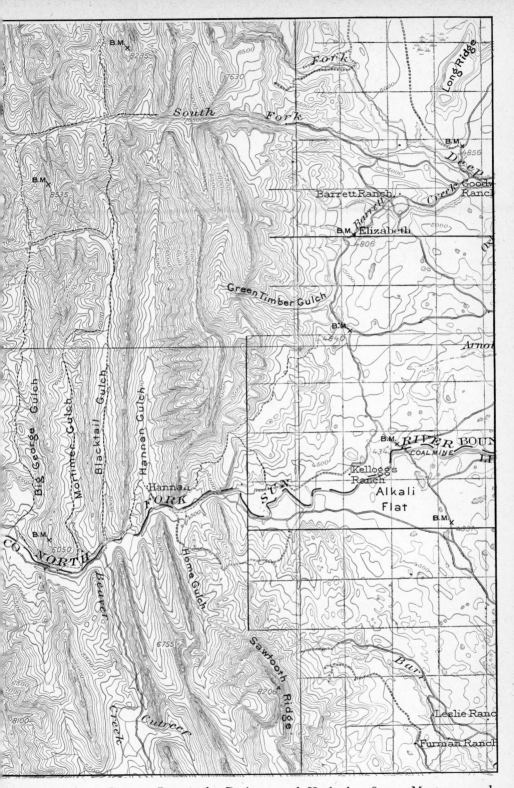

᠎TE III. Imminent Capture, Rectangular Drainage and Hogbacks. Saypo, Montana, quad-
gle map of the United States Geological Survey. Horizontal scale 1/125,000, contour inter-
100 feet. The North Fork Sun River is an extended consequent, Hannan and Blacktail
᠎ches are subsequent valleys; the ridge between them is a hogback. The stream in Hannan
᠎ch will shortly capture the South Fork Creek at its head. The drainage of this area perfectly
᠎mplifies the rectangular drainage pattern.

water portions of lesser consequents. Drainage divides creep, and then leap, as the integration of stream courses proceeds. Broad lowlands, inner and outer vales, are opened along the subsequent courses. These lowlands are bounded, downdip, by escarpment slopes, capped by the more resistant strata. The escarpment, or inface, and the backslope together form a cuesta. Consequent streams cross the cuestas in water gaps. The pattern of parallel strips made by the alternation of vales and cuesta ridges constitutes a belted coastal plain.

The site where a lesser consequent is diverted is the elbow of capture. What remains of the original lesser consequent after the capture is a beheaded consequent. A beheaded consequent has its (new) source in the wind gap, former water gap, next below the elbow of capture. From the wind gap to the elbow of capture the former consequent flow is turned back on itself and becomes a reversed consequent.

Independent streams descending the inface slope also have courses directly opposite that of the consequent flow. These are obsequent streams. Obsequent streams are very effective in headwater erosion. They regularly capture and divert higher level subsequents.

The general effect of these concurrent developments is to bring about a more and more complete adjustment of drainage to structure. The valley lines that mark this adjustment form a rectangular pattern of drainage.

BIBLIOGRAPHY

CLASSICAL

Davis, W. M. (1899 a) *The Drainage of Cuestas,* Proceedings of the Geologists' Association, Vol. XVI, Part 2, pp. 75–93.
Davis, W. M. (1899 b) *The Geographical Cycle,* Geographical Journal, Vol. XIV, pp. 481–504.
Abbe, C. Jr. (1899) *A General Report on the Physiography of Maryland,* Maryland Weather Service, Vol. 1, Part 2, pp. 41–216.

RECENT

Davis, W. M. (1915) *The Principles of Geographical Description,* Annals of the Association of American Geographers, Vol. 5, pp. 61–105.
Barton, D. C. (1930) *Surface Geology of Coastal Southeast Texas,*

Bulletin Association of American Petroleum Geologists, Vol. 14, pp. 1301–1320.

Zernitz, E. R. (1932) *Drainage Patterns and their Significance,* Journal of Geology, Vol. 40, pp. 498-521.

Maxon, J. H. (1935) *Terminology of Surface Forms of the Erosion Cycle,* Journal of Geology, Vol. 43, pp. 88–96.

Baulig, H. (1938) *Questions de Terminologie—Consequent ou Cataclinal,* etc., Journal of Geomorphology, Vol. 1, pp. 224-229.

Flint, R. F. (1940) *Pleistocene Features of the Atlantic Coastal Plain,* American Journal of Science, Vol. 238, pp. 757–787.

Chapter Eight

THE NORMAL OR FLUVIAL GEOMORPHIC CYCLE ON A COASTAL PLAIN (*Continued*)

B. REGIONAL DEVELOPMENT

Introduction.   The Atlantic Coastal Plain of the United States, which extends from northern New Jersey to Florida, is from 50 to 100 miles wide.   It appears to be the product of discontinuous uplift.   Indicative of such intermittent upheaval is the succession of flat terraces, each terminated by a short, steep rise, that constitute the seaward border of the plain.

The dip of the rock layers and the surface slopes of the plain become steeper as the inner border of the plain is approached. The edges of successively older beds outcrop as the oldland is neared.   The altitude of the inland edge of the plain is approximately 500 feet.   The inner portions of the plain are stream-dissected to a far more advanced stage than the coastal areas.

Valley Deepening—Grade.   The history of numerous slight uplifts, separated by considerable time intervals, in the Atlantic Coastal Plain, warrants the inference that master, extended consequent streams tended to maintain their courses so regularly at a *profile of equilibrium,* that is, *at grade,* that the effect of the uplifts on their functioning was negligible (Fig. 54).

Grade, as a geomorphic term, is not synonymous with the words "gradient" and "slope," which signify simply an inclination, or departure from the horizontal.   The general idea of grade, in the technical sense, is not difficult to grasp.   It means the continuous curve of descent of a stream floor which everywhere is just steep enough to serve the need of the current for its flow and the transportation of its sediment load.   But the precise and concise definition of grade is difficult.   It is commonly said that a river is at grade when its active downcutting ceases.   That, broadly, is what was implied by the statement in the preceding paragraph that the

133

master, extended consequent streams were able to maintain their courses across the coastal plain at grade in opposition to the successive uplifts. But downcutting does not completely cease once grade is attained. Instead a slow reduction in level of the valley bottom continues to be effected indefinitely thereafter. The grade equilibrium is maintained without interruption but the altitude of the valley floor and the steepness of the gradients are reduced all along the course. Not, however, reduced at the same rate at all points of the profile. Nor is the grade slope necessarily on the rock floor. It may be over sedimentary fill as well.

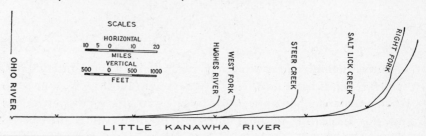

FIG. 54. PROFILES OF THE LITTLE KANAWHA RIVER AND ITS TRIBUTARIES IN WEST VIRGINIA

The curves are almost ideally representative of the graded condition of these streams. The slight break in the curve, in the headwaters section, indicative of failure to attain grade there, proves to be the line of outcrop of exceptionally resistant beds in the Pottsville series. The regional dip is toward the headwaters of the streams, so this is an obsequent system. Grade profiles of a consequent system might show somewhat differently inflected curves. Constructed by Laurence Nugent.

Maintenance of grade consists of a continuous, infinite series of adjustments between volume, slope, and sediment supply. These adjustments are made by variations and alternations in downcutting, deposition, transportation. Grade is the preservation of a balance between the various phases of a stream's activity reflected in a continuous curve of descent which when achieved is continually subject to modification, but always retained. It is not a particular declivity; it is not the ultimate lowest declivity. Its first attainment marks a stage in valley development but it is not itself the stage.

J. E. Kesseli (1941) argues that the postulate of grade, as a balance between power and load, cannot be authenticated, and proposes that the term should be considered to mean only the absence of waterfalls and rapids in the stream course.

Although grade, when first established, is not necessarily the lowest slope ever attained by a stream, it is a profile of equilibrium and, as such, is only slightly and slowly modified by later developments. Grade in the master consequents thus serves as the local base level for streams tributary to them. Just as the main streams have their erosive activities finally governed by the grand base level of the sea, so tributaries are limited in their downwearing by the levels of their junctions with the trunk streams. If a trunk stream is at grade the local base level it fixes is essentially stable. Tributaries develop their profiles of equilibrium with reference to the local base level that the grade of the main stream establishes.

Valley Widening. As soon as any stream channel is eroded below the level of the initial surface on which its course started, the cut that has been made begins to be widened at the top by weathering action. At the sharp edge of the top of stream cut, weathering processes can attack the rock substance from two sides. The edge is crumbled away almost at once. K. Bryan (1940, pp. 258–259) insists that rounding at the top edge occurs only if the rock is fragile. This would be true of coastal plain sedimentary beds. It is his conviction that in strongly consolidated rocks the only effective action is on the inclined slope. The corner stays sharp.

As the cut is deepened the weathering agencies progressively gain access to rock exposures at lower and lower levels in the valley sides. Meanwhile the reduction at the top continues and extends farther back from the site of the original cut. The pro-

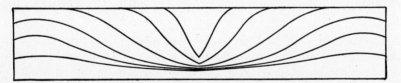

FIG. 55.   CHANGES IN THE SLOPE PROFILES AND THE WIDENING OF VALLEYS DURING THE PROGRESS OF THE FLUVIAL GEOMORPHIC CYCLE
Slightly modified from Davis. Drawing by Laurence Nugent.

gressive deepening of the channel, by providing a continuously steep slope for the removal of weathering waste, facilitates the recession at the top. These conditions apply until the stream has attained grade. It should be appreciated, however, that although downward erosion is preponderant at this stage, lateral erosion by the stream is then also vigorous, and in weak rocks contributes significantly to the widening of the valley while the deepening proceeds apace (Fig. 55).

If grade is assumed to mark the approximate maximal depth of downcutting possible, then the major portion of the stream's erosive activity after grade is attained will be directed to lateral planation.

It follows that after grade is established valleys are widened at the top by weathering, at the bottom by lateral erosion.

Transition from Youth to Maturity — Valleys. The features that mark youthful, consequent valleys in a coastal plain are steep sides, a bottom width measured by the current width, alternation of flat reaches and steep descents, interruptions by expansion in consequent lakes.

The process of transition from the youthful to the mature stage of form is, however, in progress from the first inception of the valley. It consists of the crumbling back by weathering action of the top edge of the valley side, wearing down and elimination of the rapids sections, conversion of the consequent-lake areas to portions of the stream channel by filling in with sediment and outlet downcutting.

It will be perceived that because of initial irregularities of topography and structure, different parts of the valley of a coastal-plain stream will vary in form according to how far the transition from youth to maturity has proceeded. A durable bed may resist weathering attack so effectively as to retain nearly vertical valley sides the while those on weaker beds have been developed to comparatively gentle slopes. In the channel of the stream the strong bed is also a *temporary base level.* (This phrase is synonymous with local base level.)   Until it has been worn down to conformance with the eventually achieved, general profile of equilibrium the altitude of the outcrop of the strong bed in the stream channel limits downward erosion above that point (Fig. 56). Thus long reaches of the valley may be graded, each with reference to the altitude of a particular resistant bed downstream which constitutes its local and temporary base level. The reach of a valley which is graded in respect of a local base level has attained maturity; the valley as a whole will be mature when the rapids sections are eliminated by downward erosion and an uninterrupted profile of equilibrium extends over the full length of the stream course. The presence of narrow strips of alluvial deposit, *flood plain* (Fig. 57), along the valley floor at all points below the headwaters section is the particular earmark of the graded condition. The change from downward erosion, primarily, to that of lateral enlargement of the floor signifies the end of youth and the beginning of maturity of valley development.

FIG. 56. TEMPORARY BASE LEVEL AND IMMINENT DISAPPEARANCE OF A WATER-
FALL BY INTERSECTION WITH THE GRADE PROFILE. SHOWN BY A MINIATURE
EXAMPLE

The stream is graded above and below the fall and the fall will disappear when its crest is broken back to the point where the slopes of the upstream and downstream graded reaches, projected, will intersect. From a photograph. Drawing by Elizabeth Burckmyer.

Transition from Youth to Maturity — Divides. Broadly considered, the topographic aspect of newly uplifted portions of a coastal plain is that of flat surfaces, gently inclined seaward and separated by short, steep slopes. In other words, they comprise widespread low terraces. The channels made by the parallel consequents cut the originally continuous flat surfaces into strips, referred to as *interfluves*, or *doabs* (Davis, W. M., 1889, p. 75) (Fig. 58). Coastal plain divides in the earliest stage of youth consist of these wide undissected doabs. Sheet wash makes the surfaces of such doabs faintly convex upward toward the centers of the areas between the dissecting streams. As tributaries to the consequents develop, the doabs are gradually separated into smaller areas. In the flat, new, coastal plain sections, where the beds have a very gentle dip, these tributaries will be insequent, following irregular courses. They in turn will receive insequent tributaries and so on, each tributary to a tributary being of smaller size. The

FIG. 57.   INCIPIENT FLOODPLAIN, DOE RIVER, TENNESSEE
Coarse gravels, the beginnings of a floodplain, are visible in the channel of the stream in the immediate foreground. The valley slopes have the open "V" profile appropriate to the approach to maturity in valley form. Photograph from the United States Geological Survey.

pattern of drainage that then ensues is *dendritic,* having stem, branches, limbs, and twigs; it is like an oak tree in the organization of its parts (Fig. 44a). The doab flats experience continual reduction of area and their outlines are made exceedingly irregular. In this stage the divide areas may be called *fringed doabs.*

The actual number of streams will be greater in the earlier stages of the dissection of the doabs. Through valley widening, by weathering back of the valley sides, the larger and deeper valleys will engulf the lesser, shallower, higher level channels.

This process of consolidation is called **abstraction** (Figs. 45, 114) and results in a complete consumption of the divide flats at sites where it has operated.

When, either by multiplication of stream courses or by abstraction, doabs are converted to sharp-crested ridges the divide areas have attained the stage of maturity.

FIG. 58.   UNDISSECTED INTERFLUVE OR DOAB, WITH FAINTLY CONVEX SURFACE FROM SOIL WASH AND SHEET EROSION
In the Atlantic Coastal Plain west of Savannah, Georgia.

Regional Maturity.   Failure to make a clear distinction between the stages of development in the fluvial geomorphic cycle as these apply, on the one hand, to valley forms and to divides, and on the other to regional aspects, is a common source of confusion in geomorphic discussion.   It is appropriate to call a valley mature when the stream in it has attained grade (Fig. 57).   A divide is mature when the initial surface has been changed to a ridge.   Thus full regional maturity is attained when all initial forms have disappeared.   Identification of stage with reference to regional aspects involves first a correlation of valley- and divide-development and then consideration of further factors of structure and process (Fig. 27).

According to Davis (1899, *Essays,* 1909, pp. 258–259) "When the trunk streams are graded, early maturity is reached; when the smaller headwaters and side streams are also graded, maturity is far advanced; and when even the wet-weather rills are graded, old age is attained." This analysis applies to regional interpretation. It may be supplemented by correlation with divides, in that early maturity will witness the first conversion of the flat interfluves, doabs, of a coastal plain to ridges; in middle maturity all divides are ridges (Fig. 3); at the end of maturity ridge divides are being rounded and lowered.

If further uplift occurs after the cycle of development is well advanced on a previously existing coastal plain a *rejuvenation* of both valley and divide forms will result. In that event the area could be regarded as entering upon a new cycle. But it may be assumed that the number and magnitude of uplifts is such that only a beginning is made on the dissection of the larger doabs at the low altitudes. The master consequents may be expected to maintain their courses at grade, practically without interruption, under these circumstances. The measure of downcutting that maintenance of grade entails will bring the trunk streams into contact with deeper, more strongly consolidated beds having relatively steep dips. When this occurs the development of insequent streams on resistant beds will be checked and the drainage pattern will rapidly change from the dendritic to the rectangular arrangement. In other words, subsequent streams will gain ascendency, and bring about captures and integration of drainage in the manner described above.

Herein is presented an additional characteristic indicative of regional maturity, namely adjustment to structure. As before, there will be grading of stream courses and sharpening of divides to earmark the stage of maturity. But if the geomorphic unit is possessed of structural differences sufficient in magnitude to exercise a control over valley development, then full maturity is not achieved until such adjustment to structure is made complete. Adjustment to structure means also the integration of drainage; by capture and diversion many original, small, independent systems are linked up into a few large units.

One more factor must be taken into account in evaluating regional maturity. It is that of the relief, considered with regard both to its vertical measure and to the degree of topographical irregularity. When regional maturity is fully attained the master streams will be graded; they will have reached their approximate limit of downcutting. The headwater reaches of the smallest streams will have just encompassed the last remnants of the initial flat doabs. The altitude of the ridge crest separating two of the smallest streams will not, as yet, have been degraded below the level of the original surface. With trunk streams at their greatest depth and with ridge lines in headwater areas still remaining at the original altitudes, the region, in full maturity, exhibits its maximal possible relief.

At the same time it presents its greatest topographic irregularity. The valley system has been expanded to realize every possibility of development. Divides everywhere are converted to the ridge form. Cuestas exhibit escarpment and dip slopes, water gaps and wind gaps. During the remainder of the cycle these features will be gradually subdued; at the stage of full regional maturity they have their greatest prominence.

Summary of Regional Maturity. To summarize: A geomorphic region in the stage of full maturity will have trunk streams at grade and their valleys adjusted and oriented to structure. No areal expanse of the initial interfluves, the doabs of a coastal plain, will remain and ridge divides will separate the smaller stream valleys. The region will then present a greater measure of relief and a greater topographic irregularity than at any other stage of the cycle.

Law of Equal Declivity. After regional maturity has been attained the classical view is that change of slope *declivity* becomes the principal feature of the further progress of the cycle.

Where the structural and other circumstances are simplest it has been held that the **law of equal declivities** will be in effect. With essentially homogeneous materials, horizontally disposed, and an equal distribution of precipitation over the area so constituted, the rate of reduction of slopes is determined by the declivities. The steeper slope is degraded faster. Accordingly, when slopes of unequal steepness occur on two sides of a divide the more rapid reduction of the steeper slope will shift the divide ridge toward the gentler one. At the same time the altitude of the divide will be lowered. This action ceases, and the divide becomes stationary in position, only when the divide ridge has acquired a symmetrical, cross-section profile. Considerable thicknesses of coastal-plain sediments may be of low, uniform resistance and of horizontal structure. In these localities the operation of the law of equal declivities will be clearly in evidence in middle maturity. Traces of the symmetry then developed should be long retained and may persist to the stage of old age. (Where perfection of equal declivity is observed in regions of strongly indurated rock it is warranted to infer notably homogeneous structure.)

Law of Monoclinal Shifting. On the inner portion of a coastal plain, where the beds have considerable dip and vary greatly in resistance to degradational processes (and in other geomorphic units having the same characteristics), slopes will be asymmetrical and divides will migrate in the direction of the dip. This response is referred to as the *law of monoclinal shifting* (Fig. 46). It results from the fact that an inclined capping layer of durable rock maintains a steep escarpment slope at its outcrop edge and a gently inclined dip slope on its upper surface. In accordance with the law of equal declivities the steeper slope recedes more rapidly. But in this case the higher declivity of the steeper slope is preserved by the structure, and the divide therefore migrates constantly in the direction of the dip. (The reference here is to coastal-plain conditions but the law applies to all dipping structures, sometimes in very complex relationships.)

Rotational Deflection. Not all asymmetrical slope profiles are to be ascribed to structural differences. On the Atlantic Coastal Plain of the United States the right bank of consequent valleys is characteristically steeper than the left. This difference is considered by some students to result from the right-hand deflection of the stream current as a result of the earth's rotation. Those who doubt the adequacy of *rotational deflection* to produce such a result suggest that prevailing winds drift water more strongly toward one side of the channel. In favor of the rotational deflection interpretation it may be noted that the Mississippi, the Yukon, and large Russian rivers, where they flow across weakly consolidated, little resistant materials, regularly have steep and high, right banks independent of wind direction.

Slopes Climatically Conditioned. In arid regions the north-facing slopes (Northern Hemisphere) of east to west valleys are regularly less steep than those facing south. The reason for this difference is fewer hours of direct insolation on the north-facing slope; hence less evaporation, and more vegetation cover. These circumstances favor the retention of weathering waste on the north-facing slope.

It has also been argued that the vicinity of the 32° F. line of January average temperature (Russell, R. J., 1931) is a critical belt. There the north-facing slopes (Northern Hemisphere) should be steeper because a snow cover will protect them from erosion; whereas the south-facing slopes, exposed to the sun, will experience repeated thaws and melt-water gullying. South of the 32° F. belt, slopes should be symmetrical and gentler; north of it symmetrical and steeper. Limestone hills in the Trades, where the wind blows almost unceasingly from one direction, have been observed to have a gentler inclination on the windward side. This asymmetry is inferred to result from the markedly greater solution and wash brought about by the constant drive of rain against the windward slopes. North-facing and lee slopes in high latitude and high altitude regions of incipient glacierization are characteristically steeper than the opposed ones because the snow banks and glaciers, which develop there first, have a sapping effect.

Old Age Valleys. The principal phenomenon to be noted during the conversion of a region from the stage of maturity to that of old age (in the fluvial geomorphic cycle) is the progressive elimination of the structural control of relief forms. The discussion that follows refers specifically to this development as it takes place on a coastal plain, but the sequences in this portion of the cycle are, in general, the same in other geomorphic units.

In the stages of youth and early maturity of valley development when the rate of lateral cutting is negligible in comparison with that of downcutting, many streams acquire a swinging flow from changes in direction of the initial consequent courses and from the irregularities of structure they encounter as the valleys are deepened. These swings tend to become more pronounced and enlarged before grade is attained. After attaining grade, streams rapidly widen the floors of their valleys by lateral planation. At many places along the course of the graded stream more of the energy of the current is directed against one side of the valley than against the other. The original swings initiate this uneven application of force and the mechanics of stream flow keep it in operation. The significant thing for geomorphology is that the lateral erosion of the graded stream is more effective on the side against which the current impinges with the greater force. The unequal widening of the valley floor at such points tends to confirm the current in its trend and thus to enhance the effect, and so to induce a continually accelerated rate of cutting where the preponderance of energy is expended. By this set of circumstances the stream is shortly confirmed in a *regular* swinging flow; it acquires the habit of **valley meandering.**

As the lateral cutting progresses the original slight departures from a straight-line course are enlarged to pronounced meander curves. Flow around the meanders lengthens the stream. Its gradient is thus reduced. Then the grade equilibrium in relation to sediment supply and transporting power is disturbed. Deposition results and serves to build up the gradient toward restoration of the graded condition. In this way a beginning is made in floodplain development. The first accumulation is made along the inside curve of a meander bend. Deposition begins on the downstream limb of the bend and enlarges from there. The isolated patches of deposited material that first show are called **flood-plain scrolls** (Figs. 98, 101). Although "flood plain" is generally used for this development it is clear that flooding, as such, is not an essential element of the process.

There is a **limiting width of meander belt** (Jefferson, M. S., 1902) (measured from the median line of flow to the centers of the arcs of successive meanders) beyond which the meander curves cannot be enlarged (Fig. 100). This width varies with the volume and the grade profile of streams. For a small stream the limiting width may not be more than 50 feet across; for a large stream it may be a mile or more. It has been estimated to average 15 to 20 times the width of the stream current (Bates, R. E., 1939, p. 850). As the limiting width is approached in a given stream a period of high water **(freshet,** or **flood** in America, **spate** in Great Britain) tends to overflow the **neck** of land inside a meander curve. The part of the current following this shorter course has a steeper gradient than that following the channel around the curve (Fig.

59a, b, c, d).   The power of downward-erosion, acquired by virtue of the steeper descent, serves to bring about the cutting of a channel across the neck of the meander.   As the flood subsides the new *cutoff channel* is followed by the normal current.   The abandoned meander course then becomes an *oxbow lake;* called a *mortlake* in Great Britain.

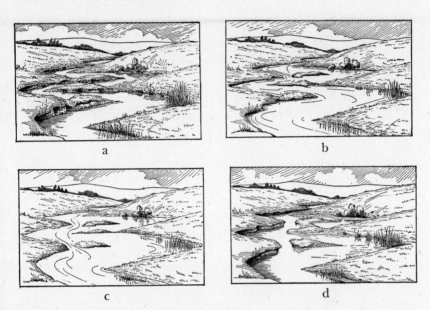

a   b

c   d

FIG. 59.   DEVELOPMENT OF A CUT-OFF CHANNEL AND AN OX-BOW LAKE

During the flood stage the strongest current is across the neck inside the meander curve.   A deeper channel eroded there then continues to be followed by the stream when the flood subsides and the longer, lower gradient, course around the meander bend becomes an ox-bow lake.   From photographs.   Drawings by Elizabeth Burckmyer.

Development of cutoffs diminishes the requirement for increase of gradient by deposition, necessitated by lengthening of the stream course from meander enlargement.   At the stage when the introduction of cutoffs is a frequent occurrence a continuous flood plain will have been built across the full width of the meander belt.   The course of the stream is then said to be one of *free meanders.*   From time to time the current is impelled to swing in new directions because of cutoffs.   These changes cause the whole meander belt to migrate back and forth across the flood-plain area. As a consequence of such migration lateral cutting is concentrated at a given time and along a given reach on the base of one valley slope; at another time or along another reach on the opposite valley slope. In this manner a wider and wider valley floor, clothed with flood-plain deposits, is produced. Meanwhile

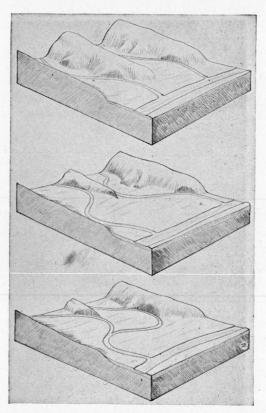

FIG. 60. DEVELOPMENT OF A CONFLUENCE PLAIN

The lateral cutting of the meandering tributary streams eventually reduces the divide ridge between their valleys to the common flood-plain level and thus produces a confluence plain of wide extent. Drawing by Steve Barker.

the level of the flood plain is being built up. The migration of the whole meander belt across the full width of the flood plain, like the flow around a single meander curve, tends to lengthen the course of the stream. The reduction in velocity of flow that results induces deposition, and so further raises the altitude and surface gradient of the flood plain. The flood-plain expanse in consequence, slowly, to be sure, but progressively, encroaches on the valley slopes.

According to Crickmay (1933) this sequence of circumstance and process is chiefly responsible for the reduction of wide areas to the ultimate peneplain stage. It will be noted that as, first, the valley meanders, and then the migrating, free-meander belt, cut along both sides of the valley, the lateral planation which results creates a nearly level valley floor over all the area involved. The effectiveness of such action may commonly be observed at sites where nearly parallel, closely adjacent, graded tributary streams

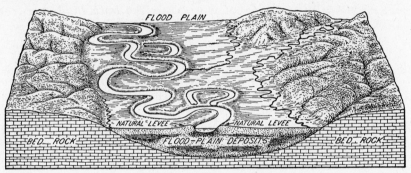

FIG. 61. DIAGRAM OF NATURAL LEVEES, OX-BOW LAKES, BACK LANDS, AND YAZOO
The back lands slope off from the natural levees to the base of the valley sides along which yazoo streams flow. After Frederick Morris.

join a main stream. At these localities it is seen that a considerable length of the divide which formerly separated the lower courses of the tributaries has been completely planed away (Fig. 60) by the combined lateral cutting of the two streams. *Confluence plain* is suggested as an appropriate genetic term for such development.

The volume of a flood may far exceed the capacity of the normal channel. The stream then spreads across the full width of the flood plain. When the rapid current of the rising waters first overtops the banks, it suffers a sudden check in velocity and, in consequence, immediately deposits a considerable proportion of its sediment load, and so builds up *natural levees* (Fig. 61). Natural levees are narrow and rather sharply defined along small streams, but in the case of large rivers may be hundreds of feet wide. Where the current of a flood locally and violently breaks across a levee a *crevasse* is cut. (Such crevasses must not be confused with crevasses in glaciers.) The higher, natural-levee accumulations, left behind by numerous shifts in the course of a stream, stand up above the general level of the flood plain, and, together with filled-in or ox-bow lakes, are prominent features in airplane photographs of such areas. The higher, dryer land of the natural levees supports plant associations unlike those on the lower channel and flood-plain lands, a difference clearly visible in many of the pictures. The building up of the general level of flood plains is by fine-textured deposits from the sluggishly flowing waters which at flood stages occupy the *back lands* between the natural levees and the base of the valley slopes.

The phenomenon of a *deferred tributary junction* (sometimes referred to as a *yazoo)* is another common feature where trunk streams have extensive flood plains. As a meander enlarges and moves progressively downstream by *meander sweep* it carries with it the mouth of a tributary. The tributary is thus compelled to a prolonged course over the back lands parallel to the main stream. A limit is set to such prolongation through capture of the tributary by the next large meander sweeping down from upstream. The section of the tributary below the point of capture then becomes an abandoned channel.

Old Age—Divides. According to W. S. Glock (1932), the progress of the fluvial cycle on a geomorphic unit of the simple type, represented by the newly uplifted, nearly flat portions of a coastal plain, is greatly dependent on *available relief* (Fig. 62). By available relief is meant the vertical distance between the altitude of the original surface, after uplift, and the level at which grade is first attained. If this distance is 200 to 300 feet or less, valley flats will appear before the interfluves are destroyed by slope retreat, that is, by weathering and wash of the valley sides. At attainment of grade the previously dominant vertical corrasion yields its pre-eminence in rate of cutting to lateral corrasion. The destruction of the flat interfluve areas, which started with the dissection resulting from stream downcutting, is thenceforward effected by lateral planation. Under these circumstances the phenomena of divide maturity and of regional maturity are eliminated from the cycle sequence. That is to say, areas with less than 200 to 300 feet of available relief pass directly from valley maturity to regional old age.

The value of the critical measure *(critical relief)* of available relief depends somewhat on the texture of drainage; in other words, on how far apart the stream channels are spaced. If the texture is coarse, available relief may be as great as 400 feet.

TOP DASHED LINE: INITIAL UPLAND–FLAT LEVEL

BOTTOM DASHED LINE: INITIAL GRADE – PROFILE LEVEL

150 FT.

Top diagram: Low to medium available relief. Over 15 per cent of the initial upland-flat level remains when the lower flat at grade first develops.

300 FT.

Middle diagram: Critical relief. Disappearance of the initial upland-flat levels coincides with the appearance of the lower flat levels. Regional maturity and valley maturity coincide.

600 FT.

Bottom diagram. High available relief. Upland flats and lowland flats do not co-exist. Divides and valley floors reduced in altitude concurrently as shown. The stage of regional maturity is maintained for a long time without change of aspect but with great change in altitude.

FIG. 62. DIAGRAMS TO ILLUSTRATE AVAILABLE AND CRITICAL RELIEF
From Glock. Modified drawings by Elizabeth Burckmyer.

Again, if available relief is very low the co-existence of upland flats and valley flats may extend far up the tributary arms. If available relief is high, greater by a considerable amount than critical relief, all trace of the interfluve flats will be destroyed by weathering and slope wash before any valley flat is formed. In these circumstances valley form remains unchanged until streams attain grade. Meanwhile the downcutting of valleys and the reduction in height of the line (ridge) divides are concurrent. The stage of divide maturity and approach to regional maturity may endure over long periods. But it may not be assumed that the altitude of the ridge summits during all this time is that of the initial surface. The dictum of maximal relief at full maturity, defined as the stage when the main streams are graded and the divides converted to ridges, must then be qualified. However the concept that topographic irregularity will be greatest at full maturity holds good.

A reflection of the W. Penck approaches is found in Glock's idea that if the rate of uplift is very fast the numerical value of critical relief is raised; that is, remnants of the level upland, interfluve surfaces will remain when grade is attained, with an available relief of more than 300 feet. If uplift is slow the measure of critical relief falls below 300 feet.

The level, newer parts of a coastal plain made up of nearly horizontal beds that differ very little in resistance to weathering and erosion conform to the postulates of the concept of available relief. In the older parts of the plain, where the layers have steeper dips, vary greatly in strength, and have been subject to repeated uplifts, the principle of available relief becomes subordinated to structure, and to the pattern of consequent, subsequent, and obsequent drainage. These older sections may have experienced degradation in conformance with the principle of available relief at the time of their first emergence through uplift. But under the structural control of steep dips, and varied resistance of the beds to processes of erosion and weathering, the older sections fit the characterization of regional maturity and old age, as originally supplied by Davis.

When, in extreme old age, all streams are graded, the further reduction of divides proceeds by slope wash and lateral planation. Weathering then strikes below grade and resistant formations are ultimately without significance in localizing relief. The surface everywhere is deeply mantled by a cover of rock waste and alluvial deposit. When only differences in the altitude of the cover of rock waste constitute the relief, and there is no relation between the location of stream courses and the underlying rock structure, complete peneplanation has been attained.

SUMMARY

Wide coastal plains have outer (new) and inner (old) sections. Master streams tend to maintain their courses at grade through both sections in competition with intermittent uplift. The grade profile-of-equilibrium fixes, within narrow limits, the measure of valley deepening that is possible. The grade of the master streams, hence, constitutes the local base level of erosion for tributary streams. When grade is attained valley forms arrive at the stage of maturity. Divides in the newer section of the coastal plain are, meanwhile, converted from flat interfluves to ridges; in the older parts the divide forms and the pattern of drainage are governed by adjustment of the stream courses to structure. Regional maturity implies graded valleys, ridge divides, adjustment to structure, maximal relief, and maximal topographic irregularity. Whether slopes are symmetrical or asymmetrical is determined by various factors of structure, process, and climate.

Valley meandering, developed to a limiting width of meander belt during maturity, becomes free meandering in the old-age stage. Lateral planation and flood-plain development are then the dominant in-valley processes. In the newer section of the coastal plain the factor of available relief is significant in the sequence of divide development. Drainage there is insequent, dendritic in pattern, and of coarse or of fine texture. In the older sections structural control of relief is progressively weakened and becomes wholly ineffective when the strongest rock beds have been decomposed by weathering to levels below those of the ultimately lowest profiles-of-equilibrum of the stream courses. Then peneplanation has been achieved.

BIBLIOGRAPHY

CLASSICAL

Gilbert, G. K. (1877–80) *Report on the Geology of the Henry Mountains, Utah,* United States Geographical and Geological Survey of the Rocky Mountain Region, Washington (Powell), (2nd Ed. 1880), Chapter V.

Cobb, C. (1893) *Notes on the Deflective Effect of the Earth's Rotation as Shown in Streams,* Journal of the Elisha Mitchell Scientific Society, Chapel Hill, N. C., Vol. 10, pp. 26–32.

Tower, W. S. (1904) *The Development of Cut-Off Meanders,* Bulletin American Geographical Society, Vol. 36, pp. 589–599.

Gregory, J. W. (1911) *The Terms "Denudation," "Erosion," "Corrosion," and "Corrasion,"* Geographical Journal, Vol. 37, pp. 189–195.

RECENT

Eakin, H. M. (1911) *The Influence of the Earth's Rotation upon the Lateral Erosion of Streams,* Journal of Geology, Vol. 18, pp. 435–447.

Rickmers, W. R. (1913) *The Duab of Turkestan,* Cambridge University Press, Cambridge.

Stephenson, L. W. (1926) *Major Features in the Geology of the Atlantic and Gulf Coastal Plains,* Journal Washington Academy of Sciences, Vol. 16, pp. 460–480.

Thorp, J. (1934) *The Asymmetry of the "Pepino Hills" of Puerto Rico in Relation to the Trade Winds,* Journal of Geology, Vol. 42, pp. 537–545.

Cunningham, B. (1937) *River Flow Around Bends,* Nature, Vol. 140, pp. 728–729.

Chapter Nine

FACTORS OF ROCK STRENGTH, IN RELATION TO PROCESSES AND RESULTS, IN THE FLUVIAL GEOMORPHIC CYCLE

Introduction. The contents of the two preceding chapters are organized to apply primarily to the progress of the fluvial geomorphic cycle on a coastal plain. The structure of coastal plains as a whole is weak. They are composed of little consolidated beds in simple attitudes and at low altitudes. Other geomorphic units in interior locations and at higher elevations have a similar structural make-up and experience essentially the same history of development as that of coastal plains. Specific examples are the Great Plains, a piedmont plains unit situated east of the Rocky Mountains, and the Glacial Plains of the interior of North America.

The Great Plains (Fig. 63) have an average elevation of 5000 feet along their western edge, retain wide expanses of the initial, flat surfaces (Johnson, W. D., 1900), are made up of friable beds of silt, sand, gravel, and calcareous materials and are traversed by eastward-flowing consequent streams.

So, also, are the till plains of the north central states composed of unconsolidated deposits, little differentiated as to materials, and hundreds of feet thick in places. They are, further, occupied by consequent drainage, and are still possessed of from one-half to nine-tenths of the original flat-topped surface.

But, in general, elevated, inland geomorphic units are made up of strongly consolidated rock. It is a significant fact that solid rock is present immediately below the surface of their divide areas (Figs. 3, 34, 64), and that such rock outcrops in valley slopes and floors. These circumstances warrant the positive inference that these areas, whether of simple or complex structure, have had a long denudational history. Strongly consolidated rocks, with the

FIG. 63.   ASPECTS OF THE GREAT PLAINS (*See foot of facing page*)

exception of lava flows, are formed at depth. Their existence in widespread surface exposures, devoid of any trace of an unconsolidated cover, indicates a long history of weathering and erosion preceding that of their present expression and environment.

FIG. 64.   STRONGLY CONSOLIDATED ROCK, FORMED AT GREAT DEPTH, NOW IMMEDIATELY BELOW THE SOIL SURFACE
Gneiss exposure south of Schroon Lake, Adirondacks.

Let it be assumed that such previous denudational history is related to the existing relief only in so far as it gave rise to an initial surface. Then, whether the erosional surface thus provided remained unmodified by endogenic force, or was lifted, tilted, warped, or broken, it remains that the course of the fluvial geo-

FIG. 63 (*Continued*). Top: Wide expanses of flat surface in Meade County, South Dakota. Photograph from United States Department of Agriculture, Soil Conservation Service.

Middle: Goforth Community, Caldwell County, Texas. In the soil-erosion area, abandoned because of soil losses. Photograph from United States Department of Agriculture, Soil Conservation Service.

Bottom: Somewhat dissected portion of the Great Plains, northeast of Rock Springs, Wyoming. Photograph by John Kirk.

FIG. 65. MASSIVE SANDSTONE; WINDOW ROCK, CANYON DE CHELLY NATIONAL
MONUMENT, ARIZONA
Photograph from The Atchison, Topeka and Sante Fe Railway Company.

morphic cycle in the "hard" rock will be in many respects different
from that in weak, unconsolidated materials. The specific nature
of the factors responsible for such unlikeness needs to be considered.

Hard Rock. "Hard" is put in quotation marks to indicate
that the word, as it is commonly employed in geomorphic discus-

sions, does not adequately serve the meaning it is intended to express. "Hard" is appropriate when the reference is to resistance to abrasion. Commonly this specific application is not intended. The broader relationship that the words "hard" and "soft" are usually meant to convey is better expressed by one of the pairs, "strong" and "weak," "durable" and "yielding," "greatly resistant" or "little resistant."

FIG. 66. THICK MASS OF GENESEE SHALE, TAGHANIC CREEK, NEW YORK

The fragments at the base of the cliff were weathered off its face in less than a year.

The implications of "strong" and "weak" are obvious. But it should also be clearly understood that these adjectives are used in the comparative and not in the absolute sense. They indicate which of two or many units is or are stronger, more resistant, and so on when considered in some sort of juxtaposition to other units, that is, beds, masses or structures.

Factors of Rock Strength. (1) *Massiveness.* A rock unit may be relatively strong because it is massive (Fig. 65). A massive bed or other rock unit is, so to speak, not to be disposed of out-of-hand. It tends to be geomorphically persistent. This dictum has its limitations. Thick, uninterrupted masses of shale rock are among the weakest of units under nearly all types of degradational attack and in association with almost all other units (Figs. 66, 67).

FIG. 67.   SHALE MASSES, FALL CREEK GORGE, ITHACA, NEW YORK

An exception has been made with reference to limestones (Ward, F., 1930).

(2) *Consolidation.*   True shales cohere only from compaction. Other sedimentary rocks cohere by various degrees and kinds of

cementation. Metamorphic and igneous rock cohere because of fusion and crystal adhesions and crystal interlocking. If a shale is regarded as having least strength from consolidation, quartzite perhaps has the greatest.

(3) *Composition.* A bed of limestone and a bed of quartzite may both be massive and well consolidated, but because of their difference in composition the limestone will be physically soft and chemically soluble (Fig. 68), while the quartzite will be very re-

FIG. 68. SOLUTION HOLLOWS IN THE SURFACE OF THE MASSIVE TULLY LIMESTONE, TAGHANIC CREEK, NEW YORK

sistant to abrasion and almost unyielding to solvent action. Granitic and syenitic rocks vary in durability in accordance with the volume of feldspar in their make-up; the feldspar is very susceptible to chemical decomposition of various kinds. Similarly a micaceous schist breaks down more readily than a gneiss.

(4) *Minute perviousness.* The degree of perviousness or permeability of a rock is of great importance in determining its comparative strength. "Perviousness" and "permeability" are nearly synonymous terms, but neither of them should be used interchangeably with "porosity." A rock may have a large volume of pore space but be relatively impermeable. If the pores are very

minute and discontinuous the penetration of liquids and gases will be slow and difficult. In general, rocks are more pervious than would seem probable on first inspection.

Apparently dense and impermeable rocks and minerals are shown under the microscope to have so many cracks, fissures, and tubes, and these to be so open and continuous that liquids and gases obviously have ready access to the rock interiors (Fig. 69). This perviousness permits a contrast to be drawn between rocks and minerals, as representatives of the inorganic world, and the plants and

FIG. 69. FLAWS IN THE MINERALS OF A GRANITE ROCK AS SEEN UNDER THE MICROSCOPE

animals of the organic world. The living things of the organic world are possessed of covering skins and of cell walls that protect their interior substances from exterior attack. If these covers are ruptured the organism functions to renew them; on its success or failure in effecting such healing its survival depends. If the wound is not mended, part or all of the organism decays or is disrupted. Rocks and minerals have neither protective skins nor cell wall covers. They are directly and immediately subject to attack and decomposition or disintegration by any agency of destruction to which they may be exposed. Thus the inorganic world of rocks and minerals is innately weak compared to the organic world, whose representatives can maintain themselves, more or less successfully, through possession of a skin, for a life history. Rocks are, so to speak, born dying.

The smaller passages, in general terms, are the flaws and imperfections of crystals and crystal adhesions in the crystalline rocks and the spaces unfilled by cementing materials between the particles of a sedimentary rock. Owing to their presence, rocks subjected to weathering processes ultimately break down to fine waste, popularly referred to as soil, more accurately in geologic terms a constituent part of the cover of rock debris called *mantle rock*, or *regolith*. The minute passages, and the fine rock waste they make possible, are important in the progress of geomorphic change, but

FIG. 70. WIDE-SPACED JOINTING IN OLEAN CONGLOMERATE, OLEAN, NEW YORK

are overshadowed in respect of strength differences, and the forms to which these give rise by the larger, gross breaks that rocks exhibit, notably joint- and fault-plane fissures.

(5) *Gross Perviousness.* As nearly as any such broad generalization can safely be made, it may be asserted that all consolidated rocks are jointed. The movements necessary to bring about their exposure as surface materials at considerable altitudes, following the long degradational histories alluded to above, have so racked the rock masses as to induce almost universal fissuring of the type seen when a sheet of glass is cracked, but not broken apart. Such

Fig. 71. Jointing in metamorphic rock. Hornfels outcrop in Westgard Pass, Inyo County, California, has a shattered aspect

fissures, in which the movement is almost solely at right angles to the plane of break, extend greater or less distances through the rocks and are called *joints.* Jointing may be wide-spaced (Fig. 70) or close-spaced; indeed the joints may be so numerous, though

Fig. 72. JOINTING IN BASALTIC ROCK, DEVIL'S POST PILE, NEAR BISHOP, CALI-
FORNIA
Photograph by Frashers, Inc., Pomona, California.

Fig. 73. CAYUGA PALISADES, CAYUGA LAKE, NEW YORK
Classic site for illustrations of jointing in sedimentary rock.

still of the definite joint pattern, as to cause the rock to appear shattered (Figs. 71, 72).

If joints are wide-spaced and obscure, any given type of rock will be strong in comparison with the same rock cut by close-spaced and prominent joints. The granites of the Yosemite Valley, California, are asserted to be free of joints for distances of 1000 feet in places (Matthes, F. E., 1930, p. 39). In the sedimentary formations of the Appalachian Plateau of central New York the spacing of the joints varies greatly within narrow horizontal distances. In Watkins Glen, specifically, there is indeed an alternation between sections widely open where the joints are obvious and close-spaced, and narrow gorge reaches where joints are few and poorly developed.

FIG. 74.   EROSION OF JOINT BLOCK FROM STREAM COURSE, ENDFIELD GLEN, NEW YORK

The perfect rectangular outlines indicate where joint blocks have been removed bodily from the stream bed. Photograph by Robert Underwood.

In the central New York region the joint systems intersect at approximately right angles. As a consequence the details of relief where the rocks are not covered by regolith have a very conspicuous rectangular aspect. Because, further, considerable vertical sections of the rock are very uniform in composition and texture, the joints extend in uninterrupted planes through great thicknesses of strata. Wave erosion along the lake shores of this region has given rise to cliffs which exhibit the joint phenomenon as smooth walls so perfect as to appear of artificial origin (Fig. 73). These cliffs are a classic site for illustrations of the phenomenon of jointing in sedimentary rocks. The right angle intersections and the regularity of the jointing in this area, generally, guide small, but actively downcutting streams in sharply rectangular courses, because during periods of high water joint blocks are lifted bodily out of the channel bottom and moved downstream (Figs. 74, 96).

Hobbs (Hobbs, W. H., 1911) considers the influence of jointing (and faulting) on weathering and erosion a dominant factor in the *lineamenting* of many landscapes. The repeating, rectangular pattern (Fig. 44a) (and in some instances trellis pattern) of drainage lines, is, he thinks, primarily a response to the ordering of the joint and fault systems in the rocks. Hobbs cites rivers in Connecticut, the drainage of the Lake Timiskaming, Ontario, region,

FIG. 75. FAULT-LINE SCARP, SOUTHEAST ARM OF GREAT SLAVE LAKE, CANADA

Fault in massive rock given expression in the relief of this area. Pre-Cambrian granites left back; pre-Cambrian conglomerate sandstone and diabase to right and in foreground. Royal Canadian Air Force photograph, courtesy D. A. Nichols.

parts of the Spitzbergen coast, as examples. The geomorphic aspect of the Adirondack Mountains, as a unit, gives expression to this lineamenting influence of joints and faults. The conspicuous development there is referred to a set of circumstances that Hobbs did not elucidate. The Adirondacks have experienced a long history of degradation, were perhaps repeatedly reduced to low altitudes, but never perfectly peneplaned nor ever submerged in the course of the repeated downwearings. Throughout the long history of subaerial exposure the undeviating pattern of the fracture lines persistently guided the weathering and erosional attack. The

FIG. 76. BEDDING PLANES AT A WATER-FALL SITE ON THE EAST SIDE OF SKANE-
ATELES LAKE, NEW YORK

The bedding planes are lines of discontinuity. At the crest of the fall the
variation in composition of successive beds gets expression in jutting and
overhang.

166

composite effect of such long continued directed dissection developed the marked lineamentation that now exists. The influence of a single fissure in one cycle was not determinant; the cumulative effect resulting from the repetition of this influence was ultimately so great as to give the small fissures collectively a leading role in the patterning of the landscape (Fig. 44a).

Fault planes, like joint planes, are paths for the penetration of the agencies of rock disintegration. Because they are definite

FIG. 77.   COVER MASS AND UNDER MASS, LOOKING EAST FROM OPPOSITE GRAND VIEW POINT, GRAND CANYON, ARIZONA

The horizontal sedimentary beds of the upper canyon are a cover mass over the under mass of the Vishnu schist, the top surface of which is a fossil erosion surface of low relief.   Photograph, copyright, from Spence Air Photos.

breaks, with shifts by displacement, extending, in places, with unbroken continuity through great vertical and horizontal distances the traces of faults might, *a priori*, be expected to exert marked influences on the development of relief. But observation leads to the conviction that the importance of fault breaks if not of original or cumulative large throw is relatively slight. They do in places guide erosion (Fig. 75). But, unless the displacing movement, especially if chiefly horizontal, heave, is renewed from time to time, fault breaks tend to heal up at depth by mineral filling and so tend to become lines of strength rather than of weakness.

Bedding planes and unconformities are lines of discontinuity but not of physical break (Fig. 76). They influence the progress of degradation by fixing the sites where abrupt changes in the materials subject to attack are encountered but are not of them-

FIG. 78. TEMPORARY OVERFLOW CHANNEL OF ICE-MARGIN LAKE, BROOKTONDALE, NEW YORK

The well-defined channel, now not carrying drainage, was sluiced into glacial drift by the overflow of a lake ponded (in the valley of the middle background) by a former ice margin which extended along the left of the picture. In the far background a rock hill characteristically modeled by ice erosion appears.

selves lines of penetration. The geomorphic significance of the abrupt, commonly marked in kind, transition between the materials above and below a plane of angular unconformity is indicated by the introduction of the terms *cover mass* and *undermass* (Fig. 77).

It may be here noted that, except in the case of lava floods, or of piedmont plains, undermasses that have the ruggedness of relief characteristic of late youth or early maturity seldom occur. A widespread transgression of the sea is immediately feasible over a region reduced to old age or peneplanation, or over a plain of marine erosion, but not across a region of marked relief. The upper surface (*fossil, or exhumed erosion surface*) of an exhumed undermass, hence, is characteristically one of very low relief. The origins and former attitudes of fossil erosion surfaces are commonly very difficult to determine.

Rock Variations and Downward Erosion of Streams. (1) *Grooving.* In unconsolidated rock, streams erode with some degree of effectiveness by the sweep of the current flow. This is clearly demonstrated by the well-defined channels that temporary overflows from ice-margin lakes make in glacial deposits (Fig. 78). But such sluicing is practically impotent where the rock is strongly indurated. Sediment-free water may induce some yield in such rocks by solution of their substance. However, the main process of downcutting in consolidated beds and masses is by application of sediment, rock fragments, small and large, used as the tool for grinding by streams. This abrasive action is called corrasion.

If grinding by transported sediment is directed against rocks that are very uniform in composition, and very little intersected by fissures, the result is a smooth grooving (Fig. 79) that reproduces the curving flow of the current. As such conditions of rock structure are of infrequent occurrence, examples of groove cutting are not numerous.

> However, the site of the most renowned downward erosion by a stream, the Grand Canyon of the Colorado, in the best known section, is now experiencing groove cutting to a noteworthy degree (Maxon, J. H., and Campbell, I., 1935). The Vishnu schist (Fig. 77), into which the inner canyon there is cut, has ideally the necessary homogeneity and massiveness for this process. The rock of the river channel, as seen at the foot of the Bright Angel Trail, is perfectly smoothed and polished by groove grinding.

The stream-grooved surfaces in some respects resemble the striation and polishing of rock by glacial ice. Where stream grooving is responsible, the close relationship between the forms of the surfaces and minor differences in rock durability should permit the water-formed markings to be distinguished from those due to glacial polish. Where the rock differences are marked enough the water action develops *flutings,* which more conspicu-

FIG. 79. GROOVING EROSION IN MOSAIC CANYON, NEAR STOVE PIPE WELLS, DEATH VALLEY, CALIFORNIA

These curved groovings were obviously made by the swirling flow of water coming down the canyon in flood volume. Photograph by Frashers, Inc., Pomona, California.

ously reflect variations in the rock in relation to this type of corrasion.

(2) *Potholes.* Almost every student of geology early becomes familiar with **potholes** and the mechanism of their action (Alex-

ander, H. S., 1932). The very important role that pothole grinding has in the downward excavation by streams is not, however,
generally appreciated. The pothole is examined as a specific
phenomenon. The examples pictured in textbooks, and the ones

FIG. 80. SUCCESSION OF POTHOLES CONSTITUTING THE FLOOR OF THE STREAM IN
WATKINS GLEN, NEW YORK
    The vertical erosion of the gorge is accomplished by the downward boring
of these potholes. Photograph by Douglas Rogers.

sought out for observation in the field are regularly isolated
occurrences. Such complete and intact instances do not adequately represent the significance of the pothole phenomenon.
    Where the rocks of a stream bed are nonuniform in texture, or
are frequently intersected by joints, or have any kind of localized

weaknesses, a small pit may be dug by differential erosion, or a
hollow may result from the breaking out of a large fragment.
Once a depression is formed in the bed of a stream it can become
the lodging place of sand grains or pebbles slightly too coarse for
the current to move across the low spot. The sand and pebbles
do not, however, remain at rest. They are, more or less continuously, given a circular motion around the bottom of the
hollow. By such grinding the depression is enlarged and deepened. In consequence more pebbles and more of the current are
involved. Thus a pothole, progressively deepened and widened
at the bottom, comes into being.

Once begun, the pothole persists, as such, deep below the
vertical penetration of the rock inequality by which it was initiated. Meanwhile the grooving scour of the stream lowers the
general level of the bed. Upstream or downstream, another pothole site is brought into the zone of stream action, and another
pothole is initiated. In time the whole stream bed may become
a succession of potholes (Fig. 80). Most of these will have been
descended or inherited (Elston, E. D., 1917–18) from rock conditions that are no longer in evidence. By lateral enlargement
adjoining potholes intersect at the bottom from time to time.
The miniature natural bridge that then separates the upper portions is broken down at the next period of flood flow. Shortly
the complete length of a gorge-cutting stream becomes a succession
of independent and intersecting potholes. The whole current of
the stream must, in consequence, move in a series of gyratory
swirls passing from one pothole to the next. The downcutting
erosion of the gorge thus becomes chiefly a business of pothole
grinding. When the significance of the linked potholes so regularly observed on gorge floors is appreciated, it becomes clear how
generally the pothole process of downcutting is operative and
effective.

(3) *Waterfalls.* Rock differences of greater magnitude than
those which bring about the initiation of potholes commonly get
expression in the development of rapids and waterfalls. The most
common type is that of the **cap-rock waterfall** or **cap-rock rapids.**
Somewhere between 60 and 85 per cent of the earth's land surface
has a cover of stratified rocks. It is, hence, in such materials that
the major portion of land relief is modeled. Stratified rocks char-

acteristically present alternations between shale, sandstone, and limestone beds. The downward erosion of streams in stratified rocks normally encounters these variations in the vertical section.

If the difference in resistance to erosion of the successive beds is slight, and the alternations are separated by vertical intervals that are small in the relation to the depth of the current, there will be a descent in rapids or low cascades. A weak bed will succumb faster than the more resistant overlying and underlying layers. Where it occurs the normally smooth, downward curve of the stream-bottom profile will be interrupted by a sharp downward bend. There is, further, a tendency to undermine the upper strong layer. When such undermining proceeds to a joint plane that intersects the strong bed, a block of the cap rock, deprived of support, will break out and be carried away by flood currents. The cascade crest is thus caused to retreat an appreciable distance upstream.

Where the difference in strength of layers is pronounced and on a large scale, for example, where a massive limestone or sandstone bed overlies a great thickness of very weak shales, the cap-rock fall phenomenon has its grandest expression. Then *plunge-pool* action comes into play (Figs. 81, 82). The current, in making a great vertical descent, is accelerated by gravity and hence attains a maximal velocity of flow; the ultimate speed of the plunging water increases with the height of the fall. The impact of the water at the base of the fall has great force and serves to disrupt the rock that it strikes. Sediment and rock fragments brought down by the current deal blows which much enhance the erosive action of the descending water. A hole is virtually punched in the rock below the falls. This hole is the plunge pool and may be of great depth. The water circulates in the pool in violent swirls. This churning flow, utilizing rock fragments as tools, brings about a rapid lateral enlargement of the base of the pool. The face of the fall is effectively undercut by this process. The Canadian part of Niagara Falls illustrates such development perfectly. As with the lesser examples of cap-rock falls, the crest line of Niagara is caused to retreat rapidly upstream, in consequence of the plunge-pool undermining it experiences.

There are other circumstances, some structural, some not, by which a waterfall declivity can be introduced in a stream course.

The concern here is not with the particulars of the different instances. It is, rather, to make clear that at the site of a fall a stream will attain great erosional competence.

Accordance of Junction. Owing to the searching action of the agencies of weathering and of the different processes of stream erosion, every variation, great and small, of rock composition and

Fig. 81. TRIPHAMMER FALLS, FALL CREEK, NEW YORK, LOW WATER STAGE
Only minor erosion is being effected on the projecting ledges at the base of the fall. The water fails of reaching the plunge pool.

structure is found out. Differences in rock strength and in the energy of attack by the processes of weathering and stream erosion are in nice adjustment. It appears that the range of difference in resistance is so closely suited to the intensity and rate of the "normal" decomposing and disintegrating processes as to permit a maximum of relief to develop from their interaction. The weaker zones and areas are decomposed, disrupted, and eroded in advance of the stronger ones. It could be expected that the ensuing relief would exhibit every possible variation of discordant declivity. On this basis abrupt changes of slope would be the dominant aspect of landscape. Instead, regularity, continuity, gradation are the rule. The seeming contradiction is resolved when it is realized that while the processes of the fluvial geomorphic cycle act to give prominence to rock and structural differences in the later stages of youth and in early maturity, they tend to erase the relief, so engendered, in all the following stages of the

Fig. 82.   TRIPHAMMER FALLS, FALL CREEK, NEW YORK.   IN FLOOD, JULY 1935.
   The tremendous volume of the flood-flow shoots out from the lip of the fall to plunge with terrific force into the pool, subjecting the rock at its bottom to violent erosive action.

cycle. In this relationship there is demonstrated, even if somewhat obscurely, what proves to be a basic principle, realized early by Penck (Penck, A., 1905) of all geomorphic development, namely, the ultimate ascendency of process over structure. This outcome is realized in the grading of slopes and rivers, and in the development of the peneplain. It is peculiarly well exemplified in the phenomenon of the *accordant junction* of lateral and main streams and of their valleys.

   The ability of a stream to cut a channel in consolidated rock is due chiefly to its traction of rock fragments. The transporting power of a stream for such tools is proportional to the sixth power of the velocity of the current. Thus if the rate of flow is doubled, and the stream had been carrying particles of two units of mass at the initial velocity, it will, at the doubled velocity, be able to move particles of approximately 64 units of mass. The derived power of corrasion is computed to vary as the square of the velocity. These ratios are not realized with mathematical exactness in nature but broadly speaking they are in effect. The indicated tremendous increase in corrasive power resulting from slight increases in velocity of flow is for geomorphology a relation of first importance.

If structural variations or other circumstances bring about the introduction of declivities of greater than average steepness (knickpunkte) in a stream course, the fact of such declivity, by increasing the velocity of flow at that site, immediately enhances the rate of corrasion in so disproportionate measure as to insure, in the geomorphic time sense, the almost immediate elimination of the sharper slope. In other words, rapids and waterfalls tend to be very short-lived features in a history of valley-making; graded profiles are quickly arrived at. (The German, Penckian, and Meyerhoff's and Hubbell's concept of the initiation, in response to uplift, and persistence of knickpunkte, independent of structure, is in some degree a refutation of this doctrine.)

The superiority of process, as referred to corrasive river action, does not stop with this phenomenon of rapid elimination of structurally induced declivity. It operates also to maintain continuity of grade between main streams and their tributaries. If, properly, a trunk stream is assumed to have, by virtue of its large volume and great supply of tools, considerable efficiency in downcutting, then it might be expected that its tributaries with less volume and less tools would be left hanging at the point of junction. Instead, the more rapidly the main stream tends to outdo the tributary in downcutting, hence to introduce a discordance at the point of junction, the greater will be the velocity of flow, there, of the tributary stream. Then the attendant geometric rise in corrading ability will regularly enable the minor stream to maintain its accordant level of junction.

Thus because of elimination of structural declivities and maintenance of grade at junctions, through the functioning and superiority in effectiveness over structural resistances of the corrasive processes of streams, Playfair was enabled to say (Playfair, J., 1802, p. 102): "Every river appears to consist of a main trunk, fed from a variety of branches, each running in a valley proportioned to its size, and all of them together forming a system of vallies (sic), communicating with one another, and having such a nice adjustment

FIG. 83. ACCORDANT JUNCTION OF THE NAHE RIVER AND THE RHINE RIVER AT BINGEN, GERMANY

Although both the main and tributary valleys have recently experienced active downcutting, as is indicated by the steepness of their sides, the deepening of the tributary valley kept pace with that of the main valley. Photographer unknown.

of their declivities that none of them join the principal valley either on too high or too low a level; a circumstance which would be infinitely improbable if each of these vallies were not the work of the stream that flows in it." (Fig. 83.) His statement at one and the same time makes streams responsible for their valleys and is the formulation of what is now generally known as Playfair's *Law of Accordant Junctions.*

Nevertheless, waterfalls are notable geomorphic phenomena and their sites in many instances are discordant junctions of tributary and main valleys. Accordingly, it is appropriate next to examine more closely the occurrence of waterfalls and the particular features that are characteristic of the various types.

SUMMARY

Inland geomorphic units are, in general, made up of consolidated rock. Because of a number of factors the different kinds of such rock vary considerably in durability. The range of difference in rock strength and the measure of energy exerted in degradational attack are nicely matched for effective interaction. Distinctive topographic lineamentation may result from the influence of the rock differences in effect through an extended degradational history. Rock variations also condition the processes of stream corrasion. But process ultimately prevails over structure. This outcome is basic to Playfair's Law that tributary streams normally join main streams accordantly.

BIBLIOGRAPHY

CLASSICAL

Merrill, G. P. (1897) *A Treatise on Rocks, Rock Weathering, and Soils,* The Macmillan Company, New York.

RECENT

Pirsson, L. V., and Knopf, A. (1926) *Rocks and Rock Minerals,* John Wiley & Sons, Inc., New York.

Chapter Ten

WATERFALL SITES

Introduction. Waterfall sites more than any other geomorphic feature attract and hold the interest of the general public. Because they have such a popular approval waterfalls are not given serious attention by some students of systematic geomorphology. This attitude is not to be commended. Waterfalls are significant items for geomorphic interpretation.

Discordance Sites. Playfair's Law of Accordant Junctions embodies an implication that the gradients of main streams are gentler than those of tributaries which join them. Because trunk streams tend to attain grade early in the degradational evolution of most geomorphic units this is the relation commonly observed.

If, however, circumstances are such in the initial stages of the fluvial cycle that the main stream, instead of having a lesser declivity, is actually provided with a maximal slope, one approaching waterfall steepness, it is clear that tributaries will not be able to keep pace with the main stream in downwearing. Even if the gradients of the tributaries are as steep as those of the main stream, the smaller volume and, possibly, poorer supply of cutting tools, will prevent the tributary streams from maintaining accordance. If the gradients of the tributaries are measurably inferior to those of the main stream, the rate of downcutting by the side streams is perforce less than that of the trunk stream.

The discordance of stream junction that results from these relations is commonly observed on a small scale where wet-weather, intermittent drainage joins streams that have perennial flow. In such instances the disparity in volume approaches the ultimate extreme. During and immediately after rains a discordance type of waterfall is seen at the junction of the wet-weather and the perennial stream. Between rains the perennial stream persistently deepens its valley while no erosion occurs in the side valley.

The discordant junctions of the wet-weather intermittent drain-

179

age are miniature instances of the phenomenon of *hanging valleys.* The same relation obtains on a larger scale in arid regions.
Somewhat similar developments are noted in districts underlain
by soluble chalk or limestone. There the downward erosion of a
large perennial stream may lower the ground-water level of areas
adjoining its course so rapidly that valleys tributary to it lose their
water supply by underground percolation. The lower ends of
the tributaries then become dry hanging valleys.

Particular conditions of uplift may permit a like development
of much larger dimensions. The hanging valleys and very high
falls of the Yosemite, California, site are a case in point. Before
the latest mountain-making uplift of the region that is now the
Sierra Nevada Mountains occurred, the trunk streams of the area
flowed westward at a low gradient. Uptilt then converted the
Sierra Nevada to a great, westward-sloping, mountain block. The
main streams were suddenly provided with very steep gradients.
Their lateral tributaries, with courses extending north or south,
experienced no change of bottom slope. These circumstances
facilitated rapid erosion of steep-sided gorges by the trunk streams,
and left the valleys of the side streams hanging (Fig. 84). The
waterfalls that resulted have remained at the original sites of discordant junction, in part because the massive granite of the region
prevented undermining of the crest, in part because plunge-pool
cutting would, even with other structure, have been rendered
ineffective by the continued active deepening of the main valleys.
At a later date differential glacial erosion served to magnify the
Yosemite hanging valleys to their present spectacular aspect.

The intervention of a second agency, like that of glacial action
in the Yosemite, is commonly the basic reason for a regional development of hanging valleys, and for the existence, at their
termini, of discordant-junction waterfalls. Sea (or lake) cliffs may
be made to retreat so rapidly, by the undermining erosion of the
wave attack, that streams which empty into the ocean (or lake)
where they occur are unable to keep pace with the rate of recession of the cliff in downcutting their valleys. On the northeast
shore of the island of Hawaii the strong and constant surf of the
trade wind beats against the edges of the lava flows that descend
to the sea from the slopes of the volcanic cone, Mauna Kea. An
imposing, cliffed coast has resulted from the wave attack. The

FIG. 84. YOSEMITE VALLEY

Bridalveil Falls on the right plunges from the hanging valley of Bridalveil Creek. Both main and tributary valleys were modified to U-shaped troughs by glacial erosion. Photograph from United States Geological Survey.

181

heavy rainfall on the windward slope of Mauna Kea gives rise to almost innumerable, parallel, consequent streams.   Only the exceptionally large ones of these have been able to maintain their valleys at grade in competition with the retreat of the sea cliff. The vast majority of the streams, unable to keep pace with the landward recession of the cliff, plunge into the sea from hanging valleys.   They end at different altitudes; the smaller streams have the higher falls.   The panorama of waterfalls which results is a noteworthy scenic spectacle.   Even along lake shores cliff-retreat may surpass the downcutting of small valleys by enough to introduce considerable declivities.

As is true of the Yosemite, hanging valleys and hanging-valley waterfalls are most conspicuously present in areas formerly occupied by glaciers.   This statement applies especially to regions of mountain glaciation, but the hanging-valley phenomenon also has a considerable development in at least one area of continental glaciation.

It is a safe assertion that all regions once glaciated, but now cleared of ice, with the possible exception of polar areas, had a preglacial history of valley-making by stream erosion.   The glaciated topography is, accordingly, a modification of a preglacial, fluvial-cycle topography.

The enormous acceleration of downward erosion that accompanies every slight increase in velocity of stream flow has little or no counterpart in glacial action.   It is, of course, true that, other things equal, the faster a glacier moves the more it erodes, because more ice passes over a given area in a given time.   But as tributary and trunk glaciers move at approximately the same velocities differences in the rate of glacial erosion are determined almost solely by differences in depth of the ice streams.   As the thickness of the ice in mountain glaciers ranges from 500 to 3000 feet and more, it is clear that if glacial erosion is at all effective differences in the measure of downcutting accomplished by glaciers of unequal thickness in a given time may be very large.   Unlike streams in another respect, downward erosion by glaciers is not governed by base levels, not even by the grand base level of the sea.   (Except in the very broad sense that the ends of glaciers that discharge into the ocean ultimately break off in deep water.)

It follows that throughout a period of *glacierization* (the occu-

Fig. 85.   Hanging valley waterfall into the Lauterbrunnental, Switzerland

The main valley is a great glacial trough eroded to grade.   Into it the side stream plunges nearly vertically from a great height.   The shelf at the right is a small alb.   Photograph by William Pleyer.

pation of an area by glaciers) thin tributary glaciers will erode
valleys downward much less rapidly than the thick trunk glacier
which they join. The preglacial accordance of valley junctions is
destroyed immediately the glacial occupation becomes effective,
and thenceforward the discordances are progressively magnified
by continuation of the differential erosive action of the dissimilar
ice streams. When the ice melts off after a long period of
glacierization, the rock bottoms of the tributary valleys are discovered to end at levels high above those of the main valleys. The
restored stream drainage then makes a waterfall plunge from each
hanging-valley lip into the main valley (Fig. 85).

A dissentient minority of geomorphologists holds that hanging
valleys in glaciated areas result from the protection that a cover of
glacier ice affords, instead of from glacier erosion. They assert that
in high-level tributary valleys, glaciers linger and protect the rock
floors from erosion, while in the main valleys stream erosion cuts
rapidly downward. In other words, streams are competent erosive
agencies; glaciers little, if at all, capable of deepening valleys.
This interpretation is contradicted by the observation that in
regions of continental glaciation hanging valleys result from
divergent ice-streaming at the bottom of the glacier. In the central
New York State plateau, or in the Scottish Highlands, the bottom
ice of the continental glaciers was guided in its motion by the
preglacial valley systems. The larger valleys that were in line with
the general direction of ice-advance are found to be greatly overdeepened. Side valleys, tributary to the overdeepened channels,
hang with a measure of discordance that depends on the local conditions. As with similar valleys in regions of mountain glaciation the hanging-valley termini of continental glaciation are waterfall sites in postglacial time. Whether or not the manner of motion of the bottom ice here postulated is an acceptable inference,
glacial protection is ruled out as an explanation for the occurrence
of the hanging valleys in these regions of continental glaciation.

As waterfalls at the ends of hanging valleys resulting from
differential glacial erosion owe their existence neither to structure
nor to the circumstances of stream erosion, they should be rapidly
eliminated, once stream drainage is restored, because at such sites
the water has maximal erosive effectiveness. But, in most places,
not enough time has elapsed since the close of the Pleistocene
glacial occupation to permit water action to erase the discordances. However, except in massive resistant rock, such as that of

the Yosemite Valley (Fig. 84), narrow gorges have been notched into the hanging-valley lips by interglacial and postglacial stream erosion (Fig. 86).

Where faults with vertical displacements cut across stream courses waterfalls with characteristics similar to those of the hanging valleys from differential glacial erosion result.

FIG. 86.   NOTCHING OF THE LIP OF A HANGING VALLEY BY STREAM EROSION, NUNATAK FIORD, ALASKA

The hanging valley lip is 1000 feet above the level of the fiord waters. Drawing, from a photograph, by Elizabeth Burckmyer.

Step Falls. A stream which flows through a gorge that it has cut into the lip of a hanging valley may be looked upon as a variety of extended consequent. The slope over which such a stream descends is new land. If irregularities of structure are encountered in the stream's downcutting, the rate of erosion will be unequal, and the consequent course will present a series of *step falls.* Not uncommonly such step descents ensue from the detachment of a joint-plane block as a unit mass. This phenomenon has given rise to the term *joint-plane falls,* with the implication that joint planes are responsible for the falls' declivity. It should, however, be understood that the precipitate descent which makes the falls possible is the differential ice erosion that created the hanging-valley condition. The step falls due to joint planes are merely breaks in the face of the larger declivity.

Other joint-plane falls are of similar origin. The descent of streams over the jointed rock forming the borders of lava flows is a case in point. The lava may be more resistant to stream erosion than the adjoining country rock. Then the circumstances are like those where a strong, but well-jointed, layer occurs in horizontally bedded sedimentary rocks. The joints are an element of weakness, but the rock, despite the presence of the joints, is more durable than the underlying layers. The breaking out of the joint blocks precludes the maintenance of a vertical falls at such a site but the presence of the declivity is due to the readier yield of the lower layers. Joint-plane falls are unusually picturesque and on that account have gained the distinction of a special name other than the general designation of step falls or cascades.

Cap-rock Falls. The jointed, but nevertheless durable, sedimentary bed whose edge is marked by a joint-plane falls is a special type of the class of falls called cap-rock falls. Cap-rock falls develop in actively downcutting streams wherever a strong layer (usually a sandstone or massive, commonly dolomitic, lime-

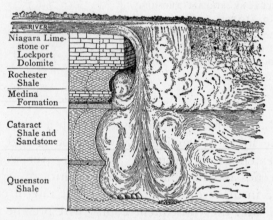

Fig. 87.   ROCK SECTION AT NIAGARA FALLS TO ILLUSTRATE THE CAP-ROCK RELATION

The massive Lockport dolomite maintains the crest of the fall. The crest recedes only as undermining from plunge-pool erosion of the weak shales below deprives the cap rock of support. Modified from G. K. Gilbert.

stone) is underlaid by weak beds (usually shales) and where the layers are horizontally disposed or have a low dip upstream. Niagara is at once the most representative and most famous example of cap-rock falls. There the thick Lockport dolomite overlies more than a hundred feet of weak shales, thin limestone, and thin sandstone beds (Fig. 87).

There are three chief varieties of cap-rock falls. Between them there is every gradation, but the type development of each variety is completely distinctive.

Where a stream has large volume and a considerable descent, the plunge-pool grinding at the base of the fall is very effective and causes rapid undercutting of the weak formations below the cap rock. The cap rock, in consequence, is deprived of support at the brink. Its own weight, together with the weight of the water,

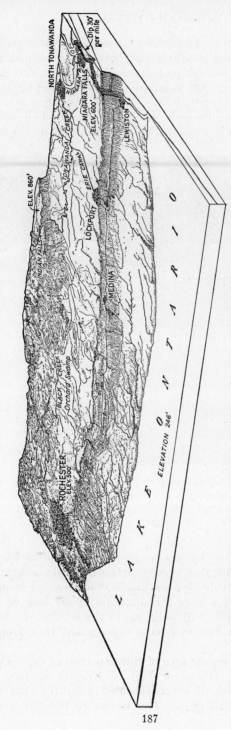

FIG. 88. THE POSITION OF THE LOCKPORT DOLOMITE IN THE GEOLOGY OF WESTERN NEW YORK

Shows how it is the cap rock which determines the line of the Niagara escarpment, and how Niagara Falls has retreated to make the gorge. Drawing by Chester Hewitt.

187

then causes it to break back. The fragments provide tools to promote the plunge-pool grinding, but only if the volume and force
of water are great enough to handle pieces of the size that break
off as rapidly as they are supplied. Niagara Falls perfectly illustrates this variety of cap-rock falls. On the Canadian side the huge
volume of water that descends over the Horseshoe Fall immediately
disposes of the debris from the breaking back of its brink, so that

Fig. 89. Tinker Falls, Labrador Hollow, New York

The wide, overhanging eaves is the Tully limestone. The fall recedes by
the weathering out of its lower layers and of the weaker Hamilton shales
underneath these.

the fall's crest retreats on the average at the rate of four to five
feet each year. The thin American Fall, on the other hand, is
unable to dispose of the cap-rock blocks that break off from its crest
and these now form a huge accumulation at the base of the falls.
In time this waste pile will build up to the level of the brink and
then the American Fall will have degenerated to a long cascade
(Fig. 88).

The geomorphic significance of this first class of cap-rock falls, as
exemplified by the Horseshoe Fall of Niagara, derives from its
characteristic creation of a vertical-sided gorge that has the same
width as the waterfall crest. The retreat of the fall is so rapid,

because of the effective plunge-pool undercutting, that at no site in the retreat is there time for weathering action of any consequence on the gorge walls.

The second variety of cap-rock falls is one that develops where the stream has very small volume. It is, hence, capable of very little or no plunge-pool excavation. Further, much of the water

FIG. 90. AMPHITHEATRE OF TAGHANIC FALLS, NEW YORK

The fall's retreat is mainly from weathering, although there is no distinct cap rock and though there is some plunge-pool action at flood stages. The amphitheatre at the fall, and the wide gorge below, are the characteristic results of the retreat of the fall from weathering. Photograph by Don Cascio.

coming over the brink is converted to spray by air friction during its descent or by dashing on the rock at the base. The undermining of the cap rock is accomplished almost solely by the weathering of the weak beds. These are slowly crumbled into fine bits. Such crumbling is facilitated by the constant wetting from the spray. So wide an eaves is often formed by the cap rock that it is possible to go behind the water curtain of the fall. Such great overhang is made possible by the delicate, bit by bit, abstraction of the supporting rocks. But as the spray-promoted weathering is not confined to the area of rock section immediately behind the waterfall curtain, and as the cap rock is a continuous cover, the overhang extends on each side far beyond the width of the water at the fall's crest (Fig. 89).

These circumstances bring about the development of a wide amphitheater below the falls, a hollow that is very much broader than the water current. A gorge of the same width as the amphitheater is formed as the crest of the fall slowly retreats. Occasional

FIG. 91. BASTION OR JUTTING TYPE OF WATER FALL, ENFIELD GORGE, NEW YORK
Note that the amphitheatre walls are retreating more rapidly than the fall's face and crest. Photograph by Henry Head.

freshets clear out most of the weathering waste, including the blocks derived from the breaking back of the cap rock at the top of the gorge. Its sides, however, are not the parallel vertical walls characteristic of the gorges resulting from recession of the variety of cap-rock fall first described (Fig. 90).

The third variety is less commonly developed (Fig. 91). It occurs where the cap rock is not a specially strong bed; i.e., where the underlying beds are approximately of the same durability as that of the fall-forming layer. Undermining by weathering is then of little effect. The water stream is one of small volume, hence not competent in plunge-pool excavation. This combination of circumstances tends to produce a fall's face that projects as a bastion, a sort of miniature stage, into an amphitheater enlargement of the valley below the fall similar to that of the second variety. It seems that the film, or sheet, of water coming over the brink is unable to erode the fall's face and serves, further, to protect the rock beneath it from weathering in both winter and summer. It prevents, especially, disintegration by frost action and by alternate wetting and drying. But, as in the second variety, the spray about the fall site promotes the wasting of the rock walls on both sides of the fall to the degree that these actually retreat faster than the water-laved brink and fall face. Considered in a slightly different way, the jutting variety of cap-rock falls is a special case of rapids, one where the rapids site and circumstances are enclosed by gorge walls.

As was noted above, the three varieties of cap-rock falls grade into each other and each occurrence has distinctive features. To note such variations and to discover the factors which occasion them will prove a good exercise in field observation and interpretation. Cap-rock falls are very widely distributed, so that this opportunity is afforded in many localities.

Vertical Barrier Falls. Waterfalls resulting from alternations in the resistance of rock to erosion develop in other than flat-lying beds. A dike of igneous rock extending vertically through great thicknesses of other formations may be so durable that downstream from the line of its outcrop the erosion of a deep valley can be effected before any appreciable lowering of the surface of the barrier is accomplished. This type of waterfall remains fixed at the site of its development.

The barrier formation may be massive. The great fall (Fig. 92) of the Yellowstone River, in Yellowstone National Park, has resulted from the presence of little-altered, durable lava beds upstream, and greatly decomposed lava downstream from the fall site (Fig. 93). The plane of demarcation between the two kinds of rock is sharply defined and vertical. These conditions make possible the imposing, straight plunge of the stream. The falls, better called rapids, of the Potomac occur where the river descends

FIG. 92. GREAT FALL OF THE YELLOWSTONE

Upstream from the fall the lava is durable, below, decomposed from hot-spring action, and easily eroded. Photograph by William H. Jackson.

FIG. 93. YELLOWSTONE CANYON BELOW THE GREAT FALL
Eroded in weak, decomposed lava beds. Photograph by William H. Jackson.

193

the moderately steep eastern border of the massive rocks of the Appalachian Piedmont area to enter on the weak beds of the Atlantic Coastal Plain (Fig. 94).

Autoconsequent Falls. There are a few instances of *autoconsequent falls.* These develop where streams carry a heavy load of calcium carbonate in solution. Warming, evaporation, and other

Fig. 94.   GREAT FALLS OF THE POTOMAC RIVER
Descent of the stream over the Fall-Line declivity marking the junction of the Fall Zone and Piedmont peneplains. Downstream are the easily eroded beds of the Atlantic Coastal Plain sediments. Photographer unknown.

factors cause part of the solution load to be precipitated at particular sites along the stream course. Such deposition is unlike that from failure to transport sediment, which is governed by velocity and acts to steepen the gradient curve of the stream bed. Neither the dissolved load of calcium carbonate nor its loss affect the current flow. The deposit, accordingly, can build up a local barrier across the stream's course and so cause a ponding upstream and a falls' descent downstream. Examples of such development are known from the limestone areas of the east coast of the Adriatic (Gregory, J. W., 1911) and at Tivoli near Rome, Italy. There are probably many unnoted occurrences of small magnitude.

Disappearance of Falls. It has been noted that the occurrence of waterfalls is a mark of youth in stream-valley history. As cap-rock falls over flat-lying beds recede, they necessarily become lower and lower because of the upward slope of the stream bed in the gorge below the fall's site. The stream in this reach will normally be at grade. It follows that the fall will disappear completely when the grade profile intersects the fall-forming, cap-rock member. The more rapidly the crest of a fall retreats the sooner will *disappearance by intersection with grade* take place (Fig. 56). It should also be realized that the altitude of the cap-rock surface constitutes a local base level for the stream above the fall's crest. If, therefore, the recession is very slow, because of great resistance of the cap rock, or small volume of the stream, the valley above the fall's site may be opened out to an advanced stage in the fluvial cycle, late maturity, or even early old age, while the gorge form of youth persists immediately below the fall.

In the case of a fall occasioned by a vertical barrier, or by a hanging valley from glaciation, the local base-level relation is not maintained above the fall's crest. In these instances, intersection with grade, and the disappearance of the fall, is achieved by the slow wearing down of the stream on and above the crest.

SUMMARY

Side streams normally have steeper gradients than the trunk streams to which they are tributary. This relation is implied when reference is made to Playfair's Law of Accordant Junctions. But such normal relation of gradient declivities may be reversed. Then discordant junctions and hanging-valley waterfalls result. However, differential glacial erosion is the chief cause of the hanging-valley type of waterfall. Step falls, resulting from the *en masse* removal of blocks of rock bounded by joint planes, are a common feature in gorges cut by stream erosion in the lips of hanging valleys.

There are probably more waterfalls of the cap-rock class than of any other type. Three distinctive varieties of cap-rock falls occur. All appear where flat-lying beds of different degrees of resistance are subject to active downcutting. However, a vertical barrier may also initiate and maintain a fall's site in a stream course. Except those which result from localized upbuilding of a stream bed by precipitation of dissolved load, all falls tend to disappear by the eventual intersection of the grade profile with their crest lines.

BIBLIOGRAPHY

CLASSICAL

Davis, W. M. (1884) *Gorges and Waterfalls,* American Journal of Science, Vol. 28 (3) pp. 407–416.

Gilbert, G. K. (1896) *Niagara Falls and Their History,* National Geographic Monographs, American Book Company, New York, pp. 203–236.

RECENT

Noyes, T. W. (1926) *The World's Greatest Waterfalls,* National Geographic Magazine, Vol. 50, pp. 29–59.

v. Engeln, O. D. (1929) *Falling Water,* The Scientific Monthly, Vol. 27, pp. 422–429.

Chapter Eleven

PHENOMENA OF THE FLUVIAL
GEOMORPHIC CYCLE ON AN OLDLAND

Introduction. It is the essence of the cycle concept that changes in land forms follow a regular succession. This orderliness permits a systematic presentation of the sequence of changes; as has been done in preceding chapters for the fluvial cycle on a coastal plain.

A coastal plain has a simple yet significant structure. Drainage systems are organized *de novo* on its surface. The whole vista of development is readily comprehended, because the structural origins are so obvious, and each of the stream types and corresponding valley forms, consequent, subsequent, and obsequent, regularly displays the characteristics of its kind.

When it is sought, in the same manner, to follow the sequence of changes in the fluvial cycle on an oldland numerous complications are encountered. The indurated rocks of the oldland geomorphic units possess compositional qualities and characteristics of structure not present, or of little consequence, in the coastal-plain formations. This chapter is, accordingly, prefaced by one in which the chief characteristics of strongly consolidated rocks are described. Another chapter is devoted to the particular phenomenon of the waterfall, because waterfalls are pertinent items in the cyclic succession. Further, waterfall processes were found to have special significance in valley development.

An oldland will have indurated rocks at the surface, or under a relatively thin mantle of waste. The presence of such rock bespeaks, as has been noted, a preceding degradational history. Whatever that history was, the beginning of a new cycle would be concurrent with, or following, an uplift. If uplift is assumed to inaugurate a cycle it is at once relevant to ask: Is the uplift of the magnitude and rapidity, and does it involve structural deformation in the degree, that the previous relief and drainage are completely reordered? That could be true of uplift resulting in fold mountains. Upwarping in the form of a more or less perfect dome might also completely disrupt pre-existing drainage. Such warping could affect areas of massive rock, areas of flat-lying sediments, or areas of peneplanation underlaid by any structure. In each of these cases the progress of the new cycle would vary to conform to the structural differences. These types of uplift are all of the orogenic, that is, mountain-forming type. Other uplifts are epeirogenic in nature, that is, of the continental type, with dominant vertical movement. Less technically, epeirogenic uplift is the uplift of plains and plateaus and is usually exerted on flat-lying sediments or peneplaned areas. Then the pre-existing surface relief and drainage system are, at least in some degree, preserved. Further complications of such uplift will be the degree and direction of the tilt given the rocks, since perfect uniformity of vertical uplift over a wide area is improbable.

Nevertheless certain valley developments are common to all occurrences of uplifted oldlands. It is also found that features of a more specific kind are so directly related to the general results, that the general and particular items may appropriately be considered together.

Gorges. Where, over coherent rock, new slopes of such direction and steepness as to bring about the elimination of the pre-existing drainage pattern, result from uplift of any type, initial streams will follow the lowest hollows of the new surface. Such streams are of the consequent kind. If a stream course, so initiated, has a sharp declivity over strongly consolidated rock, waterfall recession, groove, and pothole cutting by corrasion will produce steep-sided, even overhanging, narrow, deep gorges (Fig. 95). Under these circumstances the stage of earliest youth of valley form will persist over a long period. If, on the other hand, the rocks are relatively weak, the cut produced by downward corrasion will yield rapidly to weathering at its top and a valley that has a narrow V-form in cross section will be early in evidence (Fig. 80). (How early will depend on the relative efficacies of stream downcutting and weathering attack. This problem has been discussed in previous pages as that of slope retreat.) If the rock is made up of weak and strong beds in alternation, waterfalls will interrupt the course of the stream and the form of the gorge will be modified by their presence, as has already been noted.

Valley Meanders. Over short reaches and down unusually steep slopes consequent streams originating from uplift can follow nearly straight courses. Much more commonly there will, as in consequent streams on coastal plains, be some expression of valley meandering. In strong rocks the differential lateral erosion that

FIG. 95. MYSTIC FALLS AND GORGE, OPHIR, COLORADO
Steep-sided gorge in massive rock. Photographer unknown.

results from valley meandering gives rise to *alternating* (also called *overlapping,* or *interlocking) spurs.* With curving flow the current is caused to impinge with greater erosive effectiveness on the concave bank, which it tends to undercut (Fig. 96). Even if the undermining process is not sufficiently rapid in its action to deprive the overlying rock of support it does promote the fall and removal of weathering waste where it is in operation. The concave wall of the stream that exhibits valley meanders is, consequently, maintained as a steep cliff (in massive, strong rock may indeed be temporarily overhanging) and is known as the *cut-bank* (also called *undercut slope,* or *river-cliff*) (Fig. 97).

Downward corrasion is maintained concurrently with the recession of the cut-bank. The stream channel, consequently, is lowered, as well as moved laterally away from the convex side of

FIG. 96. LATERAL EROSION OF GORGE WALLS, TAGHANIC CREEK, NEW YORK

On the far left is seen the curve of the stream directed against the gorge wall. During a period of extreme flood stage in July, 1935, the lateral erosion of the current dislodged the rock of the foreground and middle distance in great joint blocks and cut into the slope below which the figures appear.

the water course. The net result of such shift is to produce, on the convex side, a *slip-off slope* (Fig. 98). Slip-off slopes then constitute the outer faces of progressively lengthening alternating spurs (Fig. 99).

Meanwhile, lateral corrasion is enlarging the concave curve of the cut-bank, not only at its head but also on the upstream side of the spur by which the curve is terminated downvalley. This downvalley attack results from the acceleration of the current in that direction, because of the general downslope of the valley bottom. The effect of such cutting on the spurs is first to *sharpen* them by reducing their width at their tips, then to *blunt* them by nipping their ends, and finally to *trim* them off completely. When a valley reach has been cleared of spurs by this means the stream achieves the stage of free meandering. An **open valley** results. The open valley has steep walls on both sides, because it has been

FIG. 97. CUT-BANK IN FALL CREEK GORGE, ITHACA, NEW YORK

An especially conspicuous cut-bank results from the direction, by the waterfall descent, of the force of the current against the rock wall of the gorge.

subjected to the cut-bank attack at all points (Fig. 100). In this respect the valley cross profile resembles early youth. But the steep slopes of early youth lead down to a valley floor of little or no greater width than that of the stream current (in flood stage), while those of the open valley descend to a flat valley floor, the **valley plain,** with parallel walls separated by the width of the meander belt.

The history of meander development observed where the rocks are only weakly consolidated does not correspond exactly with the succession noted in strongly consolidated rocks.

The valley meandering of a stream that is eroding a channel in weak rocks, for example, recent coastal plain sediments, is inconspicuous until the graded condition is attained. From then on lateral planation becomes dominant, the meanders enlarge, cutbanks, slip-off slopes, and meander scrolls appear. Eventually the limiting width of meander belt (measured by the distance between

FIG. 98.   SLIP-OFF SLOPES OF A MEANDERING CANADIAN RIVER, FLOOD-PLAIN SCROLLS AT THEIR TIPS
Photograph from Canadian Geological Survey, Department of Mines.

lines tangent to the outer edges of the meander curves on each side of the stream) is reached. At this time the flood-plain cover of the valley floor becomes continuous and complete. Free meandering over its surface begins. The further lateral enlargement of the valley plain involves the migration of the meander belt from one side to the other of the flood plain.

In strong rock the swing of the current which inaugurates valley meandering tends to become fixed at the site where it starts. The concurrent action of downward and lateral erosion fashions

Fig. 99. SLIP-OFF SLOPE, CUT-BANK, AND INGROWN MEANDER, GENESEE RIVER, NEW YORK

The long slip-off slope provides evidence of the concurrent downward and lateral erosion. The sharper declivity at its tip indicates a recent acceleration in the rate of downcutting. Photograph by Cecil Robinson.

slip-off slopes and cut-banks in the durable rock. The slip-off slopes shortly acquire a considerable relief, and, as alternating spurs, become striking topographic features. The slip-off slopes of the early meander development of the weak rock sites, by con-

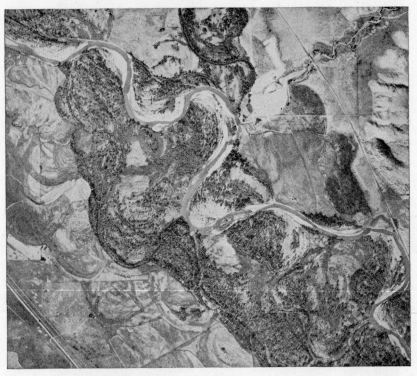

FIG. 100. FREE MEANDERING, OPEN VALLEY AND VALLEY PLAIN OF THE JEFFERSON RIVER, AT WILLOW CREEK VILLAGE, MONTANA

Look straight down on picture. Note the traces of meander swings, brought out by the photograph from the air, of an earlier development of the same kind at a higher level. Photograph from the United States Department of Agriculture, A. A. A.

trast, are low and primarily of depositional origin. The alternating spur, slip-off slopes in durable rock are exclusively the product of erosion. If the rate of downward erosion is rapid, in comparison to the rate of lateral cutting, the spur will be steep. On approach to the graded condition downward erosion almost ceases, then the slip-off slopes are flat and low, like those on the weak rocks.

In durable rock the approach to grade, when lateral erosion becomes greatly predominant, in effect matches the stage of attainment of the limiting width of meander belt in the valley developed on weak rock.

It has been suggested (Bates, R. E., 1939, p. 821) that as the ratio of limiting width of meander belt to stream width is greater for valley meanders than for flood-plain streams, the valley streams tend to become free meandering streams, with a migrating meander belt, immediately after grade is first established, or, when the limiting width of meander belt is attained.

But free meandering and the development of the open valley and valley plain in the strong rock ordinarily awaits the action of meander sweep in eliminating the rock-spur slip-off slopes by sharpening, blunting, and trimming. Thenceforward migration of the meander belt as a whole, as in the weak-rock sites, will bring about a slow widening of the valley plain.

Incised Meanders. Conspicuously developed valley meanders in durable rock are referred to as *incised meanders*. In the foregoing paragraphs the development of valley or incised meanders is discussed as a phenomenon appropriate to the erosion of consequent valleys, without reference to the existence of any earlier drainage lines. Usually, however, incised meanders are considered an inheritance from preceding conditions of stream flow. Large streams like the Ohio River apparently fail to develop real incised meander curves because they do not have the coarse sedimentary tools, with which smaller streams are supplied, available for lateral planation.

Incised meanders in strongly consolidated rocks are of two types, the *ingrown* and the *intrenched*. Both types are inferred to preserve the pattern of the stream course at the time the incising was begun. They are further regarded as derivatives of free meandering on a former flood plain. From this it follows that they indicate a revival in the downcutting power of the stream, through which its *valley* is *rejuvenated*.

It was noted that the steepness of the spurs developed as slip-off slopes is governed by the relative rates of downcutting and lateral cutting. If the rate of downcutting is not greatly in excess of the rate of lateral erosion the ingrown type of incised meander with long, more or less steeply inclined spurs will result (Fig. 99). In

this case the revival of stream erosion can properly be referred to
a tilting uplift that has affected the velocity of streams flowing in
the direction of the tilt over the whole length of their courses.

The intrenched type of meander, on the other hand, is thought

FIG. 101. INTRENCHED MEANDER, ALTERNATING SPURS, AND FLOOD-PLAIN SCROLL,
GORGES DU LOUP, NEAR TOULON, FRANCE.

The gorge was cut because of rapid, nearly vertical uplift in this region.
There is no slip-off slope; the level of the top of the gorge is the same for
the cut-banks and the spurs. Photograph by Compagnie Aerienne Francaise.

to reflect rapid, vertical, or nearly vertical, uplift (or lowering of the base level) (Fig. 101).   Such uplift could result from faulting or from monoclinal folding.   When vertical uplift is effected by either of these means, the streams of the area involved experience revival (at first) only in the belt where the transition from no

FIG. 102.   UPPER SECTION OF A VALLEY, IN A VERTICALLY UPLIFTED REGION, AS YET UNAFFECTED BY THE INCISION OF A GORGE IN ITS LOWER COURSE.   NEAR NICE, FRANCE.

The gentle slopes of the valley sides and the wide, flat floor of the valley bottom are characteristic of the stage of late maturity to old age developed in this area before a recent vertical uplift.   The lower course of this stream is a gorge like that of the preceding picture, Fig. 101, of the Gorges du Loup.

change in level to uplift occurs.   Their courses on the summit regions of the uplifted tract are meanwhile "unaware" of what has happened; that is, their gradients remain as they were before the upheaving took place (Fig. 102).   Davis (1932, pp. 419–420) described sites in France and Maryland where these circumstances prevail, and surmised that the general condition of falls' reaches in streams marginal to the upland of southern Africa derives from such nearly vertical upthrust of the great interior block of that continent.

In the transition zone, where the full measure of the uplift steepens the stream's course, downward erosion becomes extraordinarily rapid, in accordance with the rule that a geometric increase in the rate of erosion follows from every arithmetical increase in velocity of flow. The site (knickpunkt) of the almost instantaneous incision that results is moved upstream progressively, by headward, or retrograde cutting, with practically undiminished effectiveness. It follows around the meander curves of the upstream reaches without their being modified by the development of slip-off slopes or cut-banks. Where this process takes place in flat-lying, stratified rocks of unequal resistance to erosion the rapidity of headward cutting is much enhanced by waterfall retreat. Streams in the Kentucky area of the Appalachian Plateau appear to exemplify intrenching of meanders in diagrammatic perfection.

This interpretation of the development of intrenched meanders carries with it the further implication that the course of the stream is superimposed from the flood plain on the durable rock that it covers without change of the pattern of meander flow. It has been questioned (Cole, W. S., 1930) whether this assumption is always warranted. Cole contends that such superimposition will give rise, rather, to ingrown meanders; also that structural controls (valley meandering) may suffice to bring about a very pronounced meander pattern independent of inheritance from winding flow on an unconsolidated cover.

Cutoff Spur, or Meander Core. Where intrenched meanders attain marked development the geomorphically spectacular feature referred to as a *cutoff spur, meander core* (Fig. 103), or *rock island* (in German as an *umlaufberg)* may be present. Even if intrenched meanders are held to preserve the pattern of the free meanders in which they had their origin, the deeply incised cuts may have curves unlike those of the original swings. The head of a curve may gradually become bulbous in outline, or, as it is said, "fantail" to such a degree that the neck of land (not conspicuously a slip-off slope) between the upper and lower limb of a single curve is considerably narrowed, near where it joins the unbroken upland beyond the valley. Reduction of the surface by weather-

The perfect meander core in the left foreground has resulted from the cutting through of the neck that formerly connected the core with the summit level of the plateau on the right. Note that the stream is now at a distinctly lower altitude than that of the channel around the core. The neck of the existing meander is being narrowed. These are intrenched meanders; there is no slip-off slope. See also Fig. 105. Photograph from Spence Air Photos

Fig. 103. MEANDER CORE AND INTRENCHED MEANDERS SAN JUAN RIVER, UTAH.

209

ing is facilitated at the narrowed site and tends to open a col in
the summit level of the neck at that point.   From the col local
drainage descends on both slopes to the main stream.   The
gullying wash greatly enhances the rate of lowering of the altitude

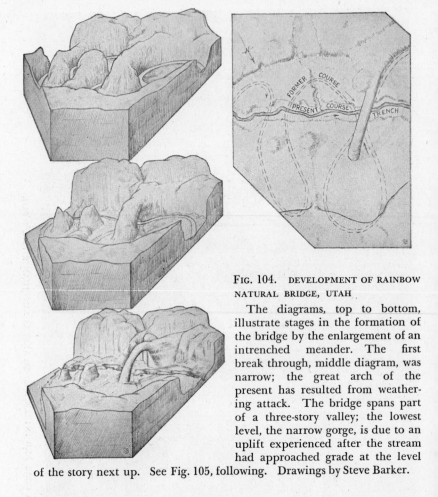

FIG. 104.   DEVELOPMENT OF RAINBOW
NATURAL BRIDGE, UTAH

The diagrams, top to bottom,
illustrate stages in the formation of
the bridge by the enlargement of an
intrenched   meander.   The   first
break through, middle diagram, was
narrow;   the   great   arch   of   the
present has resulted from weathering attack.   The bridge spans part
of a three-story valley; the lowest
level, the narrow gorge, is due to an
uplift experienced after the stream
had approached grade at the level
of the story next up. See Fig. 105, following.   Drawings by Steve Barker.

of the col area.   The lowering may be carried so far as to reduce
the height of the narrow section of the neck almost to river level.
At the time of a flood-flow some part of the main current may
take the short cut across the lowered neck.   If at the same time
the loop course is partially blocked by ice, uprooted trees, or a
rock fall, the diversion may be so great as to be almost at once

successful in opening a wide and deep channel across the neck, which is thereafter followed by the stream at all stages.   The earlier curved course becomes a dry, *abandoned, intrenched meander* and the hill which is isolated from the mainland by the cutoff is a meander core, or umlaufberg.

FIG. 105.   RAINBOW NATURAL BRIDGE, UTAH

Note the three-story valley. The second floor (from which one abutment of the bridge springs) is nearly graded, with small meander cores at this level. The top abutment of the bridge springs from the highest level. A new incision of meanders with slip-off slopes at the lowest level. Photograph, copyright, from Spence Air Photos.

There are some instances where the narrowing of necks, by the main stream itself, has proceeded to the degree of complete cutting through at river level. A *natural bridge* is thus created. The famous Rainbow Natural Bridge of Utah was so made (Figs. 104, 105). In limestone regions the cutting through is facilitated by underground solution (Fridley, H. M., 1939).

Intermittent Uplift, Terrace Flights, and Knickpunkte. In the preceding discussion, uplift, whether slow or fast, was assumed to be continuous. It is more apt to be intermittent.

With tilting uplift and production of ingrown meanders intermittence in upheaval will bring about the production of *terrace flights* on slip-off slopes. A stillstand between uplifts permits lateral cutting to continue unabated, or even to be accelerated, while the rate of downcutting declines. When uplift is resumed the immediate revival of downcutting causes a steeper section of slip-off slope to succeed a gentler one, which then becomes a terrace level. If the alternation is a number of times repeated a flight of terraces results. The front edges of such terraces, it should be noted, are convex outward and their tops slope toward the center of the valley and down stream. Several terrace fronts may merge into one where part of an upper terrace has been laterally trimmed off in the course of the development of the one next lower down.

> The same result, a terrace level, is had where the stream encounters an exceptionally durable horizontal stratum. The presence of the resistant rock inhibits downcutting, the while lateral enlargement of the meander in the weaker overlying beds continues with undiminished or even greater vigor. The upper surface of the durable bed acts as a temporary base level. When it is finally cut through some part of the flat slip-off slope developed on the top of the durable bed remains as a terrace.

With vertical uplift and intrenched meanders, intermittence results in the occurrence of a series of retreating steps in the axial profile of the stream beds. These are famous as knickpunkte, first made a topic of geomorphic dispute by Walther Penck. Penck maintained that such knickpunkte could originate in a stream course flowing over homogeneous rock on a rising dome (Fig. 106) which was experiencing continuously accelerated uplift; Davis argued that this was not possible, that a step succession of the kind postulated indicated intermittency of upheaval. Penck's untimely death prevented a reply from him to Davis's arguments. The point is one that has been much debated (v. Engeln, O. D., 1940). But whether knickpunkte may or may not result from continuously accelerated uplift, their conspicuous development is possible and probable from intermittent upheaval, as Davis contended. The existence of knickpunkte is especially significant in valleys cut in massive, uniform rock; in rock of

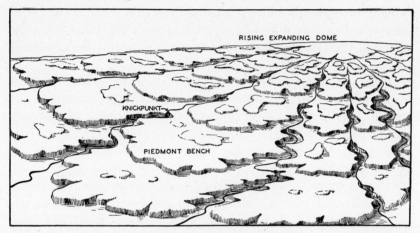

FIG. 106. DIAGRAM OF KNICKPUNKTE AND PIEDMONT BENCHLANDS ON A RISING DOME EXPERIENCING CONTINUOUSLY ACCELERATED UPLIFT
    The breaks, knickpunkte, in the stream profiles and the forward sloping piedmont benches are, according to Penck, inferred to develop with continuous uplift; Davis (also Meyerhoff and Hubbell) insisted that such forms could result only with intermittent uplift. After Davis. Drawing by Elizabeth Burckmyer.

alternating resistance the knickpunkte tend to be obscured by waterfall successions resulting from the structural differences.

Rock Terraces. Where knickpunkte from intermittent uplift are conspicuously present in the profile of a stream there may also exist a series of paired, that is matched in elevation, *rock terraces* bordering both sides of a valley. As each knick retreats it will leave behind a remnant of the valley floor developed by flow at grade, lateral planation, and slope retreat, preceding the uplift. It is assumed that the successive uplifts will be so spaced in time that each knick will retreat upstream a considerable distance, and that a graded reach will develop below it before the next uplift occurs. In turn, each graded reach will be invaded by a cut, resulting from the new vertical upheaval, along the same axis as the ones that preceded it.

If regional terraces sloping outward (down valley) to correspond with the several graded reaches of the streams, are postulated to develop as the response to a continually accelerated (in rate of uplift) upheaval of an expanding dome, the phenomenon realized is Walther Penck's *piedmont benchlands (piedmontflächen* or *piedmonttreppen).* The critical point in the formulation is the assertion that intermittence of uplift is not essential to the occurrence of the knickpunkte and associated outward sloping regional flats.

Whether such a succession of terraces will be produced in uniform massive rock, in consequence of either intermittent or progressively accelerated, continuous uplift, is, like that of the knickpunkte, still a matter for dispute. Where, however, the structure consists of alternating strong and weak beds, horizontally disposed, matched rock terraces may develop with a single uplift. For conspicuous results the strong beds should be very resistant, the weak ones very yielding. Each strong bed gives rise to a cap-rock waterfall. But, because of the great contrast in resistance, the upper surface of each strong bed will persist so long as a local base level that the valley above the waterfall crest can, meanwhile, be greatly widened at that altitude. The next lower, strong bed will bring about a repetition of this effect at its level. Meanwhile the cliff margining the higher level will have retreated by weathering so that the new terrace will not be so wide as the one above it. Terraces of this origin are also known as *structural rock benches.* The Grand Canyon of the Colorado region presents a magnificent series of matched, or paired, rock terraces (Fig. 107) because of the great differences in resistance of the rocks there cut through. The prominence of the terraces at this site results, also, in part from the great vertical measure of the river erosion; in part from the semi-arid climate. In a more humid climate (fluvial cycle) the benches would tend to be obscured by weathering waste, to be slope-graded.

Drainage Patterns. The original consequent drainage from an uplifted dome, or from a volcanic cone, has a *radial* pattern

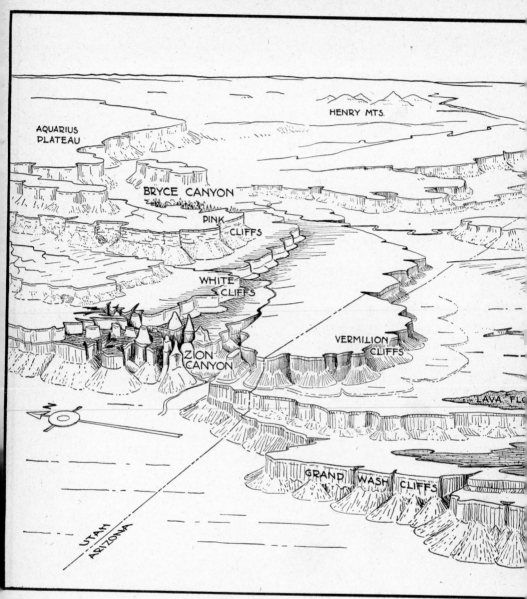

FIG. 107. THE GRAND CANYON AND COLORADO PLATEAUS DISTRICT

Large scale development of structural rock benches. Note, also, the sites of Bryce and
Steve Barker. Based on a drawing by Lathrop Douglas in *Historical Geology* by Schuche

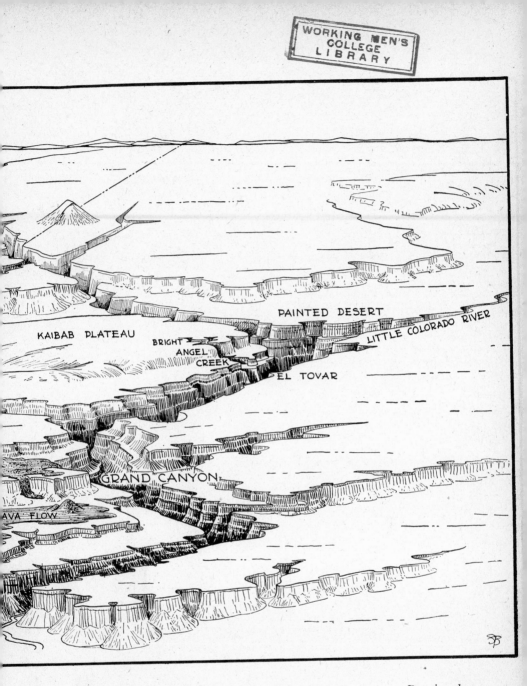

...yons, the Henry Mountains, and the weathering and fault escarpments. Drawing by
...unbar, with permission of John Wiley and Sons, Inc., publishers.

(Fig. 44b), and it, like the dendritic pattern, the parallel pattern on a coastal plain, and the *deranged* pattern in glaciated plains, indicates a development independent of structure. All the other recognized types of drainage pattern: rectangular, *trellis, annular, pinnate, contorted* are responses to structure, and result from the development of subsequent streams and subsequent valleys.

Maturity to Peneplanation on an Oldland. The cutting of gorges, development of meanders, formation of terraces, and evo-

Fig. 108. STAGE OF LATE MATURITY, CATSKILL MOUNTAINS NEAR ANDES, NEW YORK

The period of greatest measure of relief is just past; the valleys have a wide, flat "V" form in cross-section profile.

lution of drainage pattern, described above, are features and phenomena of the youthful stage of the fluvial cycle in operation where the geomorphic unit is made up of strongly coherent rocks. The reference is chiefly to in-valley aspects. But the emergence of a drainage pattern, commonly through integration of streams by river capture, involves the shaping and shifting of divides. The changes in valley forms, in pattern of streams, and in the position and characteristics of divides are effected concurrently, and, taken together, give rise to the environment of regional youth.

When control of the drainage has been achieved by graded master consequents and by graded subsequents through adjustment to structure, regional maturity is attained. As is true of the fluvial cycle on coastal plains, regional maturity in an oldland is the stage when the measure of relief is highest and topographic

FIG. 109. APPROACH TO THE STAGE OF OLD AGE, BLUE RIDGE MOUNTAINS NEAR AFTON, VIRGINIA, FROM SKY LINE DRIVE

The slopes are almost graded; the valleys are broadly open; the summits are softly rounded.

irregularity is greatest. In cross section the profiles of valleys are then characteristically of V-form, while the divides are inverted-Λ ridges (Figs. 3, 27, 108). Slopes, even in headwater sites, are uniformly graded in respect of a creeping cover of weathering waste. The larger streams have eliminated spurs from their valley sides by meander sweep, and wander freely over valley plains veneered with flood-plain deposits.

These circumstances apply to the ideal case. Rocks nearly enough alike in resistance to weathering that slopes may be evenly graded are assumed. It is also assumed that the available relief (Fig. 62) is neither too little (streams and slopes graded before all original divide surfaces are consumed) nor too great (young valleys persist long after divides are reduced to ridges). It is further understood that the drainage texture is neither so coarse nor so fine as to prevent a normal spacing of the stream courses (Davis, W. M., 1924, pp. 183-184).

After this first attainment of maturity the progress of the fluvial cycle involves mainly the rounding and lowering of divides, the flattening of slopes, the widening of valley floors, and the steady escape of stream courses from structural control.

This last is important. The evidence of complete adjustment to structure, which is the most obvious earmark of regional early maturity, becomes more and more obscure as maturity merges into old age. The pattern of the drainage may reflect adjustment to structure even in old age, but after middle maturity the direct relation between valley and rock is observed only in the ungraded reaches of small streams situated in the headwater areas of opposed trunk systems.

As late maturity softens to old age (Fig. 109) the mantle of waste becomes everywhere continuous, deep, and fine. Below it a zone of *saprolite* (decomposition products of weathering *in situ*) (Fig. 29), extends deeply into the bedrock. Finally, in peneplanation, the major streams wander over widely extended flood plains, in courses related, if at all, only to the largest units of structure. The end activities of the streams are directed to the lateral planation of the last remnants of the interstream divides.

It has been argued that a stillstand long enough to permit peneplanation of an oldland of indurated rock, with original great summit altitude, is highly improbable. This assertion is fortified by the contention that no peneplains exist at the level of their development. These objections are not well based. A remarkably perfect peneplain, albeit modified by glacial erosion, at the base-level altitude, comprises southern Finland. Ancient, deep-seated rocks, igneous and metamorphic, are there planed down to near horizontality, and the surface slopes up very gently inland, toward the north. (Glacial erosion has modeled the surface of the Finnish peneplain but neither produced the generally level expanse nor greatly reduced its altitude.) The vast, flat expanse of western Russia may be put in the same category.

The time required to bring about peneplanation has probably been overestimated. And if the levels of both continents and seas have been markedly unstable in recent geologic times, the evidence at hand indicates that this uneasiness is the exception, not the rule, in geologic history. It is not meant here to deny great orogenies, epeirogenies, and eustatic shifts in the geologic past, rather it is intended to assert that these shifts were few and of short duration in comparison with much longer intervening periods of nearly complete stability.

SUMMARY

The progress of the fluvial cycle on an oldland is conditioned by the preceding geologic and geomorphic histories of the unit, and by the nature of the uplift which inaugurates a new cycle. Nevertheless generalization with reference to the cutting of gorges in the stage of youth, in regard to the history of meandering, and the forms to which meandering gives rise, may be made on the assumption merely of a structure consisting of consolidated rock. The particular forms of incised meanders afford significant clues to understanding of the nature of the uplift that initiated their erosion, or to the structural circumstances of their development.

It is found that the factor of first importance in determining particular aspects in the form of valleys is the relation of the rate of downward erosion to that of lateral erosion. There is dispute whether the production of knickpunkte and benchlands can result from a single, progressively accelerated, uplift, but general agreement that intermittent uplift, and variation in rock resistance, permit terrace developments of various types.

In early maturity the pattern of drainage of the fluvial cycle on consolidated rock is governed by structure, to which stream courses are closely adjusted. In later maturity the peculiarities of valley form developed in youth tend to be eliminated. They are replaced by the uniformity and monotony of graded slopes. As maturity passes into old age distinctive types of relief disappear; all contact with structure is lost. The ultimate peneplain presents an undulating, low surface of wide extent.

BIBLIOGRAPHY

CLASSICAL

Marbut, C. F. (1896) *Physical Features of Missouri,* pp. 94–109
Meanders, Bulletin X, Missouri Geological Survey.

Davis, W. M. (1903) *The Development of River Meanders,* Geological Magazine (4) Vol. 10, pp. 145–148.

Davis, W. M. (1906) *Incised Meandering Valleys,* Bulletin Geographical Society of Philadelphia, Vol. IV. pp. 182–192.

RECENT

Rich, J. L. (1914) *Certain Types of Stream Valleys and Their Meaning,* Journal of Geology, Vol. XXII, pp. 469–497.

Moore, R. C. (1926) *Origin of Enclosed Meanders on Streams of the Colorado Plateau,* Journal of Geology, Vol. 34, pp. 29–57.

Leighly, J. (1936) *Meandering Arroyos of the Dry Southwest,* Geographical Review, Vol. 26, pp. 270–282.

Chapter Twelve

INTERRUPTIONS OF THE FLUVIAL GEOMORPHIC CYCLE AND THEIR CONSEQUENCES

Introduction. It appears reasonable to assume that the fluvial geomorphic cycle in an oldland may continue in operation long enough to produce a peneplain. It is not meant, however, to assert that, once started, a cycle will proceed without interruption to the end stage. On the contrary, the progress of the fluvial cycle may be halted or modified in so many ways that its evolution in unbroken sequence is probably the exception rather than the rule.

The interferences are of two kinds: interventions and interruptions. An *intervention* implies the introduction of a foreign factor that terminates the progress of the cycle. Thus arid or glacial climatic conditions may be substituted for the fluvial regime. If glaciers occupy the area the fluvial processes are stopped. When they resume, changes wrought by glacial erosion and glacial deposition may be of such magnitude as to bring about the initiation of a completely new cycle. If the climate becomes arid, the previously existing drainage systems may be dismembered and wind action will acquire a far greater importance than it has in the fluvial cycle. Or volcanic eruptions may so much alter the relief that an altogether new organization of streams must follow their occurrence. Thus it appears, that after an intervention, the fluvial cycle in the area affected is either displaced by another type of cycle, or caused to start again from the beginning.

It is impossible to make the distinction between interventions and *interruptions* completely sharp. If, because of sinking of the land and transgression of the sea, a covering mass of sediments is laid down on an undermass of oldland the effect may be that of an intervention, necessitating a wholly new drainage development,

220

or the result may be merely an interruption of the previous cycle, which resumes its former pattern when the sea withdraws. It has been proposed that the streams of the restored drainage be called *resurrected.* Again, if endogenic action greatly warps a region, without completely disrupting the existing drainage system, there is an interference which is perhaps more an interruption of the cycle than an intervention. Aside from such instances, where the modification approaches the magnitude of the intervention that compels a new start, there are interruptions which, although they break the continuity of the cycle and give rise to distinctive geomorphic results, do not terminate it.

Phenomena Resulting from Regional Uplift. A region may experience uplift, followed by a stillstand during which it is subjected to the processing of the fluvial cycle, and then be affected by another uplift. If the second uplift follows the first after a period of stillstand that sufficed only for the development of the stage of early youth in valleys and divides, the second uplift will bring about little discernible change in the broader geomorphic aspect of the region. If the upheaval of the region in youth is vertical, by faulting or by the rise of a dome, knick-punkte may be made to appear in the profiles of stream courses. If the uplift is in the nature of a tilt in one direction streams flowing in the direction of the tilt may be revived sufficiently to permit them to cut downward so fast that tributaries coming in at right angles, hence unaffected by the tilt, will have discordant junctions.

When an uplift induces rapid downcutting in the floors of middle or late mature valleys, developed during the preceding partial cycle, ingrown and intrenched meanders are an immediate consequence. Further, some portion of the open valley floor is left undissected and constitutes a more or less continuous bench on each side of the valley which merges, over a *valley shoulder* (Fig. 110), with the new stream-cut of gorge form. Such a remnantal flat, which has a surface slope downstream, may be called a *strath* or sometimes, together with the valley shoulder, a *berm.* The valley shoulder and the strath are the two distinctive form elements of the general phenomenon referred to as the *two-story valley* (Fig. 111), or the *two-cycle valley,* or the *valley-in-valley* feature. The strath level may be preserved by slope retreat of its bounding valley sides, even after the gorge resulting from the second uplift has been considerably widened at the top. In consequence of such survival a series of straths may be present in a single valley (Fig. 105) and so afford evidence of successive uplifts. It is obvious that two-cycle or *multiple-cycle valleys* provide important clues to the diastrophic history of a region.

If the strath level has greater extension than that of a narrow ribbon along one valley (in effect a remnant of the floor of a flood plain) the term *strath terrace* may be applied (Fig. 112). In this case the erosion surface extends across the interstream divides of

FIG. 110.   VALLEY SHOULDER, SUSQUEHANNA RIVER NEAR ULSTER, PENNSYLVANIA

The high ground on the right of the river, in the middle distance, is a valley shoulder, a remnant of the valley floor when the stream was graded at a higher level. Similar remnants are seen dimly in the distance. The stream, following an uplift, has again attained grade. Photograph from the Lehigh Valley Railroad.

minor drainage. (*Vide* discussion by Fenneman, N. M., 1938, p. 181.) It is then a degradational rather than a planation surface and can also be called an *incipient peneplain,* or an *uplifted local peneplain.* If the strath terrace is very extensive the phrase *graded erosion surface* should be used.

"Local peneplain" had perhaps best be reserved for the geomorphic development of the area of a strath terrace before it has experienced uplift and trenching. The valley floor of the lower Connecticut River is a good example (Fig. 113). Its status and altitude, in relation to the existing sea level, are obvious. The Asheville Basin in North Carolina, on the other hand, is a strath

Fig. 111. TWO-STORY VALLEY WITH A STRATH OR BERM, THE TARN RIVER, FRANCE

Note the old-age topography of the upland into which the upper, wider gorge was eroded to the level of the strath, lower left of picture. Then a further uplift brought about the cutting of the narrower inner gorge. See also Fig. 105. Photographer unknown.

terrace, or graded erosion surface. Its development may have been governed by a local base level owing to rock resistance rather than by sea level. Peneplanation implies grading in relation to the general base level of the sea. "Strath terrace," or "graded erosion surface," comprehends all of inference that is warranted with reference to levels developed at inland sites in an area that has experienced uplift and trenching.

If a stream course is actually dislocated, suffers an intervention rather than an interruption, a *strath valley* is left behind. The

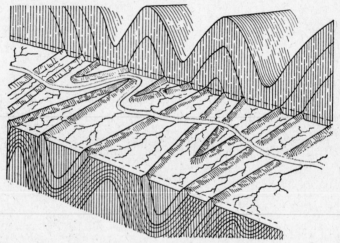

FIG. 112. STRATH TERRACE, OR UPLIFTED LOCAL PENEPLAIN, AS DEVELOPED IN THE FOLDED APPALACHIANS

The areas of plain traversed by the lesser streams are strath terraces. After W. M. Davis.

Teays Valley, north of Waverly, Ohio, and in West Virginia, is a noteworthy example.

Superimposition. In the introduction to this chapter it was pointed out that one extreme of interference with the fluvial cycle is when, at some stage, either by sinking of the land or rise of sea level, the region is broadly submerged. It is obvious that a submergence can be much more widespread if the first cycle has proceeded to the stage of old age or near to base-leveling. Further, the thickness of sediments that must be deposited, while under the sea, to insure the complete blanking out of the relief of the first cycle, will be much less with the subdued topography of old age.

Fig. 113.   LOCAL PENEPLAIN OF THE LOWER CONNECTICUT RIVER VALLEY, NEAR MT. HOLYOKE, CONNECTICUT

Over a belt of weak rock between the durable metamorphic rocks of the New England upland (foreground and far distance) the Connecticut Valley floor is a local peneplain with only slight elevation above sea level.   Photographer unknown.

Fig. 114. SUPERIMPOSITION OF STREAM FROM PLEISTOCENE GLACIAL GRAVELS ON A SPUR OF S
ROCK AT LEFT SIDE OF LOWER END OF THE GORGE

The Darkh Gorge, near Samarkand, Turkestan. Note that the original surface of the gl
fill is indicated by the matched terrace levels at the top. Rapid, post-Pleistocene, incision su
imposed the stream on the durable rock of the slate spur into which it has now cut a go
the deeper part of the preglacial valley is to the right where the path is located. The valley
the bright areas of the mountain side will shortly merge by the process of abstraction. Photogr
by W. Rickmer Rickmers.

As base-leveling is first achieved near the sea, *fossil,* or *resurrected erosion surfaces* (Fig. 77); that is, those which not uncommonly appear in stratigraphic sections, tend to be of the peneplain or near peneplain stage because the low relief of these stages can be most readily submerged.

When, as the result of a succeeding uplift, the submerged area is again exposed to subaerial processes, its drainage in the new cycle temporarily has the coastal-plain pattern and the coastal-plain type of adjustment to structure. But if the cover mass of flatlying sediments is thin and the uplift is of large vertical measure, rapid downcutting by the extended consequents very shortly, and at considerable elevations above base level, seats the erosive action of these larger streams on the surface of the oldland. This development is called *superimposition* (Fig. 114). (Also called *inherited,* or *epigenetic,* or *superposed drainage.*) The valley walls of the trenched sediments hold the stream to its previously established course. Thereafter, no matter what erosional difficulties, strongly resistant rocks, or structures are encountered in the undermass, this course is retained. Retention of a stream to the consequent course determined by the original slopes of the cover mass is more positively assured if the first downcutting in the consolidated undermass is done rapidly.

Superimposition is also more certain to result with a tilting or warping uplift than with vertical uplift. With vertical uplift the sedimentary cover of the new uplands may be stripped off by the erosive action of small streams before the flow of trunk streams is revived at points remote from the line of upheaval. The smaller streams on the upland tracts will, meanwhile, also tend to become adjusted to the oldland structure, because once this is encountered they, the small streams, will, in general, succumb to the control of the variable rock resistances of the undermass materials. Their rate of downcutting is ordinarily not fast enough to prevent the oldland structural differences, especially if these are pronounced, from exercising a guiding influence on their courses. Thus it is a regular result to find major streams obviously in superimposed courses (Fig. 115) while lesser drainage is more or less completely adjusted to the structure of the undermass. The numerous, sharply defined, and remarkably aligned, water gaps of the Middle Atlantic States section of the Folded

Appalachian Mountains are perhaps most readily explained as the result of superimposition of consequent or extended consequent streams. All about them lesser drainage courses are very closely related to the structure of the inferred oldland.

Antecedent Streams. It is conjectured that the radial drainage of the English Lake District is superimposed on an ancient

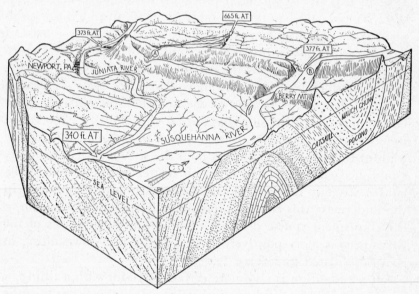

FIG. 115. FOLDED APPALACHIAN TOPOGRAPHY AND DRAINAGE NORTH OF HARRISBURG, PENNSYLVANIA

At B the Susquehanna River crosses the two resistant Pocono ridges in aligned water gaps, inferred to result from superimposition. The Juniata River is presumed formerly to have followed a similar course across these ridges at A, but is now perfectly adjusted to structure by going around the beak of the synclinal structure. As the Juniata River is at a lower altitude, 373 feet, than the Susquehanna, 377 feet, just north of the Pocono ridges, a piracy by the subsequent stream tributary to the Juniata River law of unequal declivities is geomorphically imminent. The course of the Susquehanna will then be diverted to the Juniata. Drawing by Steve Barker.

consolidated undermass from a consequent system developed on a sedimentary cover that was subjected to a dome uplift (Fig. 116). This would be a normal result where laccolithic or dome mountain geomorphic units were, at the time of their uplift, capped by a cover mass unlike the undermass in structure.

If, however, an oldland experiences an uplift by a slow folding or by faulting with the axes of the folds or the fault line athwart the courses of existing drainage, it may be possible for the larger streams to maintain their line of flow against the localized uplifts. They are then said to be **antecedent;** that is, to have been estab-

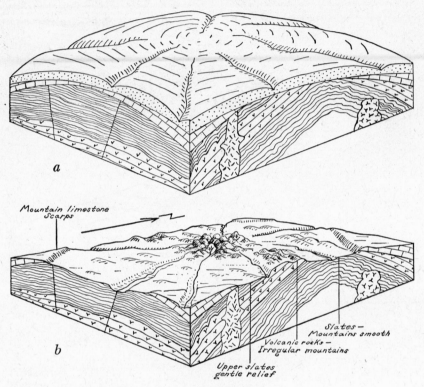

FIG. 116. SUPERIMPOSITION IN THE ENGLISH LAKE DISTRICT

This region is inferred to have been completely covered by Permian, New-Red sandstone beds on which a radial pattern of drainage developed, consequent upon a doming uplift. This radial pattern persists from superimposition on the diverse structure of limestone, slate, and volcanic beds underlying the former sandstone cover, top diagram, now completely eroded off, bottom diagram. After A. E. Trueman. Drawings by Walter Williams.

lished before the present relief came into existence, and to have persisted in their previous courses (Fig. 117). Antecedence is independent of the topographic or structural guidance of a covering mass. On the downstream side of an axis of uplift the gradient of the antecedent stream is increased, its downcutting there becoming much more vigorous. On the upstream side there may

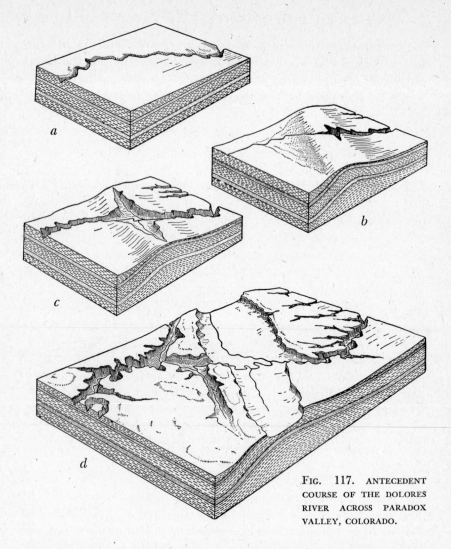

FIG. 117. ANTECEDENT COURSE OF THE DOLORES RIVER ACROSS PARADOX VALLEY, COLORADO.

In diagram (a), at the top left, the river is represented as it once flowed from left to right across a simple structure of horizontal beds, in diagram (b), at the middle right, an anticline begins to rise athwart the river's course, with the result that ponding and aggradation occur on the upstream side, rapid incision on the downstream limb of the anticline. In diagram (c), middle left, the stream has mastered the rising barrier and subsequent tributaries in the axis of the arch have begun to breach the anticline. Small new consequents are eroding gorges on the downstream limb of the anticline. The bottom diagram (d) shows the region as it now appears with the anticlinal structure converted to an anticlinal valley. The antecedent history is indicated by the perfect alignment of the water gaps and by the consequent drainage on the right flank of the anticline. Drawings by Elizabeth Burckmyer.

be a temporary ponding, but if the overflow remains at the site of the former stream course the antecedent course is not affected. Aggradation, instead of ponding, on the upstream side of the rising barrier commonly serves to bridge the relatively depressed area until the rapid incision made on the downstream limb of the fold works back across the anticlinal crest. From then on the stream is in a groove and may be presumed competent to cut through the scarp or fold as fast as uplift takes place. Tributaries entering the gorge made by the main stream during this period will commonly have hanging-valley ends, for this is a case where the trunk stream possesses all the characteristics that facilitate downward erosion: high gradient, tools, volume, so that the accelerated erosion resulting from the introduction of a declivity at the mouth of the tributary does not suffice to overcome the superior performance of the trunk stream in the like process.

Antecedence is an obvious and favorite explanation to account for streams that cut across great mountain ranges in deep, narrow gorges. It has been invoked to explain the course of the Green River across the Uintas, of the Royal Gorge of the Arkansas across the Rocky Mountains, and of the Columbia River across the Cascade Mountains. It is now held that the course of the Green is superimposed, that of the Arkansas partly superimposed, but the Columbia appears to derive its transverse course and gorges by antecedence. The Sutlej and other streams that have their sources in the interior valleys of the Himalayas but cut across the outer ranges of that mountain system in deep gorges, are cited as noteworthy examples of antecedent drainage. The southern ranges have been uplifted and linked to the Himalaya system at a comparatively recent date. The previously well-organized drainage of the older mountain belt was entirely competent to cope with the new uplift. The fact that the interior valleys of the older mountains hold vast gravel accumulations, which are now dissected into great terraces, is supporting evidence for the antecedent origin of the gorges across the new southern ranges. (L. M. Davis [1940] suggests a fault break across the main ranges.) Still another example is afforded by the course of the Meuse. From France northward toward Belgium the Meuse crosses the upwarped Ardennes Plateau in a deep gorge. The uplift, amounting to over 1500 feet, appears to have been very slow, but not so slow as to permit the former, low-level surface, which now constitutes the uplands, to be greatly dissected by the lesser drainage.   R. F. Flint (1941) presents evidence that the Mississippi River, between St. Louis and Cape Girardeau, is antecedent across the eastern flank of the Ozark dome, an upwarped peneplain surface.

Conclusive evidence of the verity of the antecedence concept is had from studies of the Rhine River gorge in the Schiefergebirge section.   Huge gravel terraces flanking the river there are found to be warped upward over an anticlinal axis athwart the river's course.   That is to say, gravel terraces that, at the time of their deposition had a one-direction, down-river, continuous slope, are now inclined in both directions from the axis of the upwarp. There is also instrumental evidence that this localized uplift is still in progress and that the river is keeping pace with it in downcutting.   (Oestreich, K., 1909; Mordziol, C., 1910; Born, A., 1930, pp. 436–439.)

Small transverse streams are unable to cope with such uplifts, hence are first ponded and then compelled to new consequent courses.   Where there is evidence that this has been the drainage history the streams so affected are said to have been **defeated.**

Aggradation.   As the preceding sections have had to do with uplifts it would appear logical to discuss next the effects of sinking of the land or rise of the sea level, that is, in a general sense, the effects of depression.   Depression brings about aggradation or sedimentation in some form; hence it is commonly assumed that the aggradation is *ipso facto* evidence of landsinking; which is not true.   Accordingly, aggradation instead of depression is chosen for the topic head of this section.

The extreme case of aggradation, that of complete submergence and burial of pre-existing relief under a cover of sediments has been described.

Where complete submergence does not take place either because the measure of relief is too great or because the sinking is of slight magnitude the water enters only the lower ends of stream valleys (Fig. 118) that open into the sea and these are then said to be **drowned valleys.**   If the depression results from a warping that does not change stream gradients inland from the new shore line the stream regime there remains unchanged.   Deposit of the stream-borne sediments is made at the mouth of streams as it was before the sinking, but with the difference that the accumulations are now laid down at sheltered bayheads; hence are little likely to

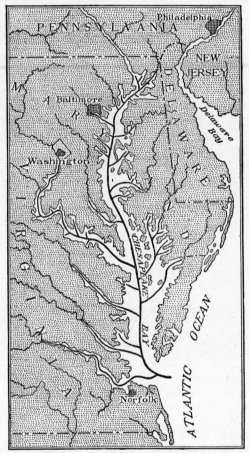

FIG. 118. THE DROWNED VALLEY OF CHESA-PEAKE BAY

The black lines in the embayed area show the probable position of the axes of the stream valleys before drowning occurred. Note how perfectly these link up with the existing drainage courses.

be carried away by longshore currents. *Delta* building (Fig. 119) is, therefore, greatly facilitated by such depression. As the deltas are built farther and farther out into the bays their top-set beds must be extended 'farther and farther upstream in order that a graded profile of sufficient steepness for transport of the sediment load may be maintained. In other words, aggradation upstream from the delta head results.

If the warping or tilting that brings about the drowning of a valley is of such nature that the whole stream gradient is made less steep, aggrading must ensue if a profile of equilibrium had previously been established. Where the middle part of a valley is warped downward that section will be subject to very rapid

FIG. 119.   DELTA OF TAGHANIC CREEK IN CAYUGA LAKE, CENTRAL NEW YORK
The stream is now confined to one channel by engineering work. The course of a former distributary leads to the lagoon. Photograph by Cecil Robinson.

aggradation, if the stream is carrying a considerable load and the downwarping is slow. If little debris is being transported, or the downwarping is rapid, a stream subjected to middle-course down-warping will be ponded. In that case the overflow of the ponded waters will commonly be in the line of the downward continuation of the valley. Ultimately aggradation, extended completely across the ponded area, will provide a slope of such steepness that the outlet site can be rapidly cut down. Then part or all of the deposits in the downwarped section will be cleared out. But parts of the lake fill, the matched terraces representing its top surface, and, if they were developed, traces of shore lines along the valley sides, will remain for a time as evidence of the warping.

If the area is one of low relief the manner of the warping may cause overflow to take place at some site along the valley side. In that case the stream is defeated, beheaded, and diverted to a new course. The old, lower course in such event is never resumed.

If the warping takes the form of an arch, or a fault, transverse to the course of a stream, the conditions are set for either ante-

Fig. 120.   Aggraded channel of the Arkansas River, at Kendall, Kansas
Photograph by H. T. V. Smith.

cedence of flow or for defeat of the river, as previously described.

In conclusion it may be noted that many, if not all of the large rivers of the world that are significantly supplied with sediment in their source areas, are at present aggrading their lower courses. This points to a general, relative depression of the land, presumably brought about by rise of the sea level. Such rise need not have been uniform in measure around the world despite the continuity of the oceans. The aggradation that has resulted from this general depression should be appreciated, but it should, on the other hand, be recognized that all aggradation has not resulted from the common sea-level rise or from the special cases of local sinking and warping to which attention has been called.

Aggradation Unrelated to Depression. After a trunk stream has attained grade in its lower course, the enlargement by head-water erosion and by capture of the drainage system that it serves as a chief artery may result in a great increase in load without a corresponding increase in transporting power through added

FIG. 121. AGGRADING STREAM ON THE MEXICAN PLATEAU NEAR MEXICO CITY

Loaded to capacity with volcanic sand from the slopes of Popocatepetl volcanic cone.

volume. In that event the lower courses of the main stream will be regraded by deposition to conform with the new conditions. This result is entirely appropriate to the normal history of a river system in the fluvial cycle. A stream may be *underloaded* in which case it will ordinarily be downcutting, or it may be *loaded to capacity* (Figs. 120, 121), in which event it is graded, but there cannot be "overloading." No more sediment load can be present in the current than can be carried. If what is brought to a certain point is capacity load for the stream there, and beyond that point transporting power is less, then some of the load is left behind at the place where transporting power is diminished. The deposited material serves to build up the gradient until the steepness of the bed insures a velocity of flow great enough to carry the larger volume of debris. Then the stream is once more at grade.

Again, if the volume of a stream is decreased by climatic change to less precipitation, the sediment supply may remain unchanged,

FIG. 122. AGGRADATION ASCRIBED TO MARKED DECEASE IN PRECIPITATION SINCE THE PLEISTOCENE GLACIAL EPOCH

Lower White Rock Canyon, Monitor Range, East Central Utah. Photograph by Laurence Nugent.

or even increase, because the diminished vegetation cover, owing to the drier climate (Fig. 122), may not hold rock waste so well on slopes. Under these circumstances aggradation will probably result all along the stream course.

But the most common cause for aggradation is the incidence of glacierization. It is safe to assume (with the possible exception of a few near-polar sites) that regions of contemporary mountain glacierization and the areas of Pleistocene mountain and continental glacierization all had a history of fluvial degradation before their occupation by ice. Stream-eroded valleys guided the advances of the glacier tongues, and, after modification by glacial action, were the sites occupied last by the retreating fronts of the ice at a given altitude or latitude. Almost without exception streams issuing from glacier ends deposit sediment in tremendous quantities as soon as they leave the ice.

The melt-waters of the glacier coming from ice caves or from channels marginal to the glacier are poured into the valley hollows leading away from the ice. When they are flowing under the glacier the waters are in confined courses and their flow is impelled by a pressure head—like water in a city water main. Marginal drainage pursues a route diagonal to the slope of the valley side, hence one much steeper than that along the axis of the valley floor. This subglacial and marginal drainage has high velocity and is capable of transporting an immense sediment load. It is also loaded to capacity because of the supply of debris from morainic sources. But as soon as the current emerges from an ice cave, or reaches the open valley floor beyond a marginal course, it drops much of this load because the velocity of its flow is there abruptly and greatly checked. If a glacier front were to remain stationary for a long time it is conceivable that so steep a slope could eventually be built up by aggradation that the melt-water streams could thereafter carry their full load forward down-valley. A very heavy fill would be required to establish grade in this manner. Commonly the ice fronts of present-day glaciers are in slow retreat. In consequence of such retreat additional fill is constantly needed to build up the lengthening, below-glacier, course. Aggrading takes place as long as the waters have a glacial source.

Alluvial Terraces. When the excess of sediment that necessitates aggradation is in any degree abated the stream regime changes. If the excess load is slowly tapered off, grade may be established on the surface of the fill. The change from a relatively arid climate to one of heavier precipitation might be indicated by this response.

If, however, the shift, by increase in transporting power or decrease in volume of load, is abrupt, as is the case when glacial melt-waters are succeeded by ordinary runoff, there is an immediate and great reversal in stream action from rapid aggradation to effective downcutting. Innumerable valleys that acquired heavy fills of coarse and fine waste during the Pleistocene glacierization have experienced this history (Fig. 123). In many of them the change from glacial-aggrading to nearly sediment-free waters has

FIG. 123. ALLUVIAL TERRACES OF THE ZARAFSHAN RIVER NEAR RARS, TURKESTAN.

Enormous fill of Pleistocene glacial gravel is being dissected by the present stream. Note that the higher terraces in the distance have a back slope toward cut-banks. An abrupt change to rapid downcutting may be inferred from the deep trench cut into the wide expanse of the lowest broad terrace. The beginning of a new wide terrace is indicated by the narrow development of a slip-off slope at the river level. Photograph by W. Rickmer Rickmers.

237

been accompanied, and the downward erosion that followed facilitated, by a tilting uplift of the land. Where these conditions governed, or where, as in the Great Lakes region, lower outlets were successively available, the glacial fills were subject to very rapid excavation. The development of *alluvial terraces* on a large scale was the direct consequence of such rapid excavation.

Where the glacial fill was deep and widespread and where the postglacial downcutting was interrupted by periods during which grade was achieved, there could be widening of the valley floor at different levels by lateral erosion. There *paired* or *matched alluvial river terraces* were developed. (The matched, surface-level terraces that result from the excavation of the filling of a lake were referred to above.) The stated conditions are met if the uplift that facilitates downcutting is intermittent. The matched alluvial terraces of this sequence give rise to a particular type of multicycle valley. It must not be thought, however, that the correlation of their levels with changes in the height of the land or rise and fall of the sea is simple. When such interpretation is attempted it is found very difficult to assign a given terrace to a particular set of circumstances or a definite place in a series.

When, after deep aggradation has been effected, there is a long period of uninterrupted downcutting unmatched alluvial terraces develop. These terraces are especially conspicuous in valleys that were not so far advanced in stage before experiencing aggradation as to have been divested of all irregularities of valley slope. An even more favorable site for unmatched alluvial terraces is a valley that before its aggradation had experienced rejuvenation, leading to the development of ingrown meanders exhibiting long slip-off-slope spurs. These circumstances are realized in many valleys subjected to glacial aggradation.

If there is to be conspicuous development of unmatched alluvial terraces it is required also that the downward cutting in the fill shall be sufficiently slow to permit appreciable, concurrent lateral erosion. Then, with an assumed initial swinging flow, the stream will develop broad meander loops. In consequence of the slow downcutting, extensive, gently inclined slip-off slopes will form inside each meander loop. If the fill at its top level is far wider than the limiting width of the meander belt broad matched terraces will be left behind at the original surface level of the fill on each side of the new cut. These will be remainders of the upper surface of the fill. If the width of the fill is less than the limiting width of the meander belt, meander sweep will in time entirely clear out the unconsolidated materials.

The majority of occurrences are not governed by either the one or the other of these extremes in breadth of fill. The downward and lateral cutting stream in the course of its meandering flow commonly encounters an in-valley projection of the rock floor on which the fill rests. That is to say, the stream at different levels from time to time, and from place to place, will impinge on buried rock spurs (Fig. 124). Where such an encounter occurs the further enlargement of a meander curve on that side of the valley will be prevented. At the level of the encounter the current will be deflected toward the other side of the valley. Downstream from the deflecting spur a new slip-off slope will be started on the fill. The inclination of this new slip-off slope will be toward the side of the valley opposite from that toward which the slip-off slope was directed before the deflection took place. The new slip-off slope will be extended across the valley until the current, at a lower level, again encounters a spur, this time projecting from the other side of the valley. The current is then once more deflected, and the slip-off slope development reversed. But at the lower level which has now been reached, the slip-off slope cannot be enlarged to the full width of the earlier one, inclined in the same direction, made at a higher level on that side, because the rock spur that caused the first deflection is, at the lower altitude, encountered farther out in the valley. In consequence of these circumstances remnants of the upper level slip-off slope are left unconsumed upstream and downstream from the rock spur. These then constitute *rock-defended alluvial terraces.* Repetition of this sequence results in a flight of rock-defended terraces on both sides of the stream. But the levels on one side do not match those on the other. Instead the successive step-ups occur in alternation, first on one side, then on the other side of the valley.

Study of the diagrams (Fig. 124) and the drawing from a photograph (Fig. 125) will lead to a clear understanding of the sequence of events leading to the development of the flights of rock-defended alluvial terraces. Such terraces will be observed to have the fol-

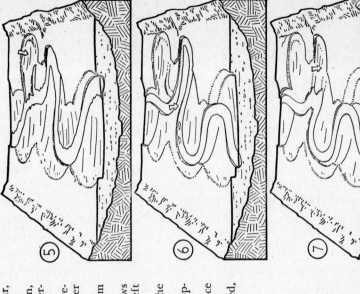

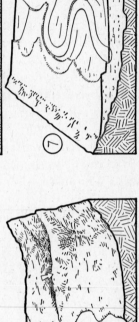

1. A stream valley eroded to the stage of late maturity with a rock spur, marked by the arrow, projecting toward its center.

2. The same valley, after receiving a deep fill of gravel by aggradation, experiencing the beginning of a slow downcutting of the fill by a meandering stream.

3. By downstream migration the meander loop has encountered the resistant rock of the spur and been deflected by it to develop a new meander swing.

4. The new curve has been enlarged to the point where it is separated from the next downstream meander only by a narrow neck, arrow.

5. At high water the stream cut a channel across this neck which it follows thereafter. A portion of the slip-off slope of the previous meandering is left as a rock-defended alluvial terrace, arrow.

6. Another upstream meander loop is compressed by the resistance of the spur which leads to:

7. A new cut-off across the neck, and the appearance of another back-sloping terrace, this time above the rock spur.

8. Now the spur is encountered again at a lower level and the sequence is repeated.

Final: Terraces, on both sides, not rock-defended, are eventually destroyed, those at spur preserved.

Drawings by Steve Barker

240

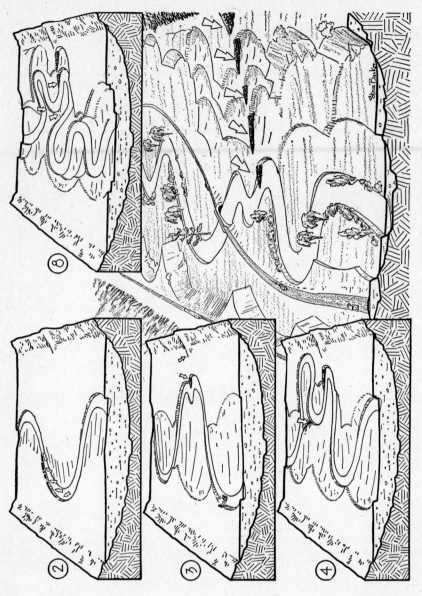

241

Fig. 124. DIAGRAMS TO ILLUSTRATE THE DEVELOPMENT OF ROCK-DEFENDED ALLUVIAL TERRACES

lowing distinctive features. The upstream and downstream terrace flats commonly meet in a cusp at the site of the ledge. The
steep slope between one terrace level and the next lower is a
former cut-bank, hence is concave in outline toward the valley
axis. At its base there is a trace, perhaps swampy, of the chan-

Fig. 125.   Rock-defended terraces of the Lucia Glacier stream, Alaska

Davis says: in "River Terraces in New England," *Geographical Essays,* p.
549, "It has not yet been possible to discover by observation how a down-
sweeping meander will make its passage past a ledge." This drawing, from
a photograph, shows a stream caught in the act. A trickle of water still
follows the former course along the cut-bank in the left foreground, but the
main current has been deflected to the right by the rock encountered at the
tip of the spur. As the stream now develops a slip-off slope toward the right
an unconsumed, rock-defended remnant of the former slip-off slope will be
left as a back-sloping terrace. An uplift of the land (September, 1899) gave
this previously aggrading glacial stream a steeper gradient, and it began the
excavation of the gravel deposits made earlier. Photograph taken in 1905
by Lawrence Martin. Drawing by Elizabeth Burckmyer.

nel followed by the current just previous to a deflection. The
top surfaces of the terraces have a back slope toward the valley
wall.

Sequence of Depositional Forms in Valleys. The broader
geomorphic significance of aggradation can best be appreciated
by giving consideration to the sequence followed in the move-

FIG. 126. ROCK FALL, TAGHANIC CREEK, NEW YORK

The fall occurred in July 1935 when a great flood undercut the gorge wall of the valley at this site. The great regularity and perfection of the joint blocks, massive, unweathered Genesee shale, is a noteworthy feature.

ment of rock waste from higher to lower altitudes and to the forms which result from this ordering of the phenomena.

From steep valley sides and unstable divides *rock falls* (Fig. 126), and *landslides* (or *landslips*) descend.   Where snow accumulates along ridge summits *avalanches* crash down.   Scars mark the

FIG. 127.   AVALANCHE TRACKS, HAYDEN AND IMOGENE PEAKS, COLORADO
Photograph by William H. Jackson.

sites from which the material was detached and the slopes in those areas are made less steep by the removal of the unstable masses. The descent is by gravity solely.   A rock fall may pile up as a heap at the base of a vertical or overhanging declivity.   The mass and momentum of landslides and avalanches overcome the frictional resistance opposed to their movement by the surfaces over which they descend, so that the courses they take are significantly eroded by the passing debris. *Avalanche tracks* (Fig. 127) and *landslide tracks* are thus scored on the steeper slopes. When the material comes to rest a characteristic, irregular landslide topography (Fig. 128) is developed. If the fall of waste, from sites sufficiently steep to permit descent by gravity only, is piecemeal instead of in large masses the mound formed at the base of the slope is called a *talus cone.* The concentration of the talus material into cones is line directed (Fig. 129). In places where the fall

FIG. 128.   LANDSLIDE TOPOGRAPHY BELOW RED MOUNTAIN, COLORADO
Photograph from United States Geological Survey.

of debris is general from the summit areas of a ridge, continuous *talus slopes* (or, British, *scree*) accumulate at the base. It is the characteristic of talus deposits that the largest rock fragments contributed to them travel the farthest distances.

On less steep slopes a *mass transport* of material similar to that of landslides is continuously in progress but at a speed so slow as to be imperceptible. It is referred to as *rock drift* (Fig. 130) and *soil creep.* The rate of movement and the differences in size of particles involved in rock drift and soil creep range between wide extremes, but the common result of their functioning

is to effect a transfer of the waste mantle downslope independent
of direct assistance by moving water. At the surface the descent
is, however, in part due to *rainwash,* by which the finer particles
are carried downslope. In polar latitudes and in glacial-border
areas where water is oozing from the ground because of ice-melting
the rain-wash phenomenon is exaggerated to the degree that it becomes a major translocation process referred to as *solifluction,* that
is, soil flow (Figs. 131, 132). The solifluction phenomenon is significantly conditioned by the presence of frozen ground at slight
depths below the surface, a circumstance which prevents the
escape of soil water to underground courses by infiltration. However, solifluction may take place under sod in the middle latitudes,
and, as Bryan (1940, pp. 262–263) points out, is a process of first

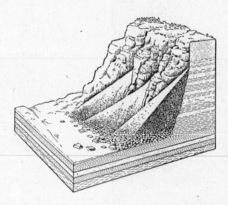

FIG. 129. TALUS CONE
   The diagram shows the tendency
of the large rock fragments to travel
farthest because of greater mass and
momentum, and less frictional surface, than the small ones. Note
also that the cones develop where
there is a line concentration of the
weathering waste. Drawing by Eliz
abeth Burckmyer.

importance in the maintenance of steep slopes in tropical regions
where solifluction functions under the cover of the rain forest.
   Many foot-of-slope accumulations are forms comprised in part
of talus fragments, in part of alluviated material. That is to say,
water at the time of rains or snow-melting, funneled on the head
of talus sites, transports debris to the talus cones and slopes that
could not be moved there solely by gravity pull. The angle of
slope of the surface of such composite forms, *alluvial cones,* is
less than that of wholly talus deposits. By water lubrication the
translocation of particles of a given size is made possible over
lower gradients than would be necessary for the movement of
dry material of the same texture. When water is present in sufficient volume to act as a buoyant medium for the transport of
sediment the term *alluvial fans* (Figs. 133, 134) is used to indi-

cate that the deposit made has even gentler slopes than those of alluvial cones.

It is to be noted that in each of these instances the downhill movement of waste is halted, and an accumulation is built up, because a change from a steeper to a gentler declivity occurs. As the debris is sporadically discharged from the upper steep runnels it spreads out laterally to develop the cone form on the lesser

FIG. 130.   ROCK DRIFT, OR DOWNHILL CREEP, OF BLOCKS OF OLEAN CONGLOMERATE, LILLIBRIDGE VALLEY, NEAR OLEAN, NEW YORK

As the blocks are successively detached by weathering from the ledges at the crest of the slope they slowly drift down the hillside.

declivity. This spreading results from the fact that on the axis where the first waste lodges the descent to the lowest level is longer and less steep than where none is present. Accordingly, the debris is shunted from side to side at the head of the accumulation so as to make the base take a semicircular outline. The net effect is to increase the steepness of slope over the area that originally had a low inclination and to shorten the steep source-slope. Talus cones and alluvial fans have the cone configuration in common, but once water becomes dominant in transport there is

FIG. 131.   SOLIFLUCTION ARTIFICIALLY INDUCED AT A SAND-WASHING PLANT NEAR TULLY, NEW YORK

As the fine, water-filled sand escaped from a crevice in the conveyor chute it flowed until draining out of the water caused it to stop as blobs.

FIG. 132.   SOLIFLUCTION AT THE HEAD OF VALDEZ CREEK, ALASKA

The pattern of the flowing soil matches that of the material from the sand washing shown in Fig. 131. Photograph from United States Geological Survey.

(*a*) stratification of the deposit, (*b*) a tendency to round the particles carried by their mutual attrition, and (*c*) the finer materials are moved to the periphery of the accumulation. In talus cones fine particles more regularly lodge at the head of the accumulation, whereas the large fragments bound far out to the base.

Material is normally moved from the lower edges of landslide, talus cone, soil creep, and alluvial fan accumulations by water flowing in a current, that is, as a stream, either of the intermittent or perennial type. Where a stream is actively downcutting it will carry the sediment load that it collects from such deposits at the base of a steep declivity, continuously forward. Ordinarily,

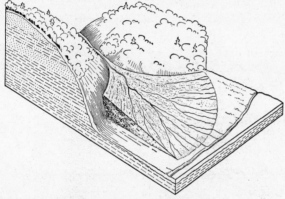

FIG. 133. STRUCTURE AND FORM OF AN ALLUVIAL FAN

The coarser sediment is deposited at the head of the fan, which has a rough stratification. Drawing by Elizabeth Burckmyer.

however, stream transport of sediment is discontinuous because the volume of streams does not remain constant. In stages of declining flow some of the coarser sediment accumulates in **river bars** at places where the declivity of the stream bed is least steep. The effect of such deposit is, as in the case of the previously described forms, to bridge across the sites of low gradient; that is, the accumulation serves to build up the slope to a declivity matching that of the steeper reaches. The steeper reaches meanwhile are being reduced by erosion.

The mechanism of river bar aggradation may commonly be observed in the courses of small streams. It is an interesting phenomenon because the functioning is so obvious. At the downstream terminus of the bar the current makes a steep descent usually referred to as a *riffle,* over the front of the deposit. Under the riffle the water is constantly combing out fine sediment so that the downstream face of the bar shows only gravel and cobbles. Upstream, mixed material is being added as the current is checked. At high water stages the coarse material of the riffle is dislodged. In consequence of this action the bar is made to migrate slowly upstream. Eventually a perfectly smooth profile should develop and the bar disappear.

When, toward the close of the stage of active downcutting, the combined erosion and aggradation evening out of the profile of the bed is perfected the stream course is said to be graded.

FIG. 134. ALLUVIAL FAN AT THE END OF HANAPUH CANYON, DEATH VALLEY, CALIFORNIA

Note the wash at the axis of the fan, indicative of different degrees of loading at different floods; also the dissection by distributaries on the upper surface of the fan. Photograph, Copyright Spence Air Photos.

If it is conceived that meanwhile all valley side-slopes have also been graded, a perfectly functioning degradational mechanism may be visualized. Rock waste will be moving continuously downstream from the highest summits to the sea. But a complete coordination of supply and transport of debris is probably never realized. Instead the stream, for one or more of the reasons given in preceding paragraphs, will begin to aggrade. Then river bars, a flood plain and natural levees are formed. If downcutting follows after aggradation some type of terrace development results.

In retrospect the manner and forms of aggradation are seen to comprise a connected series, each of which, in turn, beginning with the rock falls composed of great blocks is of (a) finer texture, (b) a gentler gradient, and (c) has a greater linear extension than the one preceding it. Stated in reverse, the slopes of the surfaces of aggradation are progressively steeper from flood plains and

FIG. 135.   DELTA OF THE VAR RIVER, NEAR NICE, FRANCE

river bars through alluvial fans to talus cones and rock falls. While it is not possible to force all the items involved to fit exactly to this pattern, for example soil creep and landslides are aberrant, the sequence it indicates is nevertheless suggestive.

Deltas.   Ultimately all waste borne by the streams which function in the fluvial cycle is deposited in the sea. If the site of discharge is one where waves and currents are active, the sediment brought by the stream is distributed by them as rapidly as it is furnished. But where the discharge is at a sheltered bayhead or in a relatively quiet site, such as the Mediterranean (Fig. 135) or the Caribbean seas, with shallow water at the mouth, the river current is completely extinguished and the sediment brought by it must settle to the bottom.

Before reaching the sea a river may be completely cleared of its sediment load by deposit in a lake along its course. The halt there, however, is temporary, for the lake basin will eventually be completely filled. Then the stream will excavate the previously deposited material, leaving first matched terraces and then, by lateral erosion, removing all the fill. But during the period of their filling lakes provide ideal sites for the accumulation of deposits at stream mouths (Fig. 119).

The sediment deposited at the stream mouth forms a delta. The sedimentation structure of deltas normally consists of top-set, fore-set, and bottom-set beds. The deposition of each of these types of beds in its particular order and place causes the delta to be extended forwards into the sea and to expand laterally. Geomorphic concern is, however, chiefly with the top-set beds. As the delta grows outward the river gradient is necessarily decreased by this addition to the length of its course. It tends, therefore, to aggrade, by building up the top-set beds, partly on the lengthening delta, partly upstream from the original discharge point. As on an alluvial fan, the channels shift from side to side as first one site, then another, is built up. Indeed the current may be split up and pursue a *braided course* (Fig. 121) over the delta top and to discharge finally at the front and sides of the delta through a number of *distributaries* (Fig. 134).

It is obvious that the piling up of the top-set beds makes dry land of areas that were sea. If the sediment brought is coarse (Fig. 119), as is usually the case in regions of considerable relief where small deltas are built into lakes, the altitude of the older part of the delta is appreciable. However, it is commonly true of large rivers that the sediment is voluminous but of fine texture. Then the gradients remain gentle, and very extensive flat, low-lying *delta-plains* are built. This applies to the Mississippi, the Nile, the Orinoco, the Rhine and other vast deltaic accumulations. The breadth and monotony of level surface such areas exhibit must be seen to be fully appreciated.

The surface configuration of deltaic deposits is nevertheless varied. Those which are rapidly built up of coarse, that is, gravelly, sandy, or silty sediments furnished by steep gradient streams have, in outline, the form of the Greek letter, delta (Δ). The front of such deltas, which constitutes the base of the tri-

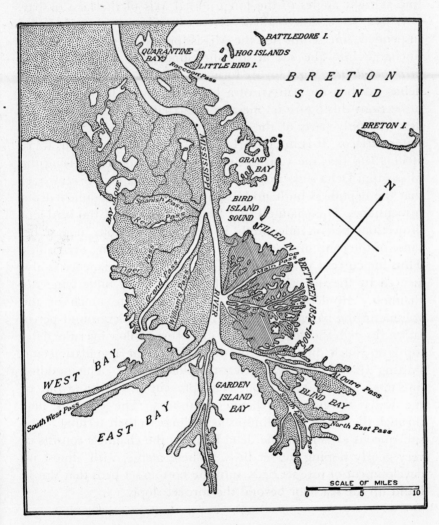

FIG. 136. BIRDFOOT DELTA OF THE MISSISSIPPI RIVER

angle, is commonly curved convexly outward. Frequently shifting distributaries are a characteristic feature. It is the type regularly developed along the sides of lakes (Fig. 119). Deltas built into the heads of narrow lakes, or the heads of estuarine bays are confined, as to lateral spread, by the bounding walls of the basin they are filling in. Such deltas are elongate in outline and are commonly terminated at the seaward end by a straight line at right angles to the longitudinal axis of the lake or bay.

Where large, low-gradient rivers, carrying a great bulk of suspended, fine sediment—the Mississippi is the type example— discharge into the sea at an unconfined site what are called *bird-foot deltas* (Fig. 136) are formed. The outer border of such deltas exhibits the pattern of a bird's talons. The long narrow projections this figure implies are in actuality the natural levees, here the only parts of the deltaic deposit to project above the water surface. It is inferred (Lawson, A. C., 1938; Russell, R. J., 1939, 1940) that the vast, fine-mud accumulation comprising the Mississippi Delta sinks isostatically at approximately the same rate that the deposit is built up by the settling of the sediment from suspension. The channels that lead to the ends of the bird-foot projections persist indefinitely in the same position, in part because of the concentrated deposit at flood stages along their sides. Thus the current is walled in. Their relative permanence is also assured by the impermeability of the fine muds underlying the channels. In deltas composed of coarser waste much of the volume of the parent stream finds escape by underground percolation through the delta deposits. The surface flow over the delta top is so much diminished by these losses that aggradation and shifting channels are characteristic phenomena. The puddled fine muds of the Mississippi Delta prevent such sieving out of the water through the channel bottoms. The currents flow through the *passes* in undiminished volume to their termini. The subaqueous expanse of the delta between the channels consists of very gently sloping top-set beds. These merge, with almost no development of fore-set beds, into the bottom-set beds that slowly build up the sea floor beyond the fore-set slope.

SUMMARY

The course of a fluvial geomorphic cycle may be terminated by an intervention, or interrupted, at any stage. A variety of topographic remnants of the uncompleted partial cycle that preceded an uplift, together with particular erosional features developed in response to the upheaval, afford evidence of this kind of interruption.

As erosional activity is associated with uplift so aggradation is held to connote depression. But aggradation is not necessarily evidence of land sinking or rise of sea level. Rock debris from weathering and erosion is consistently moving downslope. Where this waste is halted in the journey seaward its accumulation gives rise to particular relief forms. Each of these has an appropriate place in a sequential series which terminates with the building of deltaic deposits on the sea floor.

BIBLIOGRAPHY

CLASSICAL

Powell, J. W. (1875) *Exploration of the Colorado River of the West and its Tributaries*, Smithsonian Institution, Washington, pp. 152–166.

Miller, H. (1883) *River Terracing: its Methods and their Results*, Proceedings Royal Physical Society, Edinburgh, Vol. 7, pp. 263–305.

Davis, W. M. (1889) *The Rivers and Valleys of Pennsylvania*, National Geographic Magazine, Vol. 1, pp. 183–253; also in *Geographical Essays*, Ginn and Company, Boston, pp. 413–484.

Willis, B. (1889) *Round about Asheville*, National Geographic Magazine, Vol. 1, pp. 291–300.

Davis, W. M. (1902) *River Terraces in New England*, Bulletin Museum of Comparative Zoology, Vol. 38, pp. 281–346; also in *Geographical Essays*, Ginn and Company, Boston, pp. 514–586.

RECENT

Andersson, J. G. (1906) *Solifluction, a Component of Subaerial Denudation*, Journal of Geology, Vol. 14, pp. 91–112.

Tarr, R. S. and von Engeln, O. D. (1908) *Representation of Landforms in the Physiography Laboratory*, Journal of Geography, Vol. 7, pp. 73–85.

Bucher, W. H. (1932) *"Strath" as a Geomorphic Term*, Science, Vol. 75, pp. 130–131.

Stearn, N. H. (1935) *Structure and Creep*, Journal of Geology, Vol. 43, pp. 323–327.

Russell, R. J. (1936) *Physiography of the Lower Mississippi River Delta*, Department of Conservation, Louisiana Geological Survey, Geological Bulletin 8.

Sharpe, C. F. S. (1938) *Landslides and Related Phenomena*, Columbia University Press, New York.

Chapter Thirteen

THE WALTHER PENCK GEOMORPHIC
SYSTEM

Introduction. In preceding chapters the approaches and tenets of the German geomorphologists who acclaim Walther Penck as their leader have had incidental mention and, in places, somewhat extended discussion. It is, however, deemed essential, even at the cost of some repetition, to present at this point a systematic and comprehensive statement of the principles of this German system, in order that the reader may gain a clear understanding of how it differs from that of the American school, which had W. M. Davis as its preceptor.

The orderly recital of the German concept is introduced here because the Penckian analyses are concerned exclusively with geomorphic development as conditioned by weathering, rain, and rivers; namely, the processing of the fluvial geomorphic cycle as this, and its circumstances, have been described in the foregoing pages from the viewpoint of the American school. Although all accounts of arid-land, glacial, karst and other geomorphology are omitted from consideration, and the Penckian system is only part of the whole of geomorphology, it should, nevertheless, be realized that the part involved is the one which is basic for the science of land forms. On the other hand it is proper to add that the Davis system also was originally directed only to an elucidation of the fluvial cycle.

In what degree Penck and Davis are in conflict is a debatable point. Their ultimate objectives are admittedly different. Davis had as a goal the complete understanding of land forms. Walther Penck sought, through land forms, to interpret the diastrophic history of regions. It is clear that in order to achieve his end Walther Penck needed first to discover the significance of the topographic elements that presented themselves to his observation. Such inquiry is completely within the province of geomorphology.

That the two protagonists were conscious of a clash is manifest in their writings. Although the elder Penck (Albrecht) disclaims the exercise of a dominating influence on his son's work, it is clearly evident that Walther Penck inherited his approaches to geomorphic study from his father. A paper by Davis, "The Cycle of Erosion and the Summit Level of the Alps" (1923) and Walther Penck's *Die Morphologische Analyse* (1924) read in conjunction permit these relationships to be fully sensed. Walther Penck elaborated, and expanded into a divergent theory of geomorphic development, sundry criticisms that his father had leveled at the comprehensive framework that Davis had set up for the science.

For the purposes of this review it is not important to argue the question whether the two systems are mutually exclusive. It is significant that geomorphologists outside Germany have found Walther Penck's ideas provocative, hence calculated to make observation more acute and inference more cautious, and to provide geomorphic science with a broader basis than if it rested solely on the Davis precepts. The student should, therefore, be sufficiently informed about the German postulations to appreciate the bearing these may have on the future of geomorphic investigation and thought.

Specifically, Penck directed attention to slopes, their forms, their declivities, their development, their relative stability and, broadly, to the significance which attaches to their variations. Much study has since been given to this topic, and important contributions on slope analyses have been and are being made (Bryan, K., 1940; Meyerhoff, H. A., 1940) in consequence of his prompting. It is a field of great promise and much complexity. Penck's correlations between slope form and diastrophism, on the other hand, are generally discredited (De Terra, H., 1940) but a lurking suspicion appears to remain that in certain instances some such association may exist. Geomorphologists will in the future be alert to note any evidence indicating a correlation between the two. So also with regard to Penck's ideas in reference to the nature and progress of uplifts. There is general skepticism as to the validity of his postulated conditions but a residual disposition to examine the circumstances of each site with his contentions in mind. The occurrence and pertinence of knickpunkte have provoked animated discus-

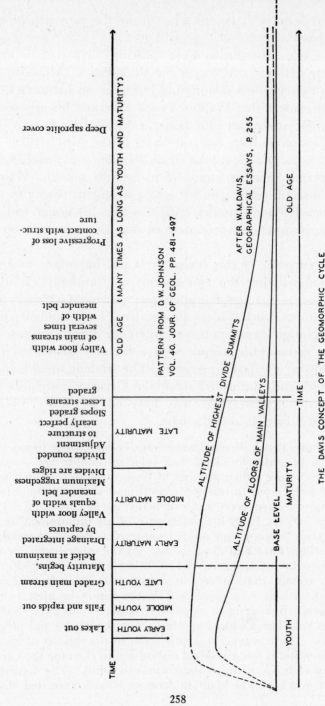

FIG. 187. THE DAVIS CONCEPT OF THE GEOMORPHIC CYCLE

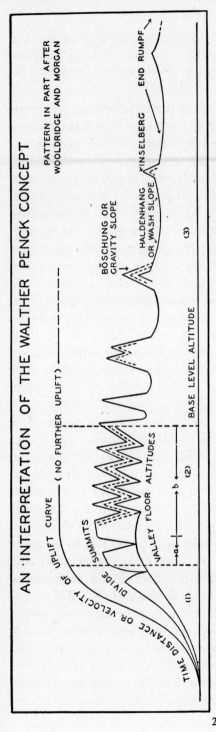

AN INTERPRETATION OF THE WALTHER PENCK CONCEPT

UPLIFT CURVE
(NO FURTHER UPLIFT)

PATTERN IN PART AFTER
WOOLDRIDGE AND MORGAN

TIME DISTANCE OR VELOCITY OF UPLIFT

DIVIDE

SUMMITS

VALLEY FLOOR ALTITUDES

a → b

(1)

(2)

BÖSCHUNG OR GRAVITY SLOPE

HALDENHANG OR WASH SLOPE

INSELBERG

END RUMPF

BASE LEVEL ALTITUDE

(3)

AUFSTEIGENDE ENTWICKELUNG

Altitudes of divide summits continuously increased. Valley deepening by erosion does not keep pace with increase of altitude of uplift, hence elevation of valley floors also raised, but by a lesser distance. Hence both maximal altitude and maximal relief increased. Slopes of *valley sides convex.*

GLEICHFÖRMIGE ENTWICKELUNG

(a) Altitudes of both divide summits and valley floors still increasing with continued uplift, but at declining velocity. Maximal altitudes attained. But valley deepening matched by divide lowering so relief remains constant. Slopes of *valley sides straight.*

(b) Uplift ceases, altitude of summit divides declines; valleys deepened, relief remains constant, valley sides retreat in parallel planes at fixed angle.

ABSTEIGENDE ENTWICKELUNG

Main streams attain grade, in Penck's terms cease downward erosion, and have thereafter an essentially constant altitude of valley floor. Parallel retreat at a fixed angle of the straight valley sides, Böschungen, or gravity slopes, continues. Divide summits are lowered by the intersection of the retreating Böschungen of adjoining valleys. The Haldenhange or wash slopes, with *concave form,* are progressively extended to the bases of the retreating Böschungen. The Böschungen and Haldenhange intersect in a sharp knick. Eventually the Böschungen are reduced to Inselbergs. When finally the Haldenhange or wash slopes are brought to intersection an Endrumpf has been developed. This phase, with the concave slopes of the Haldenhange, is *absteigende Entwickelung.*

Fig. 138.

259

sion (v. Engeln, O. D., 1940). Finally from conning of Penck's ideas the student will become familiar with many German geomorphic terms that he will encounter when he undertakes advanced reading.

The Primärrumpf. The concept of the primärrumpf has been referred to as one of Walther Penck's "magnificent generalizations." The idea of the primärrumpf derives from making an initial assumption (in regard to the circumstances conditioning geomorphic development) completely the opposite from that adopted by Davis as the type case. Although he was well aware of the range of other possibilities (as is made clear in his introduction, written in 1923, to the second edition of *Die Erklärende Beschreibung der Landformen*, (1912) Davis regularly made approximately instantaneous uplift the point of departure in his papers dealing with the fluvial geomorphic cycle. He defended this procedure on the ground that it simplified exposition of the progress of degradational change as presented in the cyclic scheme (Fig. 137). He suggested, further (Davis, W. M., 1932, p. 426) that the assumption of rapid uplift was normally valid, because geologic evidence is indicative of relatively short orogenic and epeirogenic upheaval separated by long periods of no diastrophic activity.

Walther Penck, contrariwise, conceived that the representative initial condition for the development of land forms was a long, exceedingly slow upheaval (Fig. 138). Such slow rise might be applied to two cases, (*a*) to a newly emergent, variously warped land mass, (*b*) to an earlier developed endrumpf; that is, a normal peneplain in the Davis scheme. In either case the exceeding slowness of the upheaval would permit degradation to deal with uplift as it took place. There would then be no rise in altitude and no increase in the measure of relief. No matter what the structure of the area affected might be, it would, *ab initio*, be a lowlying featureless plain and remain so indefinitely. This then would be a primärrumpf; that is, a primary peneplain, one which could, in either case, exhibit truncated beds and structures, and yet need never have had a greater altitude or a higher relief. The primärrumpf is held to be, universally, the initial geomorphic unit for any and all form sequences that may follow. It may experience an uplift rate far exceeding degradation and be reduced, with decline or cessation of upheaval, to an endrumpf, or peneplain. But always before a new form sequence develops the endrumpf is converted to a primärrumpf by the slow upheaval that initiates the new series (Fig. 139). While a primärrumpf may have the general aspect of an endrumpf it is, on closer observation, noted to have convex valley slopes, instead of the concave profiles characteristic of an endrumpf.

The idea of the primärrumpf was evidently prompted by the fact that traces of old degradation surfaces are widespread. It seemed unreasonable to Walther Penck that these should all be uplifted and partially dissected peneplains. But except as the way is paved, by this different approach, for Walther Penck's system of slope analysis, it is not clear what geomorphic economy

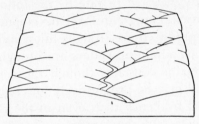

FIG. 139. BLOCK DIAGRAM OF A PRIMÄRRUMPF
After Davis. Drawing by Elizabeth Burckmyer.

is effected by changing an endrumpf to a primärrumpf before a new sequence of development may be initiated.

Aufsteigende, Absteigende and Gleichförmige Entwickelung. With the primärrumpf as a prescriptive point of departure Walther Penck found escape from the concept of cyclic change marked by the stages youth, maturity, and old age. These he replaced with the phrases *aufsteigende, absteigende* and *gleichförmige entwickelung.* It was not a substitution, because there is no direct correspondence between the two sets of terms. Penck's formulation was designed to fit the further development of his principal thesis, foreshadowed by the concept of the primärrumpf; namely that geomorphic forms are an expression of the phase and rate of uplift in relation to the rate of degradation. It is assumed that interaction between the two factors, uplift and degradation, is continuous. The land forms observed at any given site give expression to the relation between the two factors that has been or is in effect, and not to a stage in a progressive sequence. There is a real difference between the two systems.

Land forms in this scheme of analysis consist of slopes. That is to say, as the rate of uplift is accelerated or declines or is uniformly maintained, degradation follows suit and a particular type of slope profile results for each case. Aufsteigende entwickelung (waxing or accelerated development) denotes development during a period of acceleration in rate of upheaval, and is characterized by convex slopes. Relative relief, the vertical distance from valley bottom to divide summit is increased. Absteigende entwickelung (waning or declining development) indicates a slowing up of the rate of uplift; concave slopes result. Relative relief is decreased. If upheaval is maintained at an unvarying rate, and is exactly matched in rate by the induced degradation, gleichförmige entwickelung (uniform development) is in effect. The slopes then produced are straight lines, and once the slopes in retreat from two adjoining valleys are brought to intersection relative relief remains constant, though the general altitude of the region affected may be progressively lowered.

It is maintained by Penck that, even in the faint relief of the primärrumpf, the fact of slow uplift is manifest by slight convexity of slopes, whereas the endrumpf, or normal peneplain, mark of a declining rate of uplift or stillstand, will have concave slopes. Davis (1932, pp. 428, 408) disputed these deductions with reference to slope profiles on several grounds. In the first place he asserted that the forms of the peneplain, converted to a primärrumpf, are merely special types of young forms governed in occurrence, not only by the condition of very slow uplift, but also by the requirement that they must derive from a pre-existing, normal peneplain. Second, because the retreat of a valley side is usually accompanied by the development of a convex profile at its top and a concave profile at its base (Fig. 55). The shoulder at the top of the valley side, whatever its original form, yields more rapidly to the attack of weathering and gullying on its two faces and sharp edge than do the more nearly plane surfaces adjoining the shoulder. (Bryan, 1940, p. 258, as has been noted, is unwilling to accept this conclusion as valid.) Thus even an angular top edge will shortly be converted to a round shoulder of short arc, and later to one of gentler curvature. This is, in effect, the phenomenon of prevailing *convexity of hill summits,* and as such is independent of positive or negative acceleration of uplift for its development.

It should, however, be said that Penck's analysis of slope forms has aroused much interest, and a number of competent students are devoting considerable effort to its further elucidation and evaluation.

Retreat of Slopes. Gleichförmige entwickelung (uniform development) gives rise to straight line, that is, plane, valley slopes. The faster, though uniform, the rate of uplift (provided that degradation keeps pace with it) the steeper these slopes will tend to be, to the ultimate degree of vertical walls. This statement (which carries Penck's formulation to its logical conclusion, although he did not undertake such analysis) implies that, where canyon walls are present, downcutting has been so rapid that no appreciable weathering has affected the valley sides in the time required for the stream to make the cut. It is obvious that the degree of resistance of the rock to weathering processes and the relative vigor and nature of such processes, as conditioned by climatic factors, will function importantly in determining whether, with a given rate of uplift (which governs the rate of downcutting by the stream) vertical or inclined-plane valley sides will be developed.

If, now, the constant rate of downcutting, conditioned by a particular, uniform rate of uplift, is assumed to be such, with a given rock structure and climatic circumstances, that weathering and transport of waste exercise an appreciable reducing effect on the top edge of the cut made by the stream, in the time-unit required to accomplish this vertical erosion, the steepness of the valley sides must be less than vertical. Further, in the proportion that the rate of weathering approaches the rate of downcutting by the stream, the flatter the slopes will be. The hypothetical end ratio of such a series, 1:1, would then give rise to a perfectly horizontal surface.

From this analysis it appears that vertical canyon walls, with uniform rate of uplift and sufficiently rapid downcutting might rise to indefinitely great heights as plane-parallel surfaces, because the contribution of weathering-degradation to their development is zero. For all ratios intermediate between this 0:1 and the 1:1

relation, there will be a specific, unique angle of valley slope. Once established, this angle of slope will be maintained as long as the factors governing its initiation are not altered. As the valley is deepened, the slope is lengthened, and valley width is increased at the top (Fig. 80), but the angle of valley slope remains constant. In other words there is *parallel retreat of slopes.* Restoration of the previously existing slopes of the widened, upper part of the valley, in their successive positions, would reveal a series of parallel planes. These according to Penck are *böschungen,* or in English, *gravity slopes* (Meyerhoff, H. A., 1940, p. 251).

The Haldenhang. It will be noted that the degree of declivity of slope depends solely on the measure of the contribution that degradation by weathering and wash makes in a unit of time. Accordingly, as downcutting ceases with attainment of grade, the parallel retreat of the upper portions of the valley walls is not directly affected. But a new set of circumstances is introduced at the bases of the valley slopes. As the stream is no longer cutting down, no gradient is available at the foot of the slope for the continued, uniform removal of the waste supplied from above, except as, by lateral planation the stream is able to develop a flat valley floor and to remove all slope debris as fast as it is delivered. Failing that, the waste accumulates to form a talus slope (not a talus cone). But if a talus fragment comes to rest the rock slope under it is prevented from achieving its appropriate measure of retreat. The foot of the böschung, gravity slope, experiencing parallel retreat is now at the top surface of the talus fragment. At the next position of retreat the foot of the slope, theoretically considered, will be at the top of a double thickness of talus. Actually, retreat above and talus accumulation below are continuous processes. The net result of their joint operation is to bring about the development, under the talus, of a new (less steeply inclined than the parallel-retreating gravity slope) rock-surface declivity, to which W. Penck gave the name *haldenhang.* An explanatory translation of haldenhang is: undertalus rock slope of degradation.

It will be appreciated that this concept leads to the detailed study of the involved interrelations that exist between different processes of weathering, preparation and reduction of rock debris, exposure of surfaces, and translocation of waste. Collectively this set of circumstances is referred to by the Germans as **abtragung,** for which the nearest English translation is "denudation," or the part of degradation that is not directly owing to a stream erosion. Results of such studies have been published by S. O. Morawetz (1932), O. Lehmann (1934), E. Gerber (1934).

Haldenhang development is a mark of absteigende entwickelung. Eventually the concave curve of the haldenhang extends to the divide level, and the parallel retreating slopes of gleichförmige entwickelung are eliminated. Under the, now general, mantle of waste the haldenhänge undergo slow reduction in level, so that in the ultimate endrumpf (normal peneplain) long, gently concave slopes, terminating in low, sharply pointed divides are the final expression of relief.

Davis held that once the profile of grade was established in streams, and slopes were also graded, the further history of slopes was one of progressive decline in steepness. He analyzed (1932, pp. 408–410, 424–425) the Penckian concept of concave divides in peneplains and concluded that their occurrence was possible only under special circumstances, and primarily as a feature of monadnocks.

Knickpunkte and Piedmont Treppen. In accord with his concept that initial rapid uplift, followed by long stillstand and a sequential degradational development, is the representative case for fluvial geomorphology, Davis assumed that further upheaval would be intermittent and, in effect, *per saltum.* Walther Penck, contrariwise, held that the normal circumstances are a long, very slow upheaval at the start, followed by a progressive acceleration of uplift giving rise, typically, to an expanding dome. The issue here is between discontinuity and continuity of uplift. In the first case geomorphic forms are the expression of stages in a degradational sequence. In the second case they result from an unceasing interaction of diastrophic and degradational processes; there is no fixed order of progression, only continuous modification to match the interplay of the two sets of forces.

Breaks, interruptions, that is, abrupt changes in degree of declivity, are a conspicuous feature in many landscapes. In the German terminology such breaks are knickpunkte. The English phrase, **nick points,** does not exactly translate knickpunkte.

According to the precepts of the American school, knickpunkte, in the profiles of streams and in slopes, are merely the expression of an ungraded condition. As such they may be present because of marked differences in resistance to degradational attack of rock beds or structure, or are evidence of intermittent uplift. Cap-rock waterfalls, cuestas, two-cycle valleys, fault scarps are examples.

The Walther Penck doctrines hold that these explanations are inadequate. The examples cited are, in accordance with his approaches, only special cases of a general phenomenon, whose occurrence need not be conditioned by such exceptional circumstances of structure and uplift. Penck contended, instead, that knickpunkte are a normal feature in the profiles of streams that descend the slopes of a dome of homogeneous rock which is experiencing continuously accelerated, but uninterrupted, uplift, and is expanding in area. Further, the knickpunkte are matched in the interstream areas by the steep fronts of piedmont treppen (piedmont bench lands). The piedmont treppen are terraces that slope outward, and ring around the expanding dome in a series of levels (Fig. 106). The Black Forest region of southern Germany is the type instance of such development. It has been suggested that the benchlands of the Appalachian Piedmont are a parallel case.

The knickpunkte and piedmont treppen concept has aroused much controversy. However, the most ardent supporters of the Penckian system have receded from the extreme position that these features are developed as an accompaniment of continuously accelerated uplift. It is generally conceded that some degree of irregularity in rate of upheaval is essential for their occurrence, if related to fluvial degradation in homogeneous rock.

But it is still debated whether, given intermittent vertical upheavals and consequent rejuvenations, knickpunkte will develop and persist, migrating headward, in the profiles of streams eroding homogeneous rocks. The orthodox view is that the great excess of erosive energy available at the initiating point (Playfair's Law) would very shortly convert the knickpunkte to graded slopes, and so effect their elimination. It is not certain, however, that the excess of energy can be effectively applied to bring about immediate grading at the sites of the knickpunkte. If not, then knickpunkte may persist indefinitely as such, and even migrate upstream.

Development of piedmont treppen in accordance with the Penckian system, even if their initiation is ascribed to intermittent uplift, requires the acceptance of an additional principle, namely that interstream degradation, primarily the retreat of valley walls, is very rapid in relation to the rate of stream grading; that is, the extinction of knickpunkte. This relation is perhaps realized in areas where the homogeneous, fresh rock of the stream bed is greatly resistant to mechanical erosion, but is of a type that yields rapidly to chemical attack. Rich (1938) has provided a detailed analysis of these relationships, and argues against the contentions of Meyerhoff and Hubbell (1927–1928) who, in general, support the Penckian thesis.

SUMMARY

Albrecht Penck is the precursor of the German school of geomorphologists, led by Walther Penck, in somewhat the same way that Powell, Dutton, and Gilbert are in the background of the American school, led by W. M. Davis. According to Walther Penck's exposition, manner and rate of uplift are the prime factors in fluvial geomorphic development; the cyclic system of Davis is applicable only in reference to the special case of rapid uplift followed by stillstand and progressive degradation. But it may be contended, on the basis of convincing evidence, that uplift, rest, degradation is the normal sequence, the other possibilities all exceptional. In particular, Walther Penck's long continued, slow upheaval, followed by a progressively accelerated uplift, was considered very improbable of occurrence by Davis, although Penck presents it as the general expectancy. The two systems are further at variance in their interpretations of slope forms. But, in consequence of the disputation aroused by Walther Penck's contributions, slope analysis, and detailed study of processes in relation to the forms produced, are indicated as fields of geomorphic investigation that will receive much more attention than was formerly given to them.

BIBLIOGRAPHY

CLASSICAL

Noë, G. de la, and Margerie Emm. de (1888) *Les Formes du Terrain,* Service Géographie de l'Armée, Text and Atlas, Librarie Hachette et Cie, Paris.

Penck, W. (1924) *Die Morphologische Analyse,* J. Engelhorn's Nachfolger, Stuttgart.

Davis, W. M. (1932) *Piedmont Bench Lands* and *Primärrümpfe,* Bulletin Geological Society of America, Vol. 43, pp. 399–440.

RECENT

Meyerhoff, H. A., and Hubbell, M. (1927–28) *The Erosional Landforms of Eastern and Central Vermont,* Vermont State Geologist, 16th Annual Report, pp. 315–381.

Sauer, C. (1929) *Landforms in the Southern Peninsular Range of California as Developed about Warner's Hot Springs and Mesa Grande,* University of California Publications in Geography, Vol. 3, No. 4, pp. 199–290.

Rich, J. L. (1938) *Recognition and Significance of Multiple Erosion Surfaces,* Bulletin Geological Society of America, Vol. 49, pp. 1695–1722.

Baulig, H. (1939) *Sur les Gradins de Piedmont,* Journal of Geomorphology, Vol. 2, pp. 281–304.

Leighly, J. (1940) *Comments* (in Symposium on the Geomorphic Tenets of W. M. Davis and W. Penck) Annals Association of American Geographers, Vol. 30, pp. 223–228.

Johnson, D. (1940) *Memorandum* (as above) Annals Association of American Geographers, Vol. 30, pp. 228–232.

Chapter Fourteen

GEOMORPHIC FEATURES ASSOCIATED WITH WEATHERING, AND MASS TRANSLOCATIONS OF ROCK WASTE

Introduction. A number of topographic phenomena can not be directly ascribed to the operation of the fluvial or other geomorphic cycles. These features result chiefly from the action of

FIG. 140.   MANTLE ROCK, GLACIALLY TRANSPORTED, NEAR LATTINTOWN, ULSTER COUNTY, NEW YORK

The ground moraine seen here rests (at hammer head) directly on glacially striated Hudson River sandstone.   Photograph by Victor Schmidt.

weathering processes and from mass translocations of rock waste without the intervention of well-defined streams or other recognized transporting agencies.   Some of the items are *denudation forms* in the literal sense of the term, that is, rock laid bare. The mere reduction of consolidated rock to debris of greater or less fineness, ***rock preparation,*** as it has been termed, gives rise to a variety of landscape aspects. Finally that part of general degradation which consists of mass translocations without benefit of an agency that also acts to bring about specific erosive change, is responsible for the occurrence of certain characteristic topographic items.

The Mantle Rock. On the steep slopes of mountains, also in desert regions and in regions recently subjected to glaciation,

FIG. 141. THE FORMATION OF RESIDUAL SOIL

Notice that the soil, fine at the top and modified by inclusion of organic matter, and otherwise, grades downward without break into the unaltered bed rock from which its basic substance is derived.

bare, unaltered rock may be exposed over wide tracts. Far more generally a sheet of mantle rock, or regolith supplies the surface appearance of the land. This cover of rock debris has a variety of origins. Much of it has been transported to the site of the occurrence (Fig. 140). In that event the form it takes is commonly governed by the nature of the transporting medium and the erosive processes to which it has been subjected after its deposit. But over wide regions the regolith was derived from rock preparation by weathering of the underlying consolidated beds (Fig. 141). As such it is referred to as ***residual soil*** (Fig. 29), to distinguish it from ***transported soil,*** as characterized above.

The term *soil* as used in this connection is a misnomer when referred to the specific study of soil science. It is true that, by the addition of organic matter and a variety of other modifications, the top layer of the regolith commonly is made capable of supporting plant growth, and this part is properly soil. But mantle rock may extend considerable distances below the soil layer and have characteristics, even at the surface, that make it

FIG. 142. GULLYING OF RESIDUAL SOIL, HEADWATERS OF A TRIBUTARY TO THE OCOEE RIVER, TENNESSEE
Photograph by Caspar Rappenecker.

wholly unsuitable for sustaining plant life in the ordinary sense of the term, though mosses and lichens may exist on it.

The ordinary aspect of residual mantle rock as it is seen in fields and pastures, and on the forest floor, is so familiar to most persons from experience or pictures as not to require extended description. What has modernly been more acutely realized than it was formerly is that this apparently stable sheet of rock waste is everywhere moving downslope toward valley axes (Fig. 130). This is the phenomenon of soil creep, more broadly, mass translocation of weathering waste. The downhill movement is supplemented by solifluction, by rain and sheet wash, by rill and gully erosion (Fig. 142). Collectively these transfers of the granular rock substance and its included organic materials constitute the problem of soil erosion to which much attention is now given (Figs. 143, 144).

For the most part soil creep is a slow, unperceived movement

FIG. 143. SOIL EROSION IN HAMILTON COUNTY, OHIO

Up and downhill instead of contour plowing has resulted in the gullying of the soil on the slope and accumulation of silt at its base. All this damage was done by one series of spring rains. Photograph from the Soil Conservation Service, United States Department of Agriculture.

resulting from gravity pull. It is facilitated by the presence of moisture and greatly promoted by the expansion in volume of this included water when the water is changed to ice. Yield from the thrust resulting from ice formation is readier downhill than uphill, so that the net result of soil freezing is a general downslope shift. At times of great drouth and heat, *sun cracks* open because of contraction of the soil resulting from loss of its moisture

FIG. 144.   CONTOUR CULTIVATION ON THE APPALACHIAN PIEDMONT, NEAR ANDER-
SON, SOUTH CAROLINA

The furrows following the contour of the slope prevent washing of the
soil and tend to conserve moisture for the crop.

FIG. 145.   SUN CRACKS IN SOIL ON A SLOPE IN OHIO

The blocks moved slightly downhill when the cracks opened; they will
move down farther when the earth is again moistened and expanded by
rain. Photograph from the Soil Conservation Service, United States Department of Agriculture.

content. The soil units tend to move downhill when the cracks
open from drying, and again when they close by expansion after
the soil has been saturated by a succeeding rain (Fig. 145).

Soil Stripes and Polygonal Ground.   In polar latitudes (Fig. 132), and where similar climatic relations obtain in regions of lofty mountains elsewhere, solifluction, here in association with frost action, gives rise to particular patternings of the soil surface and sortings of the soil substance.   The requisite conditions for these developments are permanently frozen ground at depth, subject to deep thawing and complete saturation of the upper part in the warm season and by day, with repeated partial refreezings at night.

Under these circumstances heterogeneous rock waste experiences a sorting action which results in the development of *soil stripes* on slopes and *polygonal ground* over flat areas.

The soil stripes consist of bands of fine textured material alternating with narrower ridges of angular boulders raised slightly above the general surface.   These parallel stripes extend in the direction of the slope.

The polygonal ground on the level tracts is similarly constituted.   A many-sided or ring-shaped central area, 3 to 20 feet in diameter, composed of fine textured or undifferentiated material, is bounded by a wall composed of tightly packed rock fragments up to 6 inches or more thick and long, which rises several inches to a foot above the enclosed unit.

It is inferred that these arrangements result from the tendency of freezing to heave up the fine material and concurrently to eject included rock fragments.   Boulders thus concentrated at the surface gradually slide off the bulged mounds and ridges, hence collect at their borders.   The rock particles may also be subjected to a lateral thrust, and perhaps to the slow compulsion of a convectional circulation of the melt-water, up in the center down at the sides, resulting from density differences in the liquid in the temperature range between 32°F. and 39°F.   These deductions are only tentative; further observations may disclose other significant factors.

Felsenmeere and Rock Glaciers.   Where massive rock, with an incipient fracture or joint structure, is exposed in polar regions and on high mountain summits, frost riving is the dominant weathering process.   The rock is broken into great blocks which cover the surface in an unbroken, chaotic assemblage.   This development is called a *felsenmeer,* or rock-block field.   The finer particles that result from further disintegration are washed or blown away so that the felsenmeer retains its large-angular-boulder aspect indefinitely. The summit of Pikes Peak, Colorado, is an impressive example of felsenmeer development. In lower latitudes somewhat similar felsenmeere with rounded boulders are produced in particular rock types, chiefly those of granitic kind, by other weathering processes.

Ordinarily water furnished to the surface of talus accumulations immediately drains out at their bases because of their easy

FIG. 146. ROCK STREAM, OR ROCK "GLACIER" IN THE HURRICANE BASIN, COLORADO
Photograph from the United States Geological Survey.

permeability. If, however, the site is one where rapid alternations of freezing and thawing occur it may be possible, with adequate precipitation in the form of snow, for the spaces between the rock fragments of a talus to become completely filled with ice. The mass then acquires characteristics of motion similar to those of a glacier and is referred to as a *rock glacier* (Fig. 146). The surface of a rock glacier is marked by concentric banding and wave forms suggestive of slow flow. Indeed the rock glacier may be one of the terminal extremes of a series, the other extreme being a glacier made up of pure ice. In between, other glaciers are made up of all degrees of a mixture of ice and rock substance. J. E. Kesseli (1941) independently comes to a somewhat similar conclusion in regard to rock streams (rock glaciers) but seems to consider the phenomenon to be in effect a dying or relict phase of glacierization. For further discussion of talus at high altitudes see Behre, 1933, Bryan, 1934.

Landslide Topography. Even without the lubricating action of water or ice the mass and momentum of landslides may be such that the material develops a type of motion by flow in its descent. This flow movement is reflected in the surface forms of the deposit where the material comes to rest. The term *landslide topography* (Fig. 128) then applies. Its particular characteristic is a resemblance to short choppy waves on the surface of the sea. In some respects landslide topography is like that of irregular morainic deposits by glaciers. The materials are also similarly heterogeneous of texture. But the composition of the landslide is directly referable to the material of the higher slope from which it descended whereas the substance of the moraine usually has very diverse sources.

Stability and Instability of Slopes. It may be said that the various phases of soil creep are indicative of stability of slopes whereas landslides and even talus cones and rock glaciers are evidence of the introduction of a disturbing factor. The disturbance that brings about instability may be diastrophic, orogeny or faulting, or the intervention of agencies foreign to the fluvial geomorphic cycle, for example, glacierization or the wave attack of the sea.

The Law of Weathering. Aside from variations in the effectiveness of weathering attack on consolidated rock that arise from differences in climatic circumstances, the rate of yield is conditioned by the nature of the rock itself. This kind of variation is referred to as differential weathering. The general result of differential weathering may be expressed as a law; namely that *differential weathering causes resistant beds and structures to stand out in relief.* It is to be remembered that the operation of this law in producing geomorphic forms requires the coordinate performance of various transporting agencies for removing part or all of the rock waste resulting from weathering action. The different phenomena here under consideration are not, therefore,

FIG. 147. MOUNT WHITNEY, CALIFORNIA

This highest mountain peak in the United States has been isolated from the general line of the eastern fault scarp of the Sierra Nevada by the weathering away of the more closely jointed rock surrounding it. Photograph from Frasher's Inc., Pomona, California.

solely due to weathering, but rather to weathering supplemented
by gravity, soil creep, and stream flow.

Peaks, Ridges, Cols, and Passes. The culminating summits of
mountains, called *peaks* (Fig. 147) and *ridges,* only exceptionally
owe their superior altitude to uplift. Much more regularly they
exist as isolated, high masses because they are composed of ma-

FIG. 148. COL CONVERTED TO A PASS. BETWEEN THE HEADWATERS OF THE
GENESEE RIVER AND PINE CREEK, NEW YORK AND PENNSYLVANIA

Some structural weakness, presumably close-spaced jointing, permitted
weathering to develop an initial hollow at this site, a col. This has since
been lowered and opened to the measure of a pass by the headwater competition of the two streams. The view looks south down Pine Creek from
the high point of the pass; the Genesee River descends similarly to the north
from this point.

terial, or have a structure, that is more resistant to degradational
attack than that of surrounding areas. Basic to the disposal
of the weaker materials is the action of the weathering processes
in the preparation of rock, by disintegration and decomposition,
for removal. If more and finer stuff is made available over the
areas of easy yield, it is obvious that translocation agencies, if
these are at all competent, will move larger volumes from such
sites than from the areas of great durability. The weak areas are

thus lowered more rapidly than the strong. Monadnocks surmounting a peneplain are the ultimate expression of this sequence (Figs. 32, 33). They endure and are high because they are exceptionally resistant to weathering attack.

If the belt of weak rock extends transverse to a mountain range its summit outcrop is shortly converted to a *col.* As drainage will be directed from both of its sides toward the axis of a col, the site of a col becomes the source area for streams descending the range in opposite directions (Fig. 148). Differential weathering progressively reduces the floor of a col, but its development to a *pass* is chiefly accomplished by the competition in headwater erosion of the opposed streams. One of these will ordinarily have a steeper descent than the other. The more effective headwater attack of the steeper stream may then permit it to extend its territory far across the axis of the range and at the expense of its competitor. The height of the col is so far reduced by these means that a relatively low pass across the range is opened up.

Cols and passes across lofty mountains have commonly been widened and deepened by glacial action. Some of them, indeed, have been initiated by glacial processes. It is asserted that all of the famous passes of the Alps were enlarged by glaciers after initiation by weathering and stream action, or are the product of ice erosion solely. Passes that result from differential weathering and headwater erosion only are in many instances also water gaps.

Exfoliation Domes. Massive rocks of the granitic type subjected to long-continued degradation commonly develop the forms that stand out in relief as *exfoliation domes* (Fig. 149). The great domes of the Yosemite Valley, the Sugar Loaf of the Rio de Janeiro harbor and Stone Mountain in Georgia are well-known examples. Stone Mountain is a typical monadnock as well, in that it is surrounded by weaker rocks that have been reduced to a low-lying plain. But its form, and those of the other examples cited, is produced by the set of weathering processes called *exfoliation.*

Massive igneous rocks are predisposed to fashioning into domes by their deep-seated origin. Their exposure at the surface results only after a long history of degradation, during which an immense load of covering rock is crumbled and removed. Release from the pressure imposed by this load permits a minute expansion radially outwards from the interior of the igneous masses. The effect is somewhat analogous to the separation upward of the leaves of an automobile spring when relieved of the weight of the car. In the granitic masses the release from compression gives rise to incipient concentric joints, known to quarry-

FIG. 149. GRANITE DOME WITH CURVED SHELL FROM HYPOGENE EXFOLIATION, YOSEMITE VALLEY, CALIFORNIA
Photograph from United States Geological Survey.

men working in such rock as the "lift." Close to the surface these fissures become visible and are responsible for the curved shells, up to 100 feet thick which are characteristic features of the summits of the Yosemite domes (Farmin, R., 1937).

At the immediate surface of the dome thinner peels of rock, concentric with the great shells, are conspicuous. It is to their development that "exfoliation" is specifically applied. These peels were formerly attributed exclusively to the expansion and contraction of the surface rock under intense sun heating by day, and severe, rapid cooling at night. Rock is a very poor conductor of heat. In consequence of this characteristic the temperature changes induced by insolation and radiation are confined to a thin outer layer, with the result that this layer tends to spall off from the core mass. The universal effectiveness of such exfoliation from heating and cooling has been challenged (Blackwelder, E., 1925) especially for exposures in humid regions.

FIG. 150.   CHEMICAL EXFOLIATION OF GRANITE BOULDER
Photograph from United States Geological Survey.

Instead it is urged that chemical weathering, particularly the increase in volume brought about by the growth of new minerals resulting from the introduction of moisture in the surface layer, is responsible for the expansion and consequent curved spalling (Fig. 150). Incipient jointing and frost action probably tend to promote such chemical weathering.

Hogbacks. Perhaps the most conspicuous demonstration of the operation of the general law of weathering is the development of *hogback ridges* (Fig. 151). Where sedimentary beds, originally flat-lying, have been tilted steeply upward by the rise of a dome of igneous rock, and the beds covering the summit of the intruded mass have been eroded away, resistant beds in the flanking layers with dips greater than 35 degrees are converted to narrow ridges, with dip slopes and escarpment slopes of approximately equal steepness, by differential weathering. Such hogbacks are especially prominent where a considerable thickness of weak beds separates the resistant hogback maker from the igneous core, or

Fig. 151. HOGBACK RIDGES, GARDEN OF THE GODS, COLORADO
Photograph from United States Geological Survey.

from still more resistant lower beds, and another band of weak layers occurs on the outer side of the strong layer. The rapid yield and progressive removal of the waste of the weak beds, by wash and soil creep, on both sides of the little-affected resistant bed, leaves the strong bed to stand out high above its surroundings.

A peculiar type of interrupted hogbacks called *flatirons* develops where the basal sedimentary bed is resistant and is in direct contact with the uplifting, crystalline intrusive. The weathering of the igneous and sedimentary rock may then be nearly matched as to rate, but each is governed in pattern by its own structure. Stream erosion notches the mountain slope, cutting through both rock types. The spur ends between the valleys then retain the semi-hogback development in the arresting flatiron shape (Fig. 152).

Hogbacks and flatirons are very strikingly in evidence at various places along the eastern front of the Rocky Mountains.

FIG. 152.   FLATIRONS NEAR BOULDER, COLORADO
   The circle symbol indicates the resistant conglomeratic composition of the flatiron bed, more durable than the granite, cross symbol, of the main mountain mass to the right, which has weathered down to generally lower altitudes than those of the flanking flatirons. Drawing (based on a photograph) by Elizabeth Burckmyer.

Dike ridges are very similar in form, and in their origin through differential weathering, to hogbacks. Where a dike of igneous rock is much superior in resistance to weathering attack to the country rock it invades, a dike ridge (Fig. 153) may result. The trend of dike ridges, unlike that of hogbacks, is not necessarily related to the structural forms of the place of occurrence. This is true of the great, radiating dike ridges of the Spanish Peaks region of Colorado, and the similar ones about Ship Rock, New Mexico (Fig. 154).

Conversely, weak dikes subject to differential weathering might be expected to give rise to linear depressions. But these do not so readily ensue because on level or gently sloping lands there is no slope available for the removal of the waste in advance of that developed from the adjacent resistant country rock.

Weathering Escarpments. Where beds of varying resistance stand on end, hogback ridges result from differential weathering;

FIG. 153.   DIKE RIDGE, NEAR RAND, COLORADO
Photograph by Earl Phillips.

where they are flat-lying, *weathering escarpments* may develop. Moderately inclined strata give rise to cuestas, as has been noted.

Concisely defined, an escarpment is a precipitous slope. When geomorphic reference is made to a weathering escarpment it is further implied that there is an abrupt transition from the vertical acclivity to a horizontal surface, or gentle slope, at its summit, and that a wide plains area spreads away from the base of the cliff.

These topographic relations are conspicuously in evidence where an extensive, thick, lava flow (Fig. 155) overlies unconsolidated, fragmented volcanic materials, or rocks of other kinds readily susceptible to weathering attack. The terminal border of the lava flow is a sharply defined structural line. Outside this line normal degradation may reduce the general level of the land very appreciably while the upper surface of the flow is scarcely affected. In consequence of these conditions a sharp declivity

FIG. 154. RADIATING DIKE RIDGES AND VOLCANIC NECK, SHIP ROCK, NEW MEXICO
Photograph copyright by Spence Air Photos.

marks the edge of the lava flow. This declivity becomes an enduring element in the landscape and attains the steepness of a cliff. Differential weathering causes the weak materials under the lava cap to be disintegrated and decomposed. The debris falls to the base of the slope, whence it is removed by rain-wash and soil creep. Deprived of support, blocks from the edge of the lava bed drop and are, in turn, crumbled and washed away. The cliff is thus caused to retreat, but is maintained in its original sharpness, and may indeed be increased in height by further degradation of the region below it.

The origin of weathering escarpments under such circumstances is readily discerned. But the similar origin of other escarpments, which are in places very conspicuous geomorphic forms (Fig. 156), is not so easily comprehended. The Niagara, Helderberg, and Catskill escarpments are examples. Each of these is the product of a very long degradational history, as are many others of the same type. They occur where an extremely durable sedimentary bed of wide extent, and flat-lying, was originally capped by a

FIG. 155. WEATHERING ESCARPMENT DUE TO LAVA-FLOW CAPPING, NEAR BISHOP, OWENS VALLEY, CALIFORNIA
The capping lava bed shows clearly at the crest of the escarpment.

considerable thickness of much weaker layers. These overlying materials yield to degradation and expose the upper surface of the durable bed over wide areas. Meanwhile stream erosion, along one or more lines, succeeds in making a cut through the durable bed, and the valleys of these streams are brought to grade. If now there is a great thickness of weak beds in the section between the bottom of the resistant layer and grade level of the streams, retreat of the valley sides, as weathering escarpments, takes place in precisely the same manner that it does in

FIG. 156. WEATHERING ESCARPMENT IN SEDIMENTARY BEDS, CHIMOPOVY, ARIZONA
The strong capping bed, here, is breaking back in joint blocks. Photograph, copyright by Spence Air Photos.

287

the lava-capped areas. If the strong bed originally abutted on a crystalline mass, as the Helderberg limestones did against the base of the Adirondacks, the escarpment is effaced on that side where the massive rock is encountered. The opposite escarpment may persist for long periods, remote from the line of its origin, because of continuous retreat, and be fronted by extensive plains in which no clue remains of the sequence which gave rise to the declivity.

It will be appreciated that there can be all variations between the escarpment of mountain height and developments so low and restricted that they are more appropriately called "rock terraces." Thus the great east to west cliffs on the north side of the Colorado River (Fig. 107) remote from the canyon, are properly weathering escarpments, those within the canyon, even if of great dimensions, rock terraces. But whether of great or slight dimensions the critical requirement for these developments is that the capping layer be of such durability as to (a) resist reduction from above and (b) retreat so slowly at the edge that the waste at the base does not accumulate to form a talus, or positively stated, is crumbled and removed as fast as it is furnished.

Between weathering escarpments, cuestas, and hogback ridges there is an insensible gradation. It may, however, be said that cuestas are ordinarily associated with the development of subsequent valleys in inclined sedimentary strata and owe their existence as much, if not more, to stream erosion as to differential weathering.

The enduring existence and the sharpness of declivity of weathering escarpments and cuestas is in reverse relation to the steepness of the dip of the capping layer from zero up to approximately 35 degrees. With dips steeper than 35 degrees the hogback form develops. Its permanence and prominence, contrariwise, are enhanced with increasing steepness of inclination of the durable bed to a climax at 90 degrees.

Mesas, Buttes, Outliers. Seen from a distance weathering escarpments, of sufficient dimensions to be conspicuous elements in the landscape, present what appears to be an unbroken, sharply defined crest line. Examined in detail from close by the scarp edge is observed to be minutely nicked and grossly notched. Such sculpture of the Pink Cliffs in Utah has given rise to the celebrated Bryce Canyon (Figs. 24, 107) development with its myriad intricate forms.

Innumerable gullies and, in places, obsequent valleys of con-

FIG. 157. CAMEL ROCK, SMALL MESA, OR BUTTE, IN THE NORTHEAST OF COLO-
RADO, SOUTH OF LARAMIE, WYOMING
Photograph by Donald Rockwell.

FIG. 158. SKETCH TO SHOW RELATION OF CAMEL ROCK TO THE PARENT UPLAND
Drawing by Donald Rockwell.

siderable size breach the cliff face and facilitate the general retreat
of the escarpment by enabling the sapping attack of the weathering agencies to proceed laterally as well as from the front. If
a pair of obsequent streams, emerging some distance apart on the
escarpment front, succeed eventually in opening valleys that come
into conjunction in their headwater areas, a large tract of the

upland back of the escarpment front may be completely separated from the major development. The unit thus originally isolated by stream action is by weathering retreat of its walls converted to a *mesa* (Figs. 157, 158).

As is true of the cliffs of weathering escarpments, lava-capped regions are ideal sites for mesa occurrences because there wide, level-topped areas are initially present. The basalt-capped Mesa de Maya and Raton Mesa in Colorado east of the Rocky Moun-

FIG. 159. TWO BUTTES, POWERS COUNTY, SOUTHEASTERN COLORADO

This is an igneous intrusion rising above an old erosion surface of consolidated sediments, later alluviated. Photograph by H. T. U. Smith.

tains are well-known examples. It is also to be noted that where lava flows are very extensive consequent surface drainage may be of sufficient volume to do effective valley cutting and so to dissect the area into segments, which, by weathering retreat of their bounding walls, develop into isolated mesas. However sandstones, conglomerates, and even a cover of loose boulders can serve as the resistant material for a mesa top.

At first mesas may remain joined at the rear with the parent tableland. But eventually this connection is completely severed. From then on the mesa continually shrinks in area by retreat of the escarpments from all sides toward the center. Its last remainder persists remote from the escarpment line that gave it birth. This line has itself, meanwhile, retreated far back from the position it had when the mesa started. When the mesa has been reduced to the dimensions of a narrow isolated summit it is called a **butte**. Unfortunately "butte" is also applied to similar summits resulting from the isolation, also by differential weather-

FIG. 160. OUTLIERS OF THE LOVER'S LEAP TYPE, IN BUNTER SANDSTEIN, ELBE VALLEY, SAXONY, GERMANY

The influence of the joint planes is conspicuously evident. Photograph by Raymond Crist.

ing and degradation, of narrow vertical intrusions of igneous rock into overlying weaker beds. These may be distinctively referred to as *volcanic buttes* (Fig. 159). Ship Rock, New Mexico (Fig. 154), is such a butte. Both types of buttes are regarded as particular forms of monadnocks by some writers but this assertion implies an approach to peneplanation of the region the buttes surmount.

Inasmuch as the scarp-forming cap rock is, in common with rocks generally, always more or less cleft by joints, detachment of units of much lesser dimensions than those of mesas is possible. Where close spacing of systems of joints at right angles occurs, exceptionally rapid weathering, carried back to the intersection

FIG. 161.   OUTLIERS, MONUMENT VALLEY, UTAH

Here both caprock and joint influences may be noted. Photograph from Walter Wanger's production of "Stagecoach."

of two joint planes, one of each system, may result in the isolation of a small unit of the capping material immediately in front of the main cliff.   Such detached masses are called *outliers* (Figs. 160, 161).   More romantically, the gap that separates them from

the parent cliff may be referred to as *Indian leap,* or *lover's leap.*
Just why a harassed Indian or lover should attempt such a leap
is not clear, except, perhaps, that it would mark a limit in athletic
prowess.

Outliers ordinarily have only a fleeting existence, geomorphic-

FIG. 162. PEDESTAL ROCK, UTAH

Wind erosion may have been important in the shaping of this occurrence.
Photograph by Frederick Pack.

ally speaking, and limited development.   But with an approach
to the cuesta degree of dip, or where the joint systems are remarkably prominent, they attain striking topographic significance.
The monuments of the Perry Park and the Garden of the Gods
regions of Colorado are a collection of tremendous outliers resulting from the thorough dissection of a cuesta structure by
differential weathering along joints intersecting at right angles.

FIG. 163. ROCK CITY, OLEAN, NEW YORK

Note how the rock masses seen dimly in the distance give the effect of tall city buildings.

Some of these are reduced to very unstable pillars called *pedestal rocks* (Fig. 162), or *balanced rocks*. Balanced rocks called *perched boulders* also occur where glaciers leave behind great boulders in delicately poised positions.

FIG. 164.   BUTTRESSES AND RECESSES, FALL CREEK, ITHACA, NEW YORK
Photograph by Ward Bowen.

At Olean, New York, wide spaced but very pronounced jointing in a conglomerate rock has given rise to what are called *rock cities* (Fig. 163). In such instances the effect of weathering in opening the joint fissures is enhanced by the outward slumping

Fig. 165. Buttresses and recesses in the Yakhsu conglomerates, Panier Country, Central Afghanistan
Photograph by W. Rickmer Rickmers.

of the rectangular blocks. The rock-city appellation derives from the fancied resemblance of the widened joint fissures to the canyon streets of a metropolitan center while the rock masses

Fig. 166. BUTTRESSES AND RECESSES, ZION NATIONAL PARK
Photograph from National Park Service.

Fig. 167. CLIFF-DWELLER RUINS, ARIZONA. HOLLOW FROM DIFFERENTIAL WEATHERING; CLIFF SCULPTURE

Note that the beds in the cliff face, at the right of the picture, on the level of the cliff-dweller house, are less massive, yield more readily to weathering attack, than the beds above and below. Photograph by William H. Jackson in 1874.

FIG. 168.   HOODOOS IN YELLOWSTONE NATIONAL PARK
Photograph from United States Geological Survey.
297

are representative of the tall buildings that line such streets. The
Olean site is locally famous as a scenic wonder.

Buttresses and Recesses.   The crest lines of weathering escarpments and mesas are made up of more or less prominent salients
and re-entrants which reflect, in a lesser degree, the differential
weathering along joints which is more conspicuously in evidence
where outliers develop.   Such notching is not confined to the
particular structural relations that give rise to weathering escarp-

FIG. 169.   EARTH PYRAMIDS AT BOZEN, TYROL
This is the classic locality for this phenomenon.   Drawing (from a photograph) by Steve Barker.

ments and mesas; it is also observed on gorge walls, and there
gives rise to *buttresses* and *recesses* (Figs. 164, 165, 166).   Indeed
it may be so pronounced as to produce small outliers, called
chimney rocks, or *pinnacles.*   On gorge walls made up of flat
lying, sedimentary beds of marked alternation in resistance differential weathering along horizontal lines in places causes the
durable beds to stand out in marked relief.   The sites of the
homes of the ancient cliff dwellers in Arizona are shallow caves
weathered out between massive sandstone beds (Fig. 167).   This
may be called *cliff sculpture.*

Granite Needles. If massive granite is cut by well-defined, close-spaced, vertical joints, and only obscurely, if at all, by joints in the horizontal direction, differential weathering may give rise to *granite needles* as at Harney Peak in the Black Hills of South Dakota.

Hoodoos, Earth Pyramids, and Tepee Buttes. In the Absaroka Range to the east of Yellowstone Park a volcanic breccia, made up of dense, basic lava boulders in a friable ground-mass material has yielded to differential weathering so as to give rise to weird and grotesque puppetlike forms in a jumbled aggregate, termed *hoodoos* (Fig. 168). The knobby basic boulders disposed irregularly through the mass (which is further intersected by joints) stand out in relief

Fig. 170. EARTH PILLARS, SOUTH SHORE OF LAKE ONTARIO, NEW YORK

to produce the goblin effect which inspired the name. Similar hoodoo forms are seen in Bryce Canyon. The term is also used to designate some of the fantastic columns of the Garden of the Gods, Colorado, and for a landslide topography of the same general aspect near Mammoth Hot Springs in Yellowstone Park.

At Bozen in the Tyrol there is a remarkable development of a feature, many times duplicated in a less spectacular degree at other localities, called *earth pyramids* (Fig. 169), *earth pillars,* or *demoiselles.* Earth pyramids are tapering columns of unconsolidated clayey material capped at the summit with a boulder, commonly of larger diameter than the pedestal on which it rests. The sides of the pyramid may be studded with boulders of smaller size. The origin of such pillars is from rain sculpture of densely compacted morainic deposits (Fig. 170), or badlands clays with imbedded concretions. The large boulders or concretions preserve the clay mass below them from wetting. In between these protected columns the clayey substances are liquefied by the moisture and slump away, leaving the earth pyramids to stand out in marked relief (Fig. 171).

Of somewhat similar origin, but of seemingly unique occurrence, are the *tepee buttes* of Colorado, north of the Arkansas River, so named for their resemblance to the conical Indian tents called

FIG. 171.   EARTH PILLARS IN THE BADLANDS, SOUTH DAKOTA
Photograph from United States Geological Survey.

"tepees." Here a thick shale, otherwise of very uniform composition, contains great, fossil limestone concretions or cores, up to ten feet in diameter. These concretions protect the shale underlying them from weathering disintegration, much as the boulders do the clay of the earth pyramids. The buttes that result attain heights of one hundred and more feet rising above a plain of very low relief. Gilbert and Gulliver (1895) described them and Davis (1932, p. 409) referred to them as an example of the special circumstances necessary if sharp crests with concave slopes are to be developed in a region reduced to the low relief of old age or peneplanation in the fluvial geomorphic cycle.

SUMMARY

A numerous assemblage of geomorphic forms, ranging in measure of relief from lofty mountain peaks to the configuration of mantle-rock accumulations, is produced by weathering processes acting more or less independently of other agencies.

It is noted that when, through rock preparation, consolidated rock is reduced to weathering waste, the loose materials, subjected to gravity pull, are translocated and accumulated in various forms. The distinctive topographic aspects that the debris acquires are in accord with the particular circumstances of each case.

Consolidated rocks are found to be very unlike in the rate of their yield to the attack of weathering. In consequence of such differential yield it is the law of weathering that resistant rocks and structures are made to stand out in relief when a region is subjected to weathering action. In discussing the development of the varied land forms that result from the operation of this law it is somewhat difficult to make distinctions between what is weathering and what is not, and what part weathering and what part other agencies have had in the effect produced. But in each instance the fact remains that differential yield to weathering processes is the basic factor in the development of the feature.

BIBLIOGRAPHY

CLASSICAL

Derby, O. A. (1896) *Decomposition of Rocks in Brazil*, Journal of Geology, Vol. 4, pp. 529–540.

Merrill, G. P. (1896) *Principles of Rock Weathering*, Journal of Geology, Vol. 4, pp. 704–724; 850–871.

Tarr, R. S. (1897) *Rapidity of Weathering and Stream Erosion in Arctic Latitudes*, American Geologist, Vol. 19, pp. 131–136.

Russell, I. C. (1898) *Topographic Features Due to Landslides*, Popular Science Monthly, Vol. 53, pp. 480–489.

Howe, E. (1909) *Landslides in the San Juan Mountains, Colorado*, United States Geological Survey, Professional Paper 67.

Capps, S. R., Jr. (1910) *Rock Glaciers in Alaska*, Journal of Geology, Vol. 18, pp. 359–375.

RECENT

Allix, A. (1924) *Avalanches,* Geographical Review, Vol. 14, pp. 519–560.

Bryan, K. (1927) *Pedestal Rocks Formed by Differential Erosion,* United States Geological Survey, Bulletin 790.

Leonard, R. J. (1927) *Pedestal Rocks Resulting From Disintegration,* Journal of Geology, Vol. 35, pp. 469–474.

Taber, S. (1929) *Frost Heaving,* Journal of Geology, Vol. 37, pp. 428–461.

Russell, R. J. (1933) *Alpine Land Forms of Western United States,* Bulletin Geological Society of America, Vol. 44, pp. 927–949.

Hay, T. (1936) *Stone Stripes,* Geographical Journal, Vol. 87, pp. 47–50.

Farmin, R. (1937) *Hypogene Exfoliation in Rock Masses,* Journal of Geology, Vol. 33, pp. 793–806.

Barton, D. (1938) *The Disintegration and Exfoliation of Granite in Egypt,* Journal of Geology, Vol. 46, pp. 109–111.

Kesseli, J. E. (1941) *Rock Streams in the Sierra Nevada, California,* Geographical Review, Vol. 31, pp. 203–227.

Chapter Fifteen

THE FLUVIAL GEOMORPHIC CYCLE IN DOME AND FOLD STRUCTURES

Introduction. In the preceding chapters only incidental mention is made of the progress of the fluvial geomorphic cycle in areas of dome and fold structures. This omission is deliberate because the sequence of development follows a particular pattern in such structures and gives rise to very characteristic geomorphic forms which need to be considered separately. It is when he is working in domed and folded regions that the field geologist finds geomorphic evidence to be of great diagnostic significance for interpretation of the order and attitude of beds below the surface.

It is not improbable that all parts of the lithosphere surface are in some degree warped, or are undergoing warping. The distortion may be so slight over wide areas as to leave cover beds, composed of water-laid sediments, in their original, nearly horizontal attitudes. At the other extreme of disturbance, marked warping of the beds is finally succeeded by faulting. Then blocks of the earth's crust move in all directions along planes of fracture. Between the scarcely discernible bendings, and the ultimate complete yield and displacement from faulting, practically every gradation of warping and folding exists. From these remarks it would appear that every geomorphic unit is in some measure a warped mass. Such is, indeed, the case, but in many instances other factors of structure so effectively supervene that faint warping is obscured, or is made to play a secondary role. There remain, however, those cases which have doming or folding as the obviously dominant element of their structure. Where such units are present the pattern of the drainage and the topographic forms developed in the fluvial geomorphic cycle are intimately related to the particular nature of the structure concerned.

Doming. The simplest case of warping is that involving the upheaval of a roughly circular or elliptical dome. The forces responsible for such uplift are not fully comprehended but two kinds of domes are clearly manifest: those resulting from the rise of great masses of rock salt and those which are produced by igneous intrusions.

Deep drilling for oil in Louisiana and Texas has disclosed that

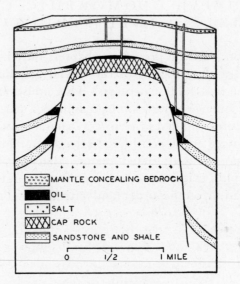

FIG. 172.   IDEALIZED DIAGRAM OF A SALT DOME

Illustrates the manner in which the overlying sedimentary beds are punched through and arched up by the rising plug of salt. The vertical tubes represent oil wells drawing their supplies from oil trapped at the sides of the plug and collecting in the domed beds above it. Modified from a drawing by Virginia Bradley.

plugs of rock salt have moved upward into the overlying sediments of those regions from depths as great as 13,000 feet (Fig. 172), presumably because salt beds thus far, or farther down were made plastic by the weight of the overburden and caused to rise at a weak spot. The energy with which the salt plugs rise is such that the sedimentary beds above them are punched through or lifted up to form *salt domes.* Salt domes range in size from scarcely perceivable swellings to bulges that rise 100 feet above the surrounding country and are from 1 to 2 miles in diameter. Some of the salt domes are evidently of very recent topographic

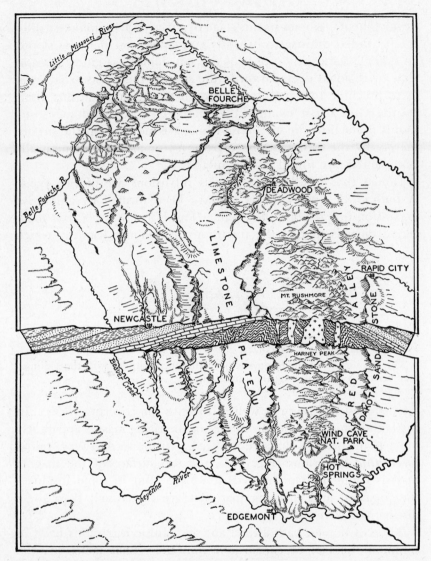

FIG. 173.   THE BLACK HILLS, SOUTH DAKOTA, WYOMING

Note that the sedimentary beds were deposited over an erosion surface developed on the crystalline rocks (wavy lines) below them.   The doming has resulted from a massive uprising of the batholithic type.   The fact of molten material at depth is manifested by the intrusions below Mt. Rushmore, the site where the heroic portraits of Washington, Jefferson, Lincoln and Roosevelt are sculptured.   This domed unit is large enough to have given rise to an independent drainage system as described.   Drawing by Elizabeth Burckmyer.

development.   Domes in this stage of early youth commonly show a faint radial drainage, obviously consequent on the new slopes. In other instances the uplift of the salt domes has either been so slow or regional degradation at the sites of their rise so vigorous as to preclude topographic expression of the dome at any time. In the Gulf Coast country the undissected young domes commonly occur near the sea; those which are indicated at the surface merely by the radial drainage patterns, or are only structurally represented, are found farther inland.

Domes that result from igneous intrusions are of two types. A **batholithic** kind appears to have been formed by a massive expansion upward of sialic magma (Fig. 173). A lesser, but more active type, is that of the intrusions, commonly basaltic, which

Fig. 174.   SECTION OF A LACCOLITH

The top surface of the magma is new; the unconformity with the sedimentary beds was developed by the intrusion.

are assumed to invade as well as to raise the covering rocks.   In the batholithic type the top surface of the rising mass is apparently older than the beds that are uplifted.   In the second type, called **laccolithic** intrusions (Fig. 174), the top surface of the magma mass is younger than the beds it warps.   But in some instances the intruded and covering materials are interfused; then these distinctions have little significance.

The salt domes, batholithic, and laccolithic intrusions have in common the fact of **concordant borders.** That is to say, the warped covering beds extend without break into the undisturbed continuation of the same rock series in the adjoining areas. Drainage lines, hence, can develop without structural interruption from the warped to the unwarped areas.

Regions of multiple folding may also have concordant borders. Thus the Folded Appalachians merge concordantly into the Appalachian Plateau on their western side, as do the Jura Mountains on their northwest side into the Jura Plateau.

Where the fold structures disappear unconformably beneath younger rocks, or where the folding terminates abruptly against a different structure the border is said to be **discordant.** The south border of the Alps illustrates the first case; the eastern border of the Folded Appalachians, where they abut the crystallines of the Blue Ridge Mountains, the second case.

Laccolithic Mountains and Arch Uplifts. Doming that results from igneous intrusion may be expressed by considerable altitudes and high dips; these conditions are characteristic of laccolithic uplifts. Or it may be represented only by very low arches such as the Nashville Dome (Fig. 176).

Whether the word "intrusion" is properly applicable to the type of warp represented by the Nashville Dome is open to question. The movement involved appears to have been deep-seated and regional, hence more in the nature of a transfer of material than an upwarp. This problem, however, is the concern of the geophysicist and structural geologist rather than that of the geomorphologist.

It may be presumed that the rise of a narrow dome of the laccolithic kind can be sufficiently rapid to disrupt pre-existing drainage. If so the new upland will acquire its own consequent drainage. But because of the limited area available for its collection and the steep slopes down which it flows, this drainage will consist of numerous gullies gashing the summit tracts. Their vigorous erosive attack will shortly strip off the cover rock completely. Then an isolated monument, comprising the igneous core, will be all that remains of the dome. Such is the nature of the Mato Tepee (Fig. 175), also called "Devil's Tower," in Wyoming, northwest of the Black Hills. But near at hand is Green Mountain (Little Sun Dance), a dome which is about 3 miles in circumference at the base, and that has had its cover stripped off in part, but not enough to expose the intruded mass of igneous rock. The classic example of laccolithic mountains is the Henry Mountains in Utah. These comprise a number of domes most of which have been sufficiently eroded to disclose their igneous centers. In the same region, Navajo Mountain, on the Utah-Arizona boundary line, retains its cover of sedimentary beds intact.

Quite unlike these laccolithic forms is the region of the Nashville Dome (Fig. 176), now represented topographically by a basin over 400 feet deep, 60 miles wide, and 120 miles long, which has, however, had a history of uplift that began in remote geologic time. The region has, in fact, rather recently experienced further upheaval, but its rise seems consistently to have been too slow to

FIG. 175.   MATO TEPEE, WYOMING, A VOLCANIC NECK, OR PLUG

All the other material has been removed by erosion, leaving the resistant lava plug standing above the surrounding country. Notice also that the stratified rocks around the base of the neck are in a perfectly horizontal position, showing that the magma made its way upward without bending or otherwise disturbing the surrounding rock.

disturb an antecedent drainage of ancient development governed by other slopes. The major streams that traversed the area before the doming began have steadily been able to maintain their courses against the uplifts. Valleys cut by the original antecedent streams were widened, and their floors made confluent, in the weak shales that underlie the resistant limestone beds which are

cap rock for the area. These structural and erosional circumstances brought about the development of an approximately circular weathering escarpment in the central region of the upwarp.
The progressive radial retreat of this escarpment has given rise
to the present basin.

The Black Hills. The examples of uplift by doming thus
far cited exhibit a drainage development that is incipient, hence
obscure, or is areally too restricted to permit the emergence of
a pattern, or one that is dominated by pre-existing water courses.
The Black Hills (Fig. 173), which straddle the north to south
boundary line between South Dakota and Wyoming, have the

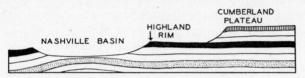

FIG. 176. SECTION OF THE NASHVILLE BASIN
Traversed by drainage antecedent to the doming.

dimensions, the measure of relief, and the degree of dissection
necessary for a representative expression of *dome mountains* as
geomorphic units.

In ground plan the dome of the Black Hills is an almost perfect
ellipse, over 100 miles long and over 50 miles wide. The mountains rise 4000 feet above the surrounding plains; Harney Peak,
the highest summit, is 7216 feet above sea level. If the covering
rocks, since eroded, were restored, the dome would be 2000 feet,
possibly 4000 feet, higher than this peak. In general the dips of
the covering beds are low near the center, steep around the
circumference.

It is clear that the rate of uplift of the Black Hills was sufficiently rapid to create adequate slopes for the development of
an independent, consequent drainage. The extensive, relatively
flat, summit area provided the gathering ground for the original
radial outflow. Coursing down the steep sides of the dome the
consequent streams developed their valleys rapidly headward by
gullying erosion. The headward extension of such channels was
uniformly directed toward the flatter area at the crest of the dome.
In this summit region competing channels were gradually merged

by abstraction, and master consequents began to function. Continuation of the degradation of the central tract eventually unroofed the igneous core below the covering sediments. This is the Harney Peak area.

Once this was accomplished the further reduction of the central area was speeded up because the granitic crystallines are actually inferior to some of the covering beds in resistance to weathering and erosion. But as the strata are themselves of unequal durability, weathering escarpments, governed by the more resistant members, began a retreat down the slopes of the dome. On the east side, where the dips are steepest, the strong beds give rise to cuestas which approximate the aspect of hogbacks. The cuesta form is most spectacularly developed on the eastern side by the Lakota and Dakota sandstones (Fig. 173). It stands as a sharp ridge, in places 500 feet above the Red Valley, next west, on weak shales. On the inner side of the Red Valley is another cuesta; in this instance formed by a resistant limestone.

The Red Valley is an extraordinary subsequent valley development. In view of what has been said on preceding pages in regard to the role of weathering processes in the formation of hog backs it is interesting to note that, despite its prominence and continuity, the Red Valley (and its less conspicuous counterparts on the western side of the dome) is either not used by water courses or only by intermittent streams. Evidently the slow translocation of weathering waste by mass movement has been competent to bring about a great enough reduction in the level of the Red Valley floor to make the cuesta hogbacks stand out in strong relief.

The Red Valley, and the similar parallel valleys, are diagrammatically perfect examples of subsequent valleys as these are developed on a simple dome uplift. The pattern of drainage they make is annular, and is linked to the radial consequent drainage. It is to be noted that the escarpments face inward, and that raingully obsequents descend them toward the center of the dome. On the stripped surfaces of the strong formations with gentle dips that are exposed on the western slope of the dome there is a slight development of *resequent streams*, that is, streams which are again (re) consequent in direction but on a new surface made available by erosion.

The actual sequence of development in the Black Hills was not so simple as it is presented above. There was an intervening period of deposition of lacustrine sediments, and a recent revival of uplift has led to a marked rejuvenation of the valleys of the radial consequents in their middle courses. Thus Spearfish Creek now flows through a canyon 1000 feet deep cut into the northern flank of the dome.

According to Monnett (1922) minor domes, or domes under a deep cover of sediments, like the more readily identifiable occurrences, get geomorphic expression in the form of hilly, agriculturally unproductive country, in regions of plains topography. This development is appropriate to the rule of prior dissection of the summits of upwarps, and provides the petroleum geologist with a clue to the location of oil fields in areas where other evidence of structure is lacking. Similarly a dome in gently inclined beds will appear as a nose in the contours of the region. In general any distinctive departure of contours, or of weathering escarpments, from their normal trend lines in a region of gentle uniform dip may be considered indicative of subsurface warping. Such irregularities have in places proved to be more reliable than refined geological measurements in determining the major elements of a warped area.

Other Dome Mountains. Somewhat smaller (30 miles across) but in other respects a dome very like that of the Black Hills, is the Lake District of western England (Fig. 116). This area was anciently a region of fold mountains then peneplaned. A submergence followed the peneplanation, and during this time a great thickness of horizontally disposed sediments was laid down. Then there was a doming uplift and a typical radial consequent drainage was initiated. In the erosional history which followed there was apparently a period of subsequent valley, annular drainage development, but this was effaced when, eventually, the cover rocks were completely stripped off. Then the persisting radial streams were superimposed on the underlying folded sediments.

The Lake District dome differs from that of the Black Hills in the nearly complete removal of the cover beds (only remnants appear in the border belts) and in that no igneous core was exposed by the stripping, although it is no doubt present underneath, for the folded sediments were invaded by granitic stocks. The perfection of superimposition of the radial drainage is also a noteworthy feature.

Of larger dimensions than the Black Hills and Lake District domes, and of different form, is the elongated uplift of the Uinta Mountains in Utah. The Uintas are comprised of a single, great, east to west arch, 150 miles long and 40 miles wide, with a strike-

fault break on their northern side. The Uintas attain altitudes
of 12,000 feet above sea level, and rise 6000 feet above the surrounding plateaus. They appear to have lost another 15,000 feet
of thickness of sedimentary covering beds by erosion. No igneous
rocks have been exposed, but like the Black Hills, the dips of the
stratified rocks at the center of the uplift are low; steep on the
flanks. Here, instead of a radial pattern, drainage is collected into
the great, transverse Green River. Its course is inferred to be antecedent to a recent renewal of upwarp, but superimposed from a
peneplaned and alluvial aggradation stage preceding this last warping. However, streams of consequent type descend the sides of the
dome in parallel courses and hogbacks separate flanking subsequent
valleys.

As the lowest formation at the center of the Uintas is pre-
Cambrian quartzite it is a fair inference that updomed granites
are the core of the range. From the Uintas it is an easy transition
to the Bighorn Mountains, representative of many of the ranges
of the Rocky Mountain system. The Bighorn uplift trends north
to south through central Wyoming, and has approximately the
same dimensions as those of the Uintas. Its central, highest peaks
are now 13,000 feet high, and once had covering rocks 15,000 feet
thick overlying them. The central region is a vast granite exposure. From low on the sides of the granite mass sedimentary
beds dip outward in both directions. They appear as encircling
hogback ridges and subsequent valley-floor exposures.

The Bighorns, and the Rocky Mountain ranges generally, have
been referred to as fold mountains. If so the folding may be designated as *monoanticlinal,* and, as such, will in no sense differ from a
dome mountain in geomorphic development. It is to be remembered that while the manner of the emplacement or uparching of
the igneous cores is a problem that troubles the structural geologist,
only the nature of the upheaval and the make-up of the resulting
unit affect the geomorphic development.

Nature of Fold Mountains Geomorphically Considered. What
may be termed the true fold mountain unit is geomorphically
unlike the dome uplift in that the structure of fold mountains
consists of stratified beds and in that the forms and patterns of
the valleys and ridges in such a unit are governed solely by the
nature and disposition of those beds, both initially and after reduction by degradation. An igneous rock core is no doubt
present but is too deeply buried to be affected by subaerial processes. However, the sequence and the features resulting from
degradation of fold mountains are, generally speaking, the same

as those developed in the covering beds of dome uplifts. The difference is a matter of greater complexity and greater variety in the fold mountains.

Origin of Fold Mountains. It is well established that regions of fold mountains begin their existence as geosynclines, of markedly linear extension, which permit the invasion of marine waters in great seaways across the continental platforms. These geosynclinal depressions become filled with sediments derived from surrounding land areas. Knowledge of the cause of the initial downwarping is hardly more than conjectural. (Experiments by Griggs [1939] make it appear that the tectogene [pp. 616–618, 643–646] hypothesis of gravity anomalies in island arcs may be generally applicable to the sequence of development of fold-mountain systems. Convectional downstreaming of the subcrustal material causes the downwarp.) Neither is there any general agreement in regard to the part that the increasing load of sediment plays in promoting or maintaining the sag. The subsidence and filling appear to proceed concurrently because the sediments eventually attain thicknesses of tens of thousands of feet but are almost solely of shallow water deposition.

After vast filling has taken place, but again at no definable point, and with no clearly discernible cause, lateral compressive movements narrow the geosynclinal trough and force the nearly flat-lying sedimentary layers into great corrugations.

The last accumulations over the geosynclinal areas appear to be of continental type, that is alluvial fan and flood-plain deposits made on land. The first subaerial expression of the fold unit, hence, is that of a widespread gently sloping plain. As uplift continues and degradation succeeds accumulation these loose covering materials are removed and rocks indurated and folded at some depth become the surface materials.

Initial Degradation. Whether the numerous corrugations of fold mountains are brought into the level of degradational attack rapidly or slowly, it is clear that the first emergence must be that of anticlinal crests. At the level of a bed of marked durability these uparchings will be gradually exhumed to the depths of the synclinal axes between them. Superimposition or antecedence may, meanwhile, permit uninterrupted traverse of the folded area by streams from adjacent oldlands. Bailey (1939) contends that antecedence is plausible because in the early stages of mountain elevation master streams cope only with unresistant sand and clay beds. When they reach the hard core rocks they are deeply intrenched and invulnerable. He says various stages of such a sequence may be observed in the Caucasus Mountains. Or the rise may be so rapid, or the durability of the resistant bed so great that an earlier drainage system will be disrupted and replaced by one fitted to the new corrugated surface.

In his classical paper entitled "The Rivers and Valleys of Pennsylvania," Davis (1889) assumed that any pre-existing stream courses were effaced when the fold mountains of that region were formed. He was then free to restore the folding to the full height and form indicated by the present structures and altitudes of the beds, and to work with all the volume of strata that appears to have been worn away since. On this basis he was enabled to fix on the site of greatest original uplift and to fit the pattern of the initial consequent drainage of this section of the Appalachians to the measure and arrangement of relief such restoration indicates. It may be doubted whether the altitudes or forms, so inferred, ever existed in the area that is now Pennsylvania; still more, whether, if they did, any relic of the drainage system to which they gave rise is now present. The concept is, however, warranted and is exemplified in the Jura Mountains of Switzerland where the sequence that Davis postulated is in actual progress.

Some structural geologists assert that the mountains composed of folded sediments, which are ultimately erected on the sites of geosynclines, gain little or nothing of their altitude from the folding action. Marked uplift, according to these students, only comes later and is comprised of a broad warping which involves the folded area, and perhaps adjoining regions, as a unit. In that case it is not improbable that the upwarped surface was reduced to a peneplain or near peneplain before its deformation and raising to high altitudes. As the degradation for the peneplanation could be assumed to take place *pari passu* with the slow original emergence (the Penckian primärrumpf concept) the later upwarping to mountain heights would present a surface for degradational attack that everywhere was on truncated anticlinal and synclinal structures. Without, of necessity, endorsing this theory of uplift it may be affirmed with considerable confidence that the present cycles of erosion of fold-mountain units were commonly begun on structures previously more or less completely beveled across.

Evolution of Drainage on Intact, Open Folds. The Jura Mountains of Switzerland (Fig. 177) are composed of anticlinal

ridges and synclinal valleys in which relief and structure correspond. This matching of form and structure is not the product
of a surface deformation of recent date. The folding appears to
have existed previously to a broad upwarping of the region. Before the upwarping the area may be inferred to have had low
relief, low altitude, and a deep cover of weak beds. (In the Jura:
"The synclines often retain Cretaceous deposits, sometimes even
Tertiaries, which are usually clayey. . . ." [Shackleton, M. R., 1934,

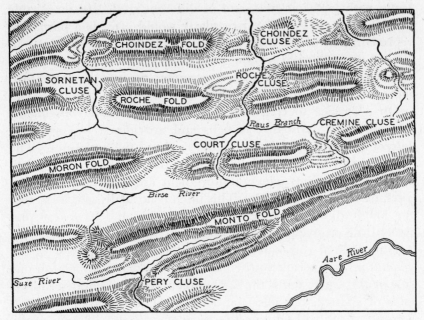

FIG. 177. PATTERN OF PART OF THE JURA MOUNTAINS NORTH OF BERN, SWITZER-
LAND
Each mountain is an anticline, each longitudinal valley a syncline.

p. 155]). With revival of active degradation, in consequence of
the upwarp, the whole thickness of the weak strata seems to have
been rapidly stripped off to the level of an exceptionally massive
and continuous limestone bed. This bed was sufficiently enduring to compel the reordering of all the drainage courses to the
anticlinal and synclinal undulations of the limestone surface.
At a few sites superimposed transverse streams persisted, but in
general the drainage was made consequent on the exhumed
folding. That is to say, the capping limestone was so resistant

that it could not be generally sectioned by stream erosion while the stripping was in progress.

The individual anticlines and synclines of a region of open folding, exemplified by the Jura, are not continuous, long, parallel ridges and valleys. Instead they are characteristically short and offset each other. Further, the crests of the anticlines rise and fall in elevation unevenly. That is, their axes pitch, incline, at various degrees. A number of loaves of bread, baked in the long form, with tapering ends, and of different sizes, laid on a table so that their ends overlap irregularly would provide a miniature representation of the arrangement. If, further, the central portion of the collection is thought of as bowed up and the separate loaves tilted endways at different angles the model would still more closely resemble the reality.

On a surface so constituted major *longitudinal consequents* flow down the synclinal troughs and are joined by secondary *lateral consequents* descending the flanks of the anticlines. The synclinal valleys are called *vals* in the Jura (Fig. 178). The gradients of the streams which follow them are determined by the pitch of the synclinal folds. This pitch is normally gentle, so that the longitudinal consequents flow sluggishly and have comparatively little erosive power.

Longitudinal consequents at high levels near the crest of the general upwarp escape to the next lower synclinal trough, on one side or the other, across the sag between the opposed, descending, ends of aligned, but offset, anticlines. The downslope of such a crossflow site will tend to be steeper than the inclination of the synclinal troughs. Accelerated erosion there results in a transection of the resistant cap rock in advance of its penetration elsewhere. Once the cap rock is cut through, the weak materials under it yield rapidly, and a deep water gap, of the type called a *cluse* in the Jura, is opened. Cluses are characteristically broad in the central section and narrow at their ends, in the direction of the dip of the beds. By successive vals and cluses the consequent drainage descends by a roundabout route, from the higher, central, to lower, marginal synclinal troughs, and to a final emergence from the folded district (Fig. 179).

Meanwhile the secondary, lateral consequents (called *ruz* in the Jura) course down the flanks of the anticlinal ridges

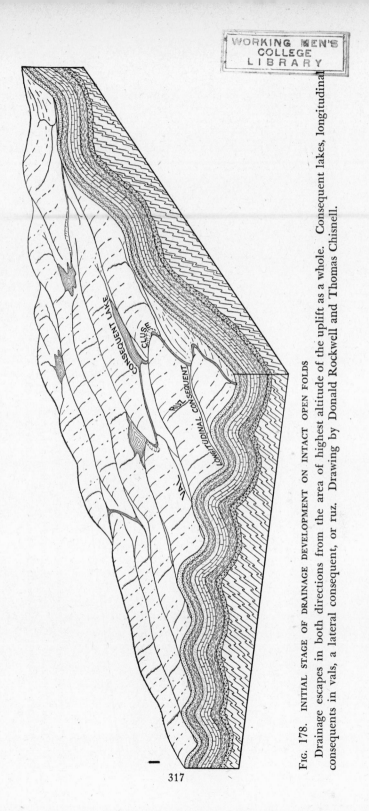

317

FIG. 178. INITIAL STAGE OF DRAINAGE DEVELOPMENT ON INTACT OPEN FOLDS

Drainage escapes in both directions from the area of highest altitude of the uplift as a whole. Consequent lakes, longitudinal consequents in vals, a lateral consequent, or ruz. Drawing by Donald Rockwell and Thomas Chisnell.

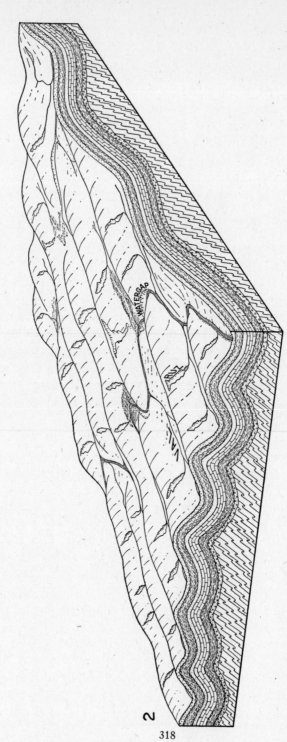

FIG. 179. SECOND STAGE OF DRAINAGE DEVELOPMENT ON INTACT OPEN FOLDS
The consequent lakes have been eliminated by sediment filling and outlet downcutting. Numerous ruz begin the dissection of the anticlines. Drawing by Donald Rockwell and Thomas Chisnell.

318

to join the main consequents in the vals. The ruz vary in size and in placing on the anticline, hence in erosive effectiveness. Those which are larger than average, and, further, are situated where a pitching anticline attains its greatest height, and where the resistant cover rock has close-spaced jointing or other structural weakness, will deepen their valleys most rapidly. As the favored transverse flows at cluse sites are able to cut through the cap rock on the anticlinal crests so these more competent ruz break through the resistant cover of the flanks of the anticlines.

A ruz which cuts through the cap rock at some point on the side of an anticline can readily extend its gash to the crest line by headwater erosion. Once the crest is reached no higher level is to be attained in the transverse direction. From that line on all drainage descends the opposite slope. Further headwater erosion is, therefore, along the axis of the ridge toward its highest summit (Fig. 180). This development, at right angles to the flow direction of the lateral consequents, is governed by structure, hence gives rise to a subsequent valley.

A number of ruz may have succeeded in penetrating the resistant cap rock of an anticline and in initiating subsequent valleys along its axis. But one of these is most vigorous, cuts the deepest gorge, has the lowest local base level at its junction with the longitudinal consequent in the val. Its subsequent will, therefore, be lengthened most rapidly and in time capture the subsequent of a neighboring, lesser ruz.

At the same time the sides of the subsequent valley are retreating, as do weathering escarpments, by the sapping process. The valley sides are also notched by minor obsequent streams. When the subsequent valley has attained such proportions that the major part of the interior of the anticline is consumed a *breached anticline* comes into existence (Figs. 181, 182). Nearly all of the precipitation that formerly descended the flanks of the anticline now follows obsequent and subsequent channels inside the arch. The steep, opposed, inward facing escarpments of breached anticlines are called *crets* in the Jura.

Anticlines are also breached by subsequent-valley development extending in both directions from the center of a cluse. (This concept is illustrated by Fig. 117c.)

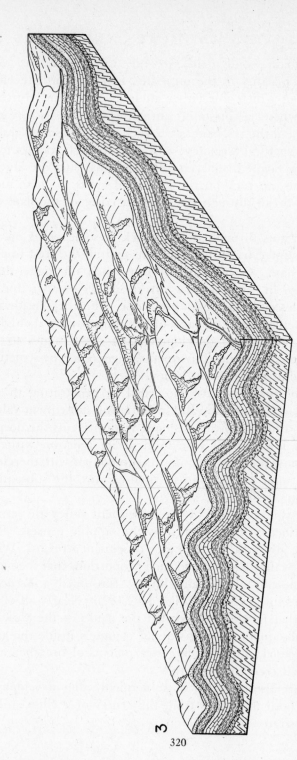

320

Fig. 180. THIRD STAGE OF DRAINAGE DEVELOPMENT ON INTACT, OPEN FOLDS
Headward erosion by ruz has reached the crest lines of the anticlines and is continued laterally along the axes. Drawing by Donald Rockwell and Thomas Chisnell.

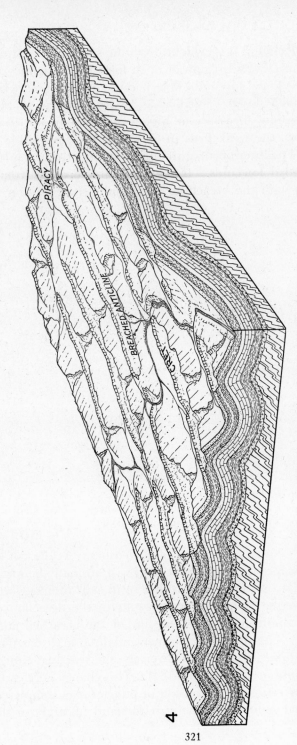

PIRACY

BREACHED ANTICLINE

CREST

4

321

FIG. 181. FOURTH STAGE OF DRAINAGE DEVELOPMENT ON INTACT, OPEN FOLDS.
Headwater erosion by subsequent streams has breached the anticlines. The drainage of lesser ruz is in part reversed. Capture of a minor drainage system has been effected at the end of one anticline. General escape of drainage is to the master transverse stream, which has made the deepest cluse cut. Infacing scarps, crests, of the breached anticlines become prominent. Drawing by Donald Rockwell and Thomas Chisnell.

Inversion of Relief. It is evident, from the succession outlined above, that in an elevated region of open folds the anticlines are first dissected. They succumb first because of their superior altitudes and steep slopes. Further, as, of necessity, weak beds below strong capping beds are at higher altitudes in anticlines than in synclines, the weak beds in anticlines are susceptible to prior erosion. The interiors of anticlines consequently are rapidly converted to broad lowlands. If the headwater erosion from a cluse site meets with the breaching that results from erosion by

FIG. 182. BREACHED ANTICLINE, ELK BASIN, WYOMING
Illustrates how perfectly the actual occurrence conforms to the analytical description. Photograph from Eklund Studio.

a ruz and its subsequent tributary, piracy ensues. As the cut of the cluse is an escape site its gradient level will normally be lower than that of the ruz system. The course of the ruz drainage will therefore be reversed. Such reversal results in the diversion of the original val drainage to the axial line of the breached anticline (Fig. 183). The site of the former anticlinal arch has now become an *anticlinal valley,* and, conversely, the synclinal trough becomes a *synclinal mountain* (Fig. 184). This change is referred to as *inversion of relief.* A succession of piracies may completely isolate a synclinal mountain leaving it to stand high above the

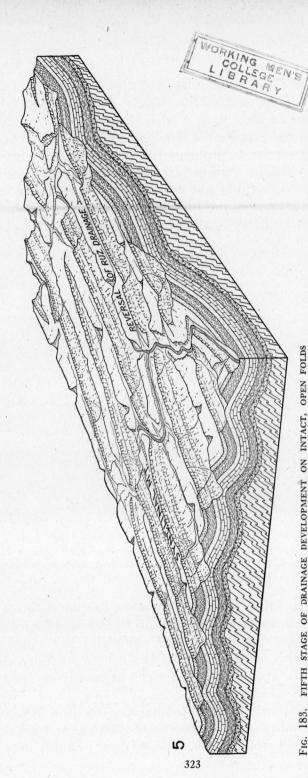

5

323

Fig. 183. FIFTH STAGE OF DRAINAGE DEVELOPMENT ON INTACT, OPEN FOLDS

Headwater erosion from major cluse sites results in the capture and reversal of subsequent drainage in the breached anticlines. This, in turn, because of the lower base level, completes the reversal of the original ruz drainage and brings about the diversion of the val drainage, original longitudinal consequents, to the subsequent streams on the axes of the anticlines. Inversion of relief is now marked; synclinal mountains are prominent. Drawing by Donald Rockwell and Thomas Chisnell.

valley floors of the anticlinal valleys and cluse gaps. (Fig. 185 makes clear how complete such inversion of relief may be.)

With reference to their stage of development in the fluvial geomorphic cycle the Jura are the youngest fold mountains in the world. (A part of the Carpathians has similar structure and measure of development.) Synclinal consequents, unbreached anticlines, and narrow cluses still exist. The distinctive nature of the geomorphic forms of the Jura is indicated by the fact that each such item is identified locally by a particular term.

FIG. 184. SYNCLINAL MOUNTAIN, MALONE MOUNTAINS, WESTERN TEXAS

This occurrence demonstrates how completely the progress of erosion in fold structures brings about inversion of relief. Synclinal summits are the rule not the exception. Photograph by Claude Albritton, Jr.

When all the anticlines have been breached and the drainage systems have been linked up into large units by successive piracies the stage of regional maturity in fold mountains is attained; when the mountains are all synclinal the end of maturity is reached. The slow reduction of the synclinal mountains comprises the stage of old age.

Features of Complexly Folded Mountains. The Jura Mountains are ideally suited for the analysis of drainage and relief development in fold mountains because of their youthful stage

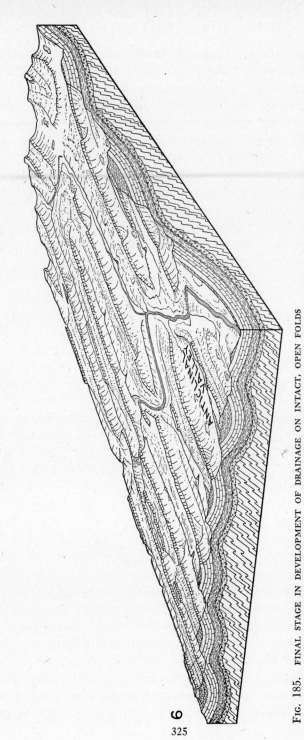

ANTICLINE

6

325

Fig. 185. FINAL STAGE IN DEVELOPMENT OF DRAINAGE ON INTACT, OPEN FOLDS

Adjustment to structure is complete and all drainage is integrated. Summits are consistently synclinal structures; valleys are over anticlinal axes. Drawing by Donald Rockwell and Thomas Chisnell.

and because of their very simple structure. The Jura folds are open and are composed of a single, massive, capping layer underlain by a great thickness of distinctly weak beds.

Other regions of fold mountains, the Folded Appalachians for example, are much more complexly constituted. The foldings are commonly tightly compressed, and a single anticline or syncline may divide into two diverging arches or basins. The pitch of the folds is commonly steep, and may be interrupted by local swellings or sags. Instead of one resistant layer underlain by weak beds solely, as in the Jura, the alternations from strong to weak beds in the Appalachians may be numerous. Finally, regions of complexly folded mountains are, apparently without exception, in a second or later cycle of erosion.

Drainage Courses and Relief Forms in Complexly Folded Mountains. The major elements of the relief and the ordering of the drainage of the complexly folded mountains are the same as those of open folding, but the pattern is much more intricate.

The trellis arrangement of drainage is developed to diagrammatic perfection (Fig. 44a). The tight packing of the folds would in itself assure this result, and the fact of an earlier cycle of erosion is sufficient warrant for assuming that the anticlines were uncapped enough to permit adjustments of stream flow to structure to be made expeditiously and minutely. The greatest streams regularly follow transverse courses (Fig. 115). Those next in size, the regional main streams, have long courses parallel to the trend of the ridges, and follow anticlinal valleys for the most part. From place to place they pass through a monoclinal ridge in a narrow gap to a parallel lower anticlinal valley. These streams are the subsequent stems on which great numbers of short obsequents and resequents are strung, to complete the characteristic trellis pattern.

Although the main subsequent valleys are on anticlinal structures, the mountains may be anticlinal, synclinal, or monoclinal.

In anticlinal structures resistant beds may be encountered at any one of several altitudes above the regional, local base level, which is fixed by the gradient of the main streams of the area. As each of these strong layers must be breached in turn, and as the breaching normally proceeds from the center toward the pitching ends, *noses,* of the anticlinal structure, the noses may long remain as summit tracts, that is, anticlinal mountains, maintained as such by one of the strong beds. The nose of a pitching anticline tends to end in a rounded point. This point has steep or gentle declivities, toward its sides and termination, accordingly as the pitch of the fold is steep or gentle. Such endings, together with the outline of the ridges bordering the breached center of the anticline, when represented on a contour map, or when included in an airplane view, give rise to a *cigar-shaped pattern* which is regularly indicative of the anticlinal structure.

The tops of synclinal mountains are commonly hollowed out at the center but the structure itself is not breached. The shallow depressed area at the summit of a synclinal mountain represents the thickness of a weak bed whose substance has been stripped off down to the surface of the underlying strong bed which governs the height of the synclinal crest. The material of the weak bed is drained away through notches made by obsequent streams working back from adjoining anticlinal valleys. The noses of synclinal mountains converge to sharp, beaklike points with outer slopes of escarpment steepness (Fig. 115). The *pattern* on contour maps made by the ridges outlining synclinal structures is called *canoe-shaped,* because it resembles a child's crude drawing of the side elevation of a double-pointed boat.

Monoclinal ridges, alternating with *monoclinal valleys,* appear where a series of resistant and weak beds all dip in the same direction. Such ridges and valleys are indicative of the incomplete dissection of a very broad anticlinal structure. Each ridge is a great cuesta or a hogback. Less prominent monoclinal ridges are developed at the borders of similarly broad synclinal structures. If the slopes on both sides of a monoclinal ridge are nearly equal, the dip of the bed is probably steeper than 45 degrees; if the two declivities are of distinctly unequal steepness, the gentler slope will be that of the dip. Monoclinal ridges marking the limbs of anticlinal structures converge down the pitch, those of synclines up, or against, the pitch.

The subsequent stream which follows the axis of an anticlinal structure made up of alternating resistant and weak beds, in turn exhumes each lower-lying resistant layer. When the stream in its downcutting encounters a resistant bed where its course is parallel to the axis of the arch and on the line of its crest, the

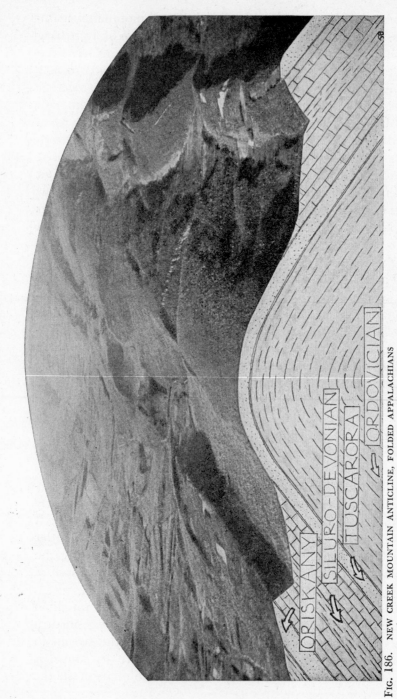

FIG. 186. NEW CREEK MOUNTAIN ANTICLINE, FOLDED APPALACHIANS

An exhumed anticlinal mountain, tapering off to a nose in the distance, cut by a structurally superimposed stream. The capping bed is the strong Tuscarora quartzite, completely stripped of its former cover of Silurian and Devonian limestones and shales. On the far right Knobly Mountain is a monoclinal ridge capped by the strong Oriskany sandstone. Photograph by John L. Rich, published in the Geographical Review, and used by permission of the American Geographical Society.

328

course will be shifted to the weak bed on the one or the other side of the axis. But if the resistant layer is encountered where the course was athwart the axial line of the arch a transverse cut will be made across the strong bed. This is the phenomenon of *structural superimposition* (Fig. 186). In consequence of such occurrences a major subsequent stream may be caused to wander back and forth across monoclinal ridges, hogbacks, from one monoclinal valley to another. Lesser subsequents develop in the

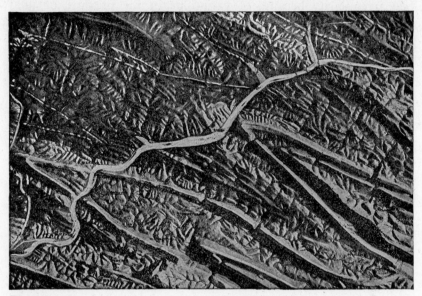

FIG. 187. ZIGZAG PATTERN OF FOLDED APPALACHIAN RIDGES, ANTHRACITE REGION, PENNSYLVANIA
Model by Harden.

monoclinal valleys that are not occupied by the main stream. The water gaps across the monoclinal ridges narrow in the direction of the dip (downdip) regardless of the direction of the stream flow. If resequent streams are observed to course down the sides of *exhumed,* intact *anticlines,* such streams will ordinarily be longer than the obsequents which come from the opposite direction and bring the drainage of the escarpment slopes.

Zigzag Pattern of Ridges. The outstanding general aspect of complexly folded mountains when their topography is represented by contour mapping or when they are viewed from an airplane, is the *zigzag pattern* (Fig. 187) made by the trace of the summits

of the monoclinal ridges.   The zigzag outline results first because the ridges converge at the ends of pitching folds.   Second,
the zigzag pattern results because the form of the convergence
of an anticline is different from that of a syncline.   Third, it
develops because the foldings overlap in the sense that the nose
of an anticline with a given direction of pitch will commonly
extend past the nose of an adjoining, parallel anticline that
pitches in the opposite direction.   The zigzag pattern is one of
great irregularity because of variations in the measure of the
offsetting, of differences in the degree of pitch, and of the frequent division of a structure into two parts with the development
of an intervening syncline or anticline.   If the anticlinal and
synclinal units have more than one resistant bed the several ridges
resulting from the presence of the strong layers follow the zigzags
in parallel courses.

Criteria.   The geomorphic features of complexly folded mountains that have been maturely dissected afford the geologist significant guides for the interpretation of underground structure.
An understanding of these phenomena has been found useful in
the solution of mining problems.   The leading criteria that may
be employed when making field or map studies of such regions
have been indicated in the preceding sections and are here sum-
marized.

The degree of compression of the zigzag pattern is indicative of
the tightness of the folding.   Cigar-shaped outlines of single
or parallel monoclinal ridges, together with infacing, opposed
escarpment slopes, mark anticlines; canoe-shaped outlines and
outfacing escarpment slopes, synclines.   The noses of anticlines
may be steep or gentle, depending on the angle of pitch but are
smooth and nicely rounded.   Those of synclines are abrupt,
escarpmentlike, and pinch out to narrow points.   The noses of
anticlines converge in the direction of the pitch; those of synclines
opposite to the pitch.

Consequent, antecedent, or superimposed master transverse
streams cut across parallel ridges and structures in a series of gaps
arranged in a line.   The gaps made by wandering subsequents in
crossing successive ridges have entirely random placement.   The
dip of beds cut by a water gap is in the direction that the gap
narrows.   Where the two slopes of a monoclinal ridge are equal

and steep, the dip is steep; if they are unlike the gentler slope
is in the direction of the dip.

Intact anticlinal mountains have rounded summits and relatively long resequent streams on their flanks; synclinal mountains
tend to have an elongated, flat top, or a summit comprised of
a shallow basin notched at the edges and drained by one or more
short, steep obsequents.

Fault movements cause sharp breaks and offsets (Fig. 188). The
direction and measure of the faulting may often be learned by
restoration of the trends of the interrupted ridges and of the struc-

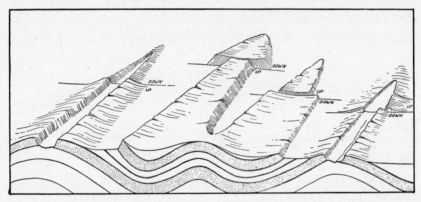

FIG. 188.   RIDGE PATTERN RESULTING FROM TRANSVERSE FAULTING OF ANTICLINES
AND SYNCLINES
The region is assumed to have been faulted before its reduction to a
peneplain. Renewed dissection following uplift of the peneplaned area
gives the topographic forms here shown. Drawing by Elizabeth Burckmyer.

ture patterns. Thus, assuming an equivalence of summit level, if
the nose of a pitching syncline is lowered by a transverse fault the
nose will be prolonged, and will widen abruptly at the fault line,
because a syncline intersected by a horizontal plane broadens in
the direction of its pitch. More concisely stated, a part of the
syncline will repeat itself beyond the fault break.

With transition from the stage of maturity toward old age the
perfection of adjustment of drainage lines to structure becomes
more complete. The large longitudinal subsequents are diverted
by capture from many of their ridge crossings; the former water
gaps then become wind gaps. Even the master transverse streams
may be released from crossing two resistant ridges in close succession by capture-diversion around the nose of the structure that gave
rise to the ridges (Fig. 115).

Nappes. In the Alps, Caucasus, and Himalaya, and in parts of the Appalachians, Andes, and Rocky Mountains compressive force has been exerted to the degree that the anticlinal folds have been upset, made recumbent, then broken and thrust forward, and finally other recumbent folds crowded ahead from the rear and piled on top of them. This complicated mountain structure is called *nappes* (Fig. 189) in French, *decken* in German. A rug or carpet subjected to rumpling by a shove from one side so that the foldings which ensue are not only forced up but are also made to overlap each other presents a partial analogy. The further fact of breaking and overriding may be conceived in terms of a pile of boards sliding over each other in one direction, the top board farthest, each board representing a recumbent fold.

Fig. 189.   DIAGRAM OF NAPPES

The arrow indicates the plane where a recumbent fold has been faulted and thrust forward.   Drawing by Elizabeth Burckmyer.

It is obvious that the erosion of mountains so constituted will give rise to distinctive geomorphic forms. The principles governing developments in the simpler dome and fold structures are applicable as well to nappes, but as the deformations are much more complex and localized the topography resulting from degradation reflects this fact.

Where a crowning nappe-fold has been thrust far forward and then almost completely destroyed by erosion, the last remnants of the structure commonly appear as a type of outlier called a *klippe.* Klippen are peculiar in that, unlike the outliers which persist beyond the main front of a weathering escarpment, and which have younger beds capping older strata, they have older beds over younger beds. Somewhat like the klippe the parallel phenomenon of a *fenster* (Fig. 190), or *window,* is an erosional opening comparable to a breached anticline, but which reverses the conditions of the breached anticline in that the fenster has a floor of rocks as young or younger than those of its rim. In general the klippen mark the topographically lower, the fensters the higher altitudes of the nappes.

Klippen may have the proportions of lofty mountain peaks. The famous Matterhorn and Weisshorn summits in the Alps are of such origin. They are referred to as examples of *mountains without roots*, because they have been shoved so far along a nearly

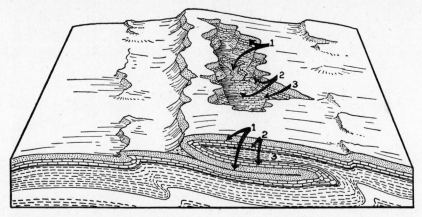

Fig. 190.   DIAGRAM OF A FENSTER

The arrows make clear how the younger beds at the rim of the fenster are repeated at depth. Where several nappes are piled one above the other such reversal of the normal order of succession of beds with depth may involve even younger beds than appear at the surface. Drawing by Elizabeth Burckmyer.

horizontal fault plane as to have lost all contact with the foundations on which they once rested. Their bases are now comprised of older rocks than the beds below the fault-plane surface.

Chief Mountain in Montana (Fig. 191) is a klippe, or mountain without roots, with a simpler history than those of the Alps but nevertheless impressive in that it is an isolated mass of pre-Cambrian (old) beds resting on Cretaceous (young) strata that was shoved eastward some 15 miles from its original position.

At the rear of the nappes, or where they have been completely stripped away, the sialic rocks that regularly underlie overfolded and overthrust masses appear. These crystallines are commonly

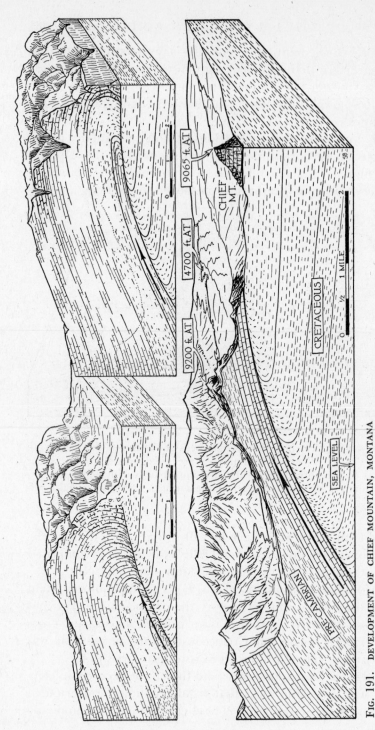

FIG. 191. DEVELOPMENT OF CHIEF MOUNTAIN, MONTANA

In the upper left diagram the thrust faulting and overriding is shown in progress. In the upper right diagram the limit of the overriding has been reached. The faint dotted line in this figure indicates the erosion surface that is shown on a larger scale in the lower diagram. This erosion has isolated the klippe, Chief Mountain, a mountain without roots, consisting of ancient pre-Cambrian rocks resting on geologically young, Cretaceous, rocks. Drawings by Steve Barker.

also lifted to high altitudes; Mont Blanc in the Alps is an example.

Ancient Mountains. The different varieties of fold mountains treated in the preceding sections are closely related in that they possess a general uniformity of structure. Also, they are made up basically of two elements, a cover of sedimentary layers, in general unaltered, and a core of crystalline rock (Fig. 192). Where a fold-mountain region is observed to be in a second or later cycle of erosion it is to be noted that these elements continue to be

FIG. 192. ADIRONDACK MOUNTAINS FROM THE SOUTHWEST

These mountains are wrapped around by a belt of metamorphosed rocks which are inferred to be part of a cover of sediments that formerly extended across the crystalline core rocks now constituting the higher peaks.

presented to the degrading agencies in essentially the original simple relationship. But some mountain regions, originally of the fold type, have experienced a history of recurrent uplift and dissection so long and so involved that they have lost nearly all semblance of their pristine structure and aspect. The heat and pressure of deep-seated folding have metamorphosed their sedimentary beds to very durable rock types; these metamorphic rocks and the underlying crystallines have been invaded by magma; the mountains have been peneplaned and then raised up again, perhaps by faulting of great displacement; again dissected; again folded; and so on. In a word, such ancient mountains present a great jumble of rocks and structures. Some of the ranges of the northern Rocky Mountains, and the mountains of northern New England are examples.

In a comprehensive view the pattern of drainage in such ancient mountains appears to be dendritic and the streams are insequent in type. The great variety of rocks and structures found within narrow areas, heterogeneously disposed, with abrupt transitions between wholly diverse units, gives rise to a mosaic. The valley erosion of such a mosaic lacks major guide lines. It is, hence, insequent, and, because the slopes are variously oriented, tends to be dendritic in pattern. But when such an ancient, multicycle, mountain region in a mature stage of dissection is studied in detail it is discovered to possess the same harmonies of valley ordering and adjustment that are found in other fold-mountain geomorphic units subject to the fluvial geomorphic cycle. The complexity, however, makes interpretation difficult.

The master streams usually prove to be consequents situated in the major structural depressions of the latest orogeny. They may even be antecedent, for a large stream is not easily defeated and disrupted. But the valley of a master consequent may alternate many times between the gorge-form of youth and the gentle slopes characteristic of an advanced stage of maturity, accordingly as the course of the stream is over very resistant or little resistant rock. The secondary streams, as elsewhere, are mostly in subsequent valleys, that is have courses determined by variations in rock structure and type. The tortuous outcrop of bands of schists or gneiss may make for a locally contorted pattern of drainage (Plate IV); elsewhere jointing and faulting give rise to a rectangular pattern.

Although the metamorphic change of the sediments, generally to rock types of high durability, precludes the existence of the strong-cap-rock, weak-interior relationship leading to inversion of relief, with development of anticlinal valleys and synclinal mountains as a consequence, it is, nevertheless, commonly the synclinal structures that persist at high altitudes (Fig. 184). This circumstance may perhaps be considered evidence of the verity of the contention, once strongly upheld, that synclinal structures are inherently stronger than anticlines, because they are subject to

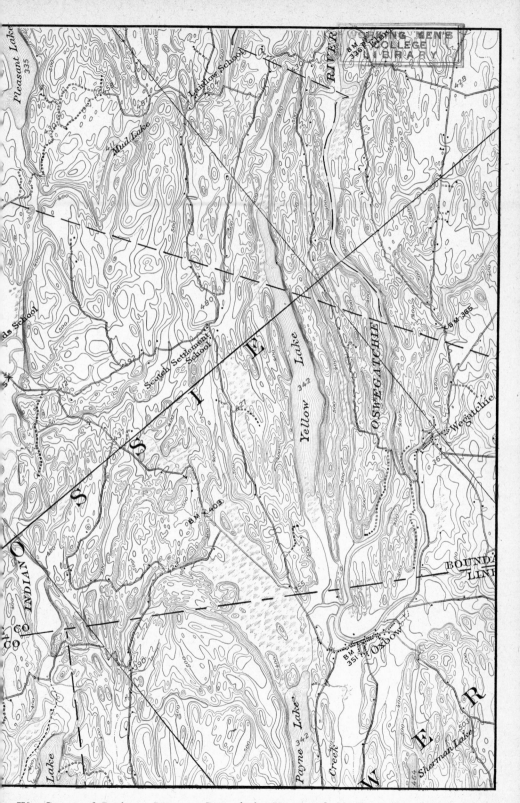

ᴛᴇ IV. Contorted Drainage Pattern. Part of the Hammond, N. Y. quadrangle map of the ᴇᵈ States Geological Survey. Horizontal Scale 1/62,500, contour interval 20 feet. The belts of ᵐorphic rock on the northwest of the Adirondacks are reflected (subsequent valley erosion) in ᵗortuous courses of the streams. This effect has probably been heightened by glaciation.

greater compression, are less broken by tension joints (Fig. 280), and are less open to weathering agencies than are anticlines.

SUMMARY

A covering mass of layered rock resting on an underlying granitic base is the normal structural aspect of a large part of the earth's land surface. The overlying sediments were, with few exceptions (irregularities of the bottoms on which the deposits were made) laid down as flat-lying or gently dipping beds, but, during or subsequent to uplift, have almost everywhere been warped in some degree. In places upwarping has been so broad, so low, and so slow that no topographic summits were produced by the upheaval. But at numerous sites uplifts have been distinctly localized, sharply delimited, steep and rapid, and accompanied by intrusion or emplacement of new rock substance, or by upmovement of the underlying granitic material.

Such localized bulges exhibit every variation in form from nearly circular domes through elongated single arches to corrugated ridgings arranged *en échelon*. The multiple foldings evidently result from lateral compression associated with uplift. The lateral compression may attain sufficient intensity to be the dominant factor in the further geomorphic development of the region affected.

Despite their diversity, the degradational history of all upwarpings is observed to follow a single unvarying sequence. The summits of the uplifts are the first areas to be dissected. By such erosion the arches are in time unroofed, then hollowed out. The uniform result of this ordered attack is to bring about inversion of relief; anticlinal valleys succeed anticlinal ridges. The numerous distinctive variations in attitude and composition of the upwarped and folded beds promote nice and manifold adjustments between valley development and structure. The reflection of these adjustments in the pattern of the topographic forms provides geomorphic evidence for analysis of the geologic elements involved.

BIBLIOGRAPHY

CLASSICAL

Lesley, J. P. (1856) *Manual of Coal and its Topography*, J. B. Lippincott and Company, Philadelphia.

Gilbert, G. K. (1877) *Report on the Geology of the Henry Mountains,* United States Geographical and Geological Survey of the Rocky Mountain Region (Powell), Washington.

Newton, H., and Jenney, W. P. (1880) *Geology of the Black Hills,* United States Geographical and Geological Survey of the Rocky Mountain Region (Powell), Washington.

Davis, W. M. (1889) *The Rivers and Valleys of Pennsylvania,* National Geographic Magazine, Vol. 1, pp. 183–253, also in *Geographical Essays,* Ginn and Company, Boston, pp. 413–484.

Willis, B. (1893) *Mechanics of Appalachian Structure,* United States Geological Survey, 13th Annual Report, Part 2, pp. 211–281, Washington.

RECENT

Willis, B. (1902) *Stratigraphy and Structure, Lewis and Livingston Ranges, Montana,* Bulletin Geological Society of America, Vol. 13, pp. 305–352.

MacCarthy, G. R. (1925) *Some Facts and Theories Concerning Laccoliths,* Journal of Geology, Vol. 33, pp. 1–18.

Collet, L. W. (1927) *The Structure of the Alps,* Edward Arnold and Co., London.

Bucher, W. H. (1933) *The Deformation of the Earth's Crust,* Princeton University Press, Princeton, N. J.

Griggs, D. (1939) *A Theory of Mountain Building,* American Journal of Science, Vol. 237, pp. 611–650.

Chapter Sixteen

HISTORY OF THE FOLDED APPALACHIANS

Introduction. The structural and geomorphic history of the Folded Appalachians is much less intricate than that of the Alps, but far more complex than that of the Jura. The Folded Appalachians are, therefore, well suited to serve as the background for a discussion of the geomorphic development of fold mountains, supplementary to the consideration previously given to the simple structural and erosional forms exemplified in the Jura, and to the extremely involved development represented by the Alps.

The Folded Appalachians are more accurately designated the Appalachian Ridge and Valley Province. This phrasing better describes the actual topographic forms. The emphasis on folds, as such, is avoided. The adjoining Piedmont and Blue Ridge provinces have also experienced folding and the Appalachian Ridge and Valley province has been thrust-faulted, especially in the south.

The Folded Appalachians have experienced one or more complete peneplanations. Their summit surfaces, in consequence, regularly truncate anticlinal and synclinal structures (Plate II). Such truncation insures that the valley and ridge development, resulting from erosional dissection, after uplift, of a peneplain surface, will exhibit a maximal degree of adjustment to rock attitudes and rock differences. Contrariwise, if the valley development and pattern of drainage in the new cycle of erosion is observed to disregard structure, such discordance may be considered evidence that some factor has operated to modify or nullify the influence of the structural elements.

The frequent recurrence of distinctive phenomena (such as accordant ridge summits, transverse stream courses, and aligned water gaps) in similar associations, yet in widely separated parts of the Folded Appalachians, is indicative of a general unity of geomorphic development for the region as a whole. It would also seem warranted to infer that adequate clues for the understanding of Folded Appalachian forms and history are at hand, because there is such repetition of distinctive features.

The two outstanding problems of Folded Appalachian geomorphology are: Why have the major transverse streams of the northern two-thirds of the province apparently experienced a reversal in direction of flow, from one southeast to northwest to one from northwest to southeast? and: Why do these transverse streams cross successive, close-spaced ridges of resistant rock in aligned, deep, water gaps? The alignment of the water gaps seems to indicate definitely that superimposition has been a chief circumstance in determining the present geomorphic expression of the Folded Appalachians. But when the assumption of superimposition is made, the problem of how it was achieved is raised. The difficulties then encountered lead to the suspicion that the assumption of superimposition may be in error, and that, perhaps, the transverse streams have always flowed from the northwest to the southeast.

That the geomorphic features of the Folded Appalachians are imposing and arresting, and that the problems they set require careful study for solution, are facts that have greatly stimulated research. Further, the ready accessibility of the region from large centers of population has served to attract many investigators. The Folded Appalachians have become classic ground for geomorphic science because of many significant papers written by these workers.

Folded Appalachian Orogenesis and Structure. In the early Paleozoic era a geosynclinal basin (Fig. 193), that extended from the St. Lawrence depression on the north to the present inner border of the Gulf Coastal Plain on the south, received sediments from an ancient land mass, called "Appalachia," situated to the south and east of the northeast-southwest axis of the trough. Sinking of the geosyncline, concurrently with deposition, permitted the accumulation of sedimentary beds to thicknesses of 30,000 to 40,000 feet, largely composed of materials laid down in shallow water. (Nelson, W. A., 1940.)

At intervals during the Paleozoic era, with culminating thrusts during the great Appalachian Revolution at its close, compression of this region buckled the stratified beds into a series of northeast-southwest trending folds, close-spaced in the eastern part of the earlier geosyncline. The force that caused this folding originated in the southeast. The sedimentary accumulations along the eastern border of the earlier geosynclinal depression were overthrust, and the width of the former depositional belt was reduced by one-half or more, that is, in places, from a breadth of 80 miles to one of 40 miles. Restoration of the folds, without loss of material, if carried upward from the present altitudes of the beds would produce mountains five miles high. But such heights were presumably never fully attained by orogenesis, either in the Appalachian Revolution, at the close of the Paleozoic, or by later uplifts. There was undoubtedly some loss of elevation by degradation during the course of the uplift. Further, the altitudes indicated by restoration of the folds are in part representative of upwarpings of later date. The significant fact is that the vast volume of material

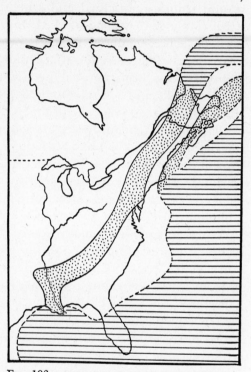

FIG. 193.   THE APPALACHIAN GEOSYNCLINE

The dotted belts indicate the sites of deposition in a representative period of the Paleozoic. The inferred extension seaward of the ancient land mass, Appalachia, is indicated by a dashed line.

necessary to fill out the original folds must have been removed by subaerial degradation.

As the altitudes of the summits of the Folded Appalachian ridges at present range between 1500 and 2000 feet in the north and are not over 4000 feet high in Virginia, it is obvious that no remainder of the original fold surface exists. But it is a reasonable inference that the highest anticlinal arches were erected at the sites where now the oldest beds outcrop at the greatest altitudes. The highest ridges in a given locality of the Folded Appalachians are observed to have a general accordance of summit level. Restoration of the beds excavated from the intervening valleys to the level of the ridge summits would develop an unbroken upland surface which would truncate anticlinal and synclinal structures indifferently. (It is contended [Ashley, G. H., 1935] that the ridge summits now seen have been reduced to levels below those of the last peneplanation. The present surface though it reflects a single old peneplain has been lowered by not less than 100 feet for the hardest rocks and several hundred feet for the softer rocks for each million years since the uplift [p. 1398]. Assuming the uplift to have been eight million years ago, that would be 800 feet for the hardest rocks [p. 1403].) This reconstructed upland surface proves to be not a plane but, instead, to be one that is warped variously according to the locality. Its bulges and basins, in general, are unrelated to the anticlinal and synclinal structures although anticlinal mountains and synclinal valleys do occur.

When an examination is made of the existing mountains and valleys they are found to exhibit the inversion of topography normal to a region of maturely dissected fold mountains. That is to say, the wider summit areas are characteristically on synclinal structures; the valley development is over anticlines.

The Appalachian ridges, as such, are for the most part monoclinal in structure. Broad folds, each one made up of a number of strong and weak beds, were first intersected by a generally horizontal surface (a peneplain) passed through their mass at some depth (actually very great) below the level of the topographic bottoms of the original synclines. A sectioning done in this manner would, on the average, cut through strong beds where they form the limbs of folds and only by coincidence where such a bed is the crest of an anticline or the floor of a syncline. Where the transection of a strong bed was through the limb of a fold, dissection, following an uplift, of the truncated structures brought about a rapid removal of the substance of the weak beds and left the strong layers behind to stand up as monoclinal ridges. The occurrences of anticlinal and synclinal mountains mark the sites where the intersection of the truncating peneplain was by chance at the level of an anticlinal crest or a synclinal floor on a resistant bed, or where there has been exhumation, in the present cycle of dissection, of an anticlinal structure capped by a resistant bed, at a level below that of the upland (Fig. 186).

Initial Consequent Stream Flow. At one time there was general agreement that the initial consequent drainage of all the Folded Appalachian region was from the southeast toward the northwest. Master streams, presumably extended-consequent continuations of oldland rivers from Appalachia, flowed across the coal swamps of the Pennsylvanian period and in the Permian brought the last of the sediments to the Paleozoic inland sea. As the thrust from the southeast first developed, and the folding began, the highest elevations continued to be on or near the eastern side of the ancient trough. But at a later period, presumably at the climax of the Appalachian Revolution, the central and western portions of the geosynclinal deposits in the Pennsylvania area were apparently (as indicated by restoration of the foldings) raised to superior elevations athwart the courses of the northwest-flowing master consequents. In the Folded Appalachian belt south of Pennsylvania the highlands on the east appear to have continued dominant, but there also the folding was transverse to the earlier consequent stream courses. If it be asserted that the original consequents maintained their southeast to northwest flow direction, undeterred by the progress of the uplift, then the manner in which the streams overcame the rise of the fold structures, athwart their courses, must be explained. If, on the other hand, it is held that the upfolding reversed the flow direction, the circumstances of such reversal need to be set forth convincingly. It is, broadly, in regard to the relative adequacy of the several answers given to these questions that discussion of Appalachian geomorphic history continues to be active.

Antecedence Theory of Folded Appalachian Drainage. An early explanation of the larger Folded Appalachian streams flowing in courses transverse to the axes of folding was that master consequents were able to maintain themselves in opposition to the corrugations of the upwarping (Fig. 117). The transverse streams are, in other words, antecedent, and have persisted in their antecedent channels down to the present time, although in most instances reversed in direction.

As the surface deformation would consist, at first, in the raising

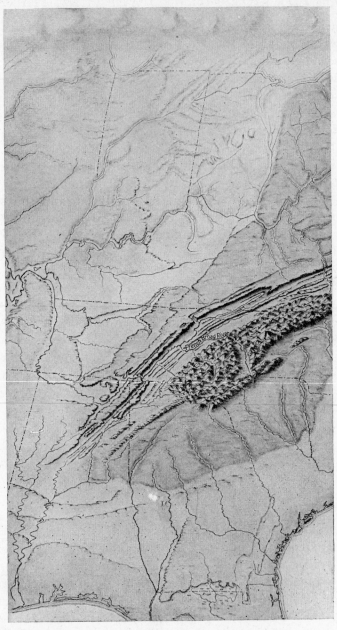

Fig. 194.   RELIEF MAP OF THE APPALACHIAN GEOMORPHIC UNITS
Drawing by Kurt Lowe and Marjorie Hooker.

344

FIG. 194 *continued.*

of broad anticlinal arches in the unconsolidated upper beds of a coastal plain it is quite appropriate to postulate such persistence. By entrenchment in the early, low folds, local superimposition on more durable layers at depth would be fostered. Once the courses of the master, northwestward streams were well established in strongly consolidated rock, the streams could survive further uplift from folding for indefinite periods. Indeed, their headwater gradients might actually be steepened and their erosive effectiveness enhanced by the narrowing of the Folded Appalachian belt that ensued from the compression that the belt ultimately experienced.

The Blue Ridge Mountains, composed of igneous and metamorphic rocks, may be considered a remnant of Appalachia (Fig. 194). In the South, where the Blue Ridge Mountains are wide, the New-Kanawha system, and the French Broad-Tennessee system have their headwaters on, and east, of the general crest line of the crystalline ranges. These river courses may be regarded as surviving examples of such antecedent drainage still following the southeast to northwest flow direction. They cross the full width of the Folded Appalachians, and that of the Appalachian Plateau on the west, to reach the Mississippi Basin.

Consequent Theory of Folded Appalachian Drainage. The significant difficulty with the antecedence theory of Appalachian drainage is that it leaves unexplained the reversal of the inferred, original, southeast to northwest courses of major transverse streams, to the northwest-southeast directions that are now followed by all such rivers from the Roanoke northward. Indeed, the antecedence principle in effect asserts the ability of streams to maintain an original direction of flow in opposition to noteworthy dismembering and reversing factors.

In the consequent theory of Appalachian drainage set forth by Davis (1889) in his classical paper, "The Rivers and Valleys of Pennsylvania," this difficulty is met in two ways. Davis assumes, first, that the folded belt was uplifted at the time of the Appalachian Revolution with such rapidity and to such altitudes that its highest parts, rather than Appalachia, became the divide sites and initiated a wholly consequent drainage, governed by the elevations, forms, and pattern of the folding. Although the divide area was by this means in part shifted to the Folded Appalachian belt, the major drainage was, nevertheless, postulated to have a northwestward flow.   The reversal to southeastward courses is held to have resulted from the development of the Newark depression, in the headwater sections of the streams, when, during Triassic time, the northwestward streams had only a moderate declivity.   Previously Appalachia had remained a barrier to escape of drainage eastward to the Atlantic.   Now Appalachia subsided generally and a great downsinking occurred immediately to the east of the folded belt.   As a result of these developments a steep eastward descent to sea level was introduced.   It was Davis's speculation that this downwarping sufficed to reverse the direction of flow of the middle courses of the transverse streams.

The fact of eastward downtilting of Appalachia, in the times following the Appalachian Revolution, is not disputed.   It is also recognized that the down movement was more pronounced in the north than in the south.   But there is objection to the assumption that such tilting could readily bring about the reversal of previously well-established trunk streams.   As has been suggested above, such streams tend to resist adverse tilting by steadily deepening their valleys.   They are dismembered or reversed only by relatively rapid and large scale diastrophism.

These and other considerations led Meyerhoff and Olmstead (1936) to propose a different theory of consequent Appalachian drainage development.   Its thesis is that the Appalachian Revolution terminated all connection, in the central and northern sections of the Appalachian belt, with stream sources in Appalachia.   A new divide was raised west and northwest of the Folded Appalachian belt and from it streams, *ab initio,* pursued southeastward courses (Fig. 195).

In support of this contention the authors urge that inliers composed of infolded and infaulted early Paleozoic sediments are present in New England and the Piedmont.   From these occurrences it appears that early in the Appalachian Revolution accumulation of sediments took place to the east as well as to the west of the Blue Ridge axis of uplift.   As has been pointed out, the fold structures are overturned and thrust-faulted northwestward.   Meyerhoff and Olmstead argue that such thrust-faulting was far more extensive than has heretofore been appreciated and that by this means the drainage divide established by the Appalachian Revolution was shifted westward beyond the present western border of the Folded Appalachian belt.

Consequent drainage then flowed southeastward down the dip slopes of the asymmetric folds and thrust sheets. The Susquehanna, Potomac, Schuylkill, and Delaware are cited as the descendants of such streams located on sites where there is evidence of structural sags, that is, a lower altitude of the Blue Ridge (Reading Prong) at those points, and transverse downfaulting.

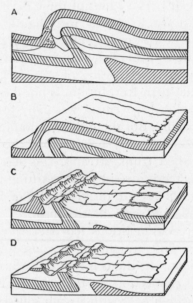

FIG. 195.   STREAM SUPERIMPOSITION FROM THE DIP SLOPES OF ASYMMETRIC FOLDS

The successive positions of the erosional surface and the drainage divide, d_1 and d_2 are indicated in A.   The development and superimposition of the consequent drainage is shown in B, C, D.   Drawing by H. A. Meyerhoff and E. W. Olmstead.

Progressive Piracy Theory of Folded Appalachian Drainage.
H. D. Thompson (1939) shows that in the southern Appalachians the main transverse streams are located at sites where escape of drainage from the interior to the Atlantic Basin is easiest with respect to the barriers imposed by structure and the relative resistance of different beds to erosion.   This evidence is in accord with the contentions made in support of the Meyerhoff and Olmstead consequent theory of Appalachian drainage evolution.   But

the application that Thompson makes of this evidence is different. He conceives that instead of being transposed far westward by overfolding and thrust faulting the divide at the close of the

FIG. 196.   THE BLUE RIDGE ESCARPMENT, BLUE RIDGE PARKWAY, ABOVE MEADOWS OF DAN, VIRGINIA
Shows steep eastward slope of the Blue Ridge escarpment.

Appalachian Revolution was at the summit of an anticlinorium marked by the axis of the Blue Ridge (Fig. 196). In line with the classical view, the major drainage slopes are considered to have been originally northwestward. It is pointed out that Triassic and later geologic history, as determined from sedimentary records and by geophysical exploration, is clearly one of progressive downward tilting of the sections of Appalachia situated east of the Blue Ridge (Fig. 19).   Thus the eastward slopes, toward the Atlantic, have consistently been shortened and steepened.

By virtue of the steeper gradients thus provided, the erosive effectiveness of the Atlantic-slope streams was made far superior to those pursuing long northwestward courses over gentle declivities.   The successive piracies through headwater erosion (Fig. 197) achieved by the east-flowing streams have brought about the migration of the main drainage divide of the Appalachians, north of the New-Kanawha system, to its present far western position.   The

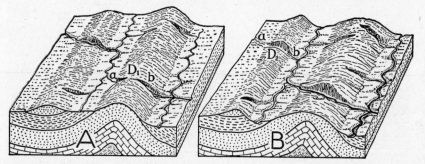

FIG. 197.   PROGRESSIVE PIRACY MIGRATION OF APPALACHIAN DIVIDES
    The gradient of stream b is several hundred feet lower than that of stream a.   By progressively undercutting the headwaters of stream a, stream b has pushed the divide from D_1 in A to D_2 in B.   Drawing by H. D. Thompson.

Thompson theory is not one of reversal in direction of previously established drainage courses.   Instead it argues the replacement, through a series of piracies, of the original northwestward drainage by one directed to the southeast.

As Thompson notes, the idea is not new.   Davis (1889, also *Essays*, pp. 417–418, 444), referring in turn to Löwl, considered it important.   Tarr (1915, p. 566) applied it specifically to the development of Appalachian drainage.

The distance to which the divide has been pushed back westward increases from south to north for two reasons: the greater width and obduracy of the resistant Blue Ridge barrier in the south and the greater downtilting of the eastward slope in the north.   Thus the Roanoke and James rivers have cut back 40 to

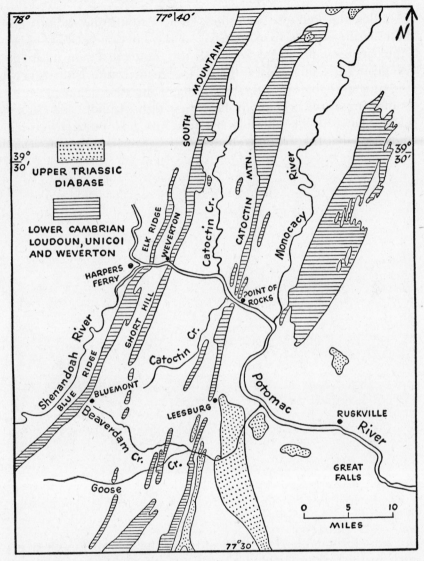

FIG. 198. MAP TO SHOW THE COURSE OF THE POTOMAC IN RELATION TO BELTS
OF RESISTANT ROCK

The ruled and dotted areas are belts of resistant rocks. At the Harpers
Ferry water gap the hard, quartzitic Lower Cambrian rocks of the Blue
Ridge are seen to be narrower and farther separated than in the regions to
the north or south. At Point of Rocks, and farther east, the river crosses at
places where the strong rocks are not present. Drawing by H. D. Thompson.

75 miles, the Potomac 100 miles. The Potomac headwaters are now in the Appalachian plateau on the far side of the Folded Appalachian belt. To accomplish this shift the Potomac divide would need to migrate less than 4 feet in each thousand years of the time available since the beginning of the encroachment.

Plotting of the geology to show the width, altitude, and degree of resistance of the durable barriers that had to be overcome indicated that the stream courses are situated where these barriers

Fig. 199.   HARPERS FERRY WATER GAP
   The Potomac River crossing the narrow belt of resistant rocks of the Blue Ridge at this point.

are least formidable (Fig. 198) and that the line of flow jogs in such manner as to avoid the more difficult crossings of a direct route (Fig. 199). The headwater erosion did not claw in a straight line directly westward. Instead, successive piracies were effected by little tributaries of the east-flowing streams as these came upon sites (Figs. 115, 197), (first to one side, then the other, of the course of the main river) where the headwaters of the westward drainage could be tapped and diverted with minimal cutting through of strong beds. At some sites, in limestone regions, the original piracy may have been due to solution action in under-ground courses, as described by Fridley (1939) with reference to the South Branch of the Potomac River.

Superimposition Theory of Appalachian Drainage Evolution. The preceding paragraphs are framed to direct attention mainly to the problem of apparent drainage reversal which was stated to be a major item in the elucidation of Appalachian drainage his-tory. Alignment of water gaps (Figs. 115, 187) across successive, close-spaced ridges of resistant rock was indicated to be the other feature of critical significance in the development of Appalachian topography.

There are two broadly opposed schools of thought in respect to aligned gaps. One holds that such gaps are indicative of super-imposition of the transverse streams of the present from a widely extended cover mass. The other school denies the validity of the assertion that there is a general alignment of the gaps, and main-tains that such alignment of gaps as does exist comes from local superimposition (Fig. 186) incidental to the erosion of the fold structure. Analysis of the conflicting contentions in regard to the alignment question requires that consideration be given to a third major problem of Folded Appalachian history, that of the pene-planations.

Students of Appalachian geomorphology are generally in agree-ment that the Folded Appalachian belt has been one or more times reduced to peneplain altitudes and topography (Fig. 30). There is some dispute in regard to the measure of relief such peneplains would exhibit if reduced by degradation to the ulti-mate degree. The consensus of opinion is, probably, that the strongest beds and structures would persist as monadnocks with elevations 100 feet, or perhaps even 400 feet, above the river plains even at a very advanced stage of peneplanation.

The surface of the general peneplanation, if there was only one, or the last one of a series, if multiple, is represented by the summit levels of the existing ridges. In later years much has been written to emphasize the point that the top surfaces of the ridges now are not remnants of the actual peneplain. The ridge sum-mits, like the intervening lowlands, it is urged, have been since lowered by erosion, and represent the peneplain surface only in that they remain parallel to that surface (Figs. 31, 112, 187), having been uniformly (with reference to a particular bed and a particular width of that bed) reduced in level.

A restoration of the surface that is representative of the peneplain, achieved by filling in the valleys to the elevations of the highest ridges, would not be level or show a gentle inclination in one direction. Instead there would appear a broad unsymmetrical dome with its summit over toward the eastern side of the Folded Appalachians in the south, toward the western side in the north. Its longer arc would extend from north to south, the shorter one east and west, with the declivity toward the east steeper than that toward the west.

It has been computed that the bulk of material removed by erosion in reduction of the Folded Appalachians to the peneplain surface is 70 times that lost by dissection since. It is obvious from the magnitude of this ratio that the peneplain surface must have transected the fold structure far below the level of any of the original synclinal basins. The surface presented for renewed erosion by reason of the upwarping was one cutting anticlines and synclines indifferently. The folds, in general, are large in comparison with the thickness of the stronger beds. With reference to any given resistant bed there are three general possibilities of transection. It may be somewhere near the middle of an anticlinal or synclinal limb. Then the strong bed will appear at the surface in a zigzag line making a pattern determined by the plunge of the folds. Postpeneplain dissection will convert these outcrops to monoclinal ridges. Or, if the transection is at or only a short distance above the crest of an anticline, intact with reference to the strong bed, any cover of weak materials will shortly be stripped off and an anticlinal mountain will result. The third possibility is that of transection of a strong bed at, or slightly above, the bottom level of a synclinal trough. Then a synclinal mountain should appear. This form will persist especially long if the synclinal floor is flat and broad. As the folds in general pitch, anticlinal and synclinal mountains, developed at the peneplain summit level, resolve at some point along their axes into diverging monoclinal ridges, because the pitch causes the transection by the peneplain surface to be progressively at a more nearly intermediate level, as referred to the fold form.

The consequent and antecedence theories of Appalachian drainage development explain the existing transverse courses of the major streams and their water gaps as persisting from prepeneplain times; that is, they are antecedent not only with reference to the latest uparching but also with reference to the original upfolding. The progressive piracy theory presumes that the drainage could have developed its present characteristics without reference to peneplanations or coastal plain superimposition. The effect of the various warps is considered to have consistently accentuated the eastward slope and so enhanced the piracy of the original northwestward drainage.

But the supporters of all these theories are troubled by the aligned water gap phenomenon. Granting the probability of persistence of the major streams in their peneplain courses, or of water gaps developed by piracy at the least difficult transverse sites, the fact remains that the aligned gaps are an anomaly in view of the adjustment to structure that should have been possible in the long prepeneplain and postpeneplain history of dissection. Escape is sought from this quandary by (a) minimizing the phenomenon by, for example, ascribing it to transverse faulting or other weakness; (b) accounting for it by local superimposition; that is, from exposure of resistant beds in different positions as degradation proceeds; (c) postulating a general, postpeneplanation superimposition.

Dodging the issue by appeal to particular structural circumstances in explanation of each instance of the occurrence of aligned gaps amounts to a denial of uniformity in their origin. But the general resemblance of the aligned gaps and the several times repetition of the phenomenon within narrow areal limits tend to make this interpretation unacceptable. Local superimposition serves to explain occurrences below the level of the reconstructed ridge-summit, Schooley, peneplain surface (Plate II). For aligned gaps that cut across these highest ridges some type of general superimposition appears to be indicated.

Davis (1889, also in *Essays*, pp. 469–473) realized that the course of the middle Susquehanna across the apical curves of two Pocono synclinal ridges (Figs. 115, 187, 194) could best be accounted for as resulting from superimposition. He postulated a transgression of the Atlantic far inland from the present coast line, and, in consequence, a widespread flood-plaining of the lower courses of

the great rivers.   Deltaic and flood-plain deposits buried the low
monadnock relief of the Pocono and Blue Mountain ridges on
the peneplain.   The courses of the rivers would then be independent of the underlying fold structure, and, in the succeeding
uplift, they would be superimposed at random from the cover
mass.   Willis (1895, p. 190) generalized that all the transverse
streams from the Roanoke to the Delaware had been superimposed from their own flood-plain deposits, in the peneplain
stage, on the sandstone and quartzite beds disposed athwart their
courses.

It is now considered improbable that flood-plain accumulation
and panplanation (Crickmay, C. H., 1933) combined (Fig. 60),
could completely dispose of all relief in a penepланed region.   To
permit superimposition on the scale asserted there would need
be, as Davis recognized, depression and marine sedimentation on
a considerable scale.

Davis (1899, *The Peneplain,* also in *Essays* p. 356 and p. 373)
quoting Darton, recognized the existence of a peneplain of earlier
development than that now represented by the levels of the summit ridges.   This earlier peneplain is the surface on which the
Atlantic Coastal Plain sediments rest (Fig. 19).   Its existence was
further asserted by Renner (1927) on the evidence from records
of wells bored through the younger beds to a floor of underlying
strongly consolidated rock.   Later geophysical explorations confirm these inferences.

The older surface has become known as the Fall Zone peneplain
(Sharp, H. S., 1929) and its distinctly angular intersection with
projection of the ridge-summit (Schooley) peneplain to the eastern
edge of the Piedmont Province is the Fall Line or Fall Zone.

With these facts as his point of departure D. W. Johnson (1931)
elaborated a theory of sufficiently general superimposition to
comprehend all the water gap phenomena.   He argued that the
Fall Zone peneplain originally had a wide extension inland.   In
Cretaceous time it experienced submergence and received a thick
deposit of sediments across the full width of the Folded Appalachian belt.   An upwarp in the form of an elliptical dome followed.   A divide between eastward and westward drainage was
established along a line extending approximately southwestward
from the Adirondacks to southwestern Pennsylvania and beyond.

From this height of land consequent streams flowed across the emergent coastal plain toward the Atlantic. Favored consequents eventually became the major transverse rivers superimposed on the underlying fold structure. The eastern border of the Fall Zone peneplain failed of emergence in the uplift. On it had been piled also the Tertiary sediments of the later erosion cycle that eventually produced the Schooley peneplain. Then the Schooley peneplain was warped up into a new dome, essentially the duplicate of its predecessor. In so far as this uplift was adverse, athwart their courses, the transverse, superimposed streams maintained an antecedent-flow direction. For the rest their erosive effectiveness was enhanced by the new eastward declivity.

The merit of this sequence is that it provides in a simple way for the generally parallel southeastward transverse courses of the major streams. It accounts for the absence of any of the Cretaceous cover sediments, inland, by postulating their complete stripping off in the deep degradation necessary to produce the Schooley peneplain. It asserts (Ver Steeg, K., 1930) that the transverse streams had their present trends before the Schooley peneplain was upwarped, because the accordant summit ridges, which define the Schooley peneplain, regularly decline in level toward the axes of the transverse streams. The jogging of the transverse streams is explained as resulting from partial adjustments to structure achieved in the Fall Zone to Schooley peneplain erosion cycle.

Against unqualified acceptance of this thesis Thompson (1939, p. 1330) urged that the faint slope of the ridge crests toward the master gaps is not valid evidence for pre-Schooley or later superimposition.

"The stream in the watergap is local base level for the longitudinal subsequents, which in turn are base level for the resequents and obsequents. Since the longitudinal subsequents descend toward the master stream, the resequents and obsequents have greater power to cut into and lower the ridge as it approaches the watergap. The differential lowering within a few million years should be sufficient to make a discernible slope toward the watergap."

Nevertheless the alignment of close-spaced gaps cut across the summit ridges finds its most plausible explanation in an hypothesis of superimposition. Also, the verity of the Fall Zone peneplain

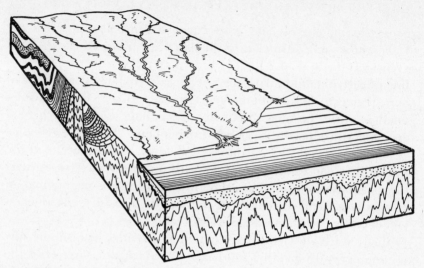

FIG. 200. THE FALL ZONE PENEPLANATION OF THE APPALACHIAN GEOMORPHIC UNITS

Drawing by Steve Barker.

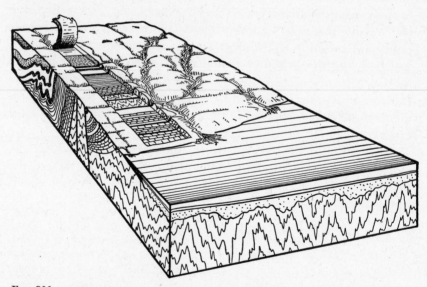

FIG. 201. WARPING OF THE FALL ZONE PENEPLANATION

The former peneplain surface has been downbent on the Atlantic side so that it is in part submerged. The upwarped region to the west is experiencing renewed dissection. The peeled strip reveals the divers rocks and structures to which this and later dissections become adjusted. Drawing by Steve Barker.

appears to be established. No cogent objection to widespread submergence of a peneplaned surface has been voiced. If the sequence is made: Fall Zone peneplanation, upwarp, Schooley (or Upland peneplanation [Frontispiece and Fig 30], if the Schooley is considered a subsummit, ridge-top surface [Cole, W. S., 1941]) peneplanation, submergence and sedimentation, reuplift and superimposition on the Schooley surface (Figs. 200–205, inclusive) the significant difficulty of the Johnson succession is disposed of without detriment to the superimposition idea. It is obvious that a remarkable measure of adjustment of drainage courses to structure has been achieved in the several part-cycles of erosion of post-Schooley time; that such adjustment, with reference to structures and beds available at the level of the Schooley surface, is still in active progress (Fig. 115); and that major transverse streams will be diverted from aligned gaps in the near geomorphic future. If a peneplanation as widespread and complete as that of the Upland-Schooley erosion cycle is postulated for a postsedimentation time, it would seem (by analogy with what has occurred, and is in progress, during the post-Schooley dissection period) that drainage could, and would, have escaped all superimposition compulsions and restraints, in view of the relief indicated to be available, and the time required to accomplish so complete a reduction.

Stose (1940) (Plate II) resolves this problem by postulating that the Schooley peneplain was cut chiefly in Jurassic time, that its eastern border was then submerged while further reduction of the still-exposed (and perhaps slightly uparched) surface was achieved in Cretaceous, Eocene, and Oligocene time. The main upwarp of the Schooley surface is postponed until after mid-Tertiary, and only late Tertiary and Quaternary time has been available for the dissection of the Schooley peneplain. This explanation, however, leaves the aligned water gaps unaccounted for, except as their presence is referred to structural weaknesses such as cross faults, and, in effect, merely reduces the measure of discordance between the Schooley and Fall Zone peneplain surfaces.

But if the sediments are assumed to have been spread over the Upland-Schooley surface, the superimpositions would be with reference to those surfaces, and, appropriately, be still in course of elimination. This is the observed condition. Post-Schooley adjustment to structure and progressive piracy (Figs. 197, 198)

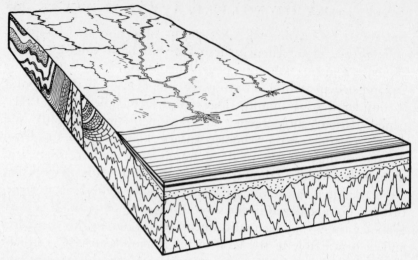

FIG. 202. THE SCHOOLEY (OR UPLAND) PENEPLANATION

The Appalachian units are again worn down to a complete peneplanation, the surface of which meets that of the submerged, sediment-covered, Fall-Zone peneplanation at an angle. (Relief of the Fall-Zone peneplanation is unduly exaggerated to show the unconformity.) This line of intersection is the Fall Line Zone of today. Drawing by Steve Barker.

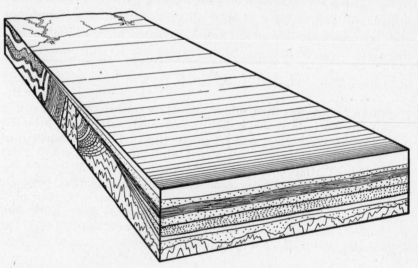

FIG. 203. SUBMERGENCE OF THE SCHOOLEY PENEPLAIN

A general sinking, without significant warping, permits a transgression of the sea across the full width of the Folded Appalachian belt. A cover of sediments is deposited over the Schooley peneplain surface. The angle of intersection of the Fall Zone and Schooley surfaces is faintly indicated in the left-hand section. Drawing by Steve Barker.

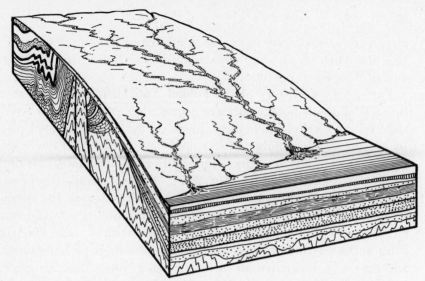

FIG. 204. UPWARP OF THE SCHOOLEY PENEPLAIN AND ITS SEDIMENT COVER

A new drainage system that is consequent upon the surface and slopes of the sedimentary beds develops. Its courses are unaffected by the nature and structure of the underlying Appalachian formations. Drawing by Steve Barker.

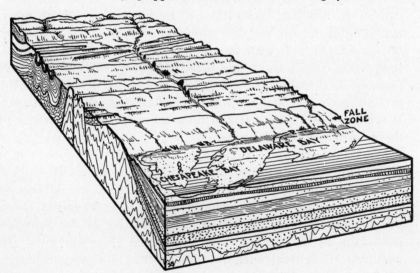

FIG. 205. PRESENT RELIEF OF THE PENNSYLVANIA REGION OF THE APPALACHIANS

Degradation has removed all of the postulated sedimentary cover beds west of the Fall Zone. Upwarp has made the angle of intersection of the Fall Zone and the Schooley peneplains more pronounced (exaggerated in the diagram). The aligned water gaps of the Susquehanna River are conspicuously in evidence. Valleys and ridges are developed in relation to structure. This adjustment is not yet complete. Drawing by Steve Barker.

361

account for the disappearance or nondevelopment of the aligned-gap phenomenon at some sites, without precluding its presence and persistence at others.

Post-Schooley History of the Folded Appalachians. Since the upwarp of the Schooley surface, degradation is thought to have reduced the level of the highest ridges, on the most resistant beds, by a considerable number of feet, and developed broad lowlands (Fig. 116), referred to as the "Harrisburg erosion surface," on the weaker beds and structures (Fig. 206). These lowlands represent a near-base-level altitude, in that they developed with the main streams at grade, and the interstream areas crumbling down to the elevations fixed by the profiles of these main streams. The Harrisburg surface is better developed than a strath; is perhaps more appropriately designated an incipient peneplain. Another uplift has brought about its trenching and the larger streams have again attained grade in the cuts they have made below the Harrisburg surface.

It is obvious that the complete truncation of the folded structure in the Schooley cycle, followed by upwarping, affords maximal possibilities for the development, by differential dissection, of cigar-shaped anticlinal mountains, canoe-shaped synclinal valleys, zigzag ridges, water gaps, wind gaps (Fig. 52), and the other phenomena of maturely eroded, fold mountains described in the preceding chapter and in preceding paragraphs of this chapter. It remains to consider a few of these more specifically because of their particular significance.

Where the summit peneplain surface truncated the floor of a broad, low-dip, gently pitching syncline a wide, flat-topped, synclinal mountain developed. Such structures are difficult to reduce by erosion, and commonly survive as monadnocks above the general level of the surface representative of the Schooley peneplain, as indicated by the monoclinal ridge summits. In northeastern Pennsylvania the most northerly of the anthracite fields are broad, flat, synclinal, summit-level areas capped by resistant conglomeratic rock which has preserved the coal immediately below it. This relation is also a feature of the extension of the folded Appalachian belt into the plateau section of southern New York. In that region the folds die out concordantly and broad, undulating flats represent undissected though perhaps low-

Fig. 206. SHENANDOAH RIVER AND VALLEY, NEAR ALMA, VIRGINIA

Views looks west to Massanutten Mountain. The Shenandoah is a subsequent stream on a broad lowland representing the Harrisburg erosion surface. Massanutten Mountain is a ridge of resistant rocks in the middle of the lowland.

ered, parts of the peneplain level. But the highest parts of these uplands are, almost without exception, the floors of synclinal troughs. (Incidentally, this phenomenon indicates that the truncated uplands are not plains of marine erosion.)

Where a syncline with steep dips was transected by the peneplain surface at a level significantly above the bottom of the trough, as delimited by a particular resistant bed, and the rimming bed was notched (as it must be) by escaping drainage, a synclinal valley developed. Its excavation would not be rapid if effected only by the small drainage that could collect in the area bounded by the rim of strong rocks. Its easy excavation could then proceed only to the upper surface of the resistant bed that floors it. The bottom would tend to remain at a relatively high altitude. The Wyoming Valley of Pennsylvania, in which the Scranton and Wilkes-Barre anthracite areas are situated, is an example of such a valley but one that has been excavated to an exceptional depth because it is double-notched by the transverse course of the Susquehanna River. Lookout Mountain on the Fort Payne, Alabama-Georgia quadrangle of the United States Geological Survey topographic sheets is a more representative occurrence. The mountain here is the floor, at the general altitude of 1200 feet, of a synclinal valley two or three hundred feet below the summit level of the rimming ridges. This shallow, upland valley is drained chiefly by Little River Gulf (gorge and water gap) through the eastern rim to the Coosa River by a descent of some 600 feet.

It is somewhat exceptional to have weak beds of such massiveness, between notably resistant formations, that a single, strong rim outlines either an anticlinal or a synclinal valley. Very frequently there is a double or even a triple rim of resistant beds, with intervening weak formations that have been weathered and eroded below the rim levels. The several strong formations will themselves differ in resistance to degradation. The secondary hollows and ridges which result from the differential reduction of these beds, together with the notching of the rims which ensues from drainage escapes, plus linkages of streams brought about by captures, give rise to a very complicated topographic picture. A prominent expression of such development is shown on the adjoining Lykens and Pine Grove, Pennsylvania, quadrangles of the topographic sheets of the United States Geological Survey.

Trellis Drainage Pattern. It is obvious that, given an erosion surface truncating the folds, and transverse master streams extending across the full width of the folded belt as they do in the Folded Appalachian region, longitudinal subsequent valleys, geologically *strike valleys,* will, after uplift, quickly be opened to sizes rivaling those of the transverse streams. This enlargement of subsequents is no less true of a Jura sequence, but is not so quickly achieved. With the master streams at or near grade, and all weak rock masses exposed by truncation to immediate attack by the degrading agencies, rapid reduction of the weak beds must follow. The larger anticlines, cut across by the trunk transverse streams will very shortly be breached and excavated to the gradient level. The clearing of the lesser and more remote anticlines is delayed because drainage from them must discharge into secondary transversals flowing at higher elevations. The smaller synclinal sites will be emptied very slowly if the resistant rock enclosing the basin is notched only by outflow drainage.

But where an adjoining subsequent has, meanwhile, eroded a deep valley, synclinal sites will be reduced in area by the retreat of the escarpment walls which bound the breached anticline. Further, obsequent streams coursing down these walls may, at weak spots, that is, where close-spaced jointing, cross faults, or thinning of the resistant beds occur, develop re-entrants by headwater erosion deep enough to capture all the drainage of the synclinal interior.

The arrangement in detail of drainage at such sites is then of the trellis pattern (Fig. 44a). The main stems of the trellis arrangement are characteristically the subsequents over the anticlinal areas. Short obsequent laterals, some of which penetrate synclinal basins that stand at higher levels, and are there fed by two subsequents draining from each end of the syncline, constitute the lesser units of the trellis form. It is in the fact that short tributaries are so numerous that the trellis pattern differs from the rectangular pattern of drainage.

SUMMARY

Because they perfectly illustrate many and varied phases of the progress of the fluvial cycle in fold mountains that have had a

long and involved history, because they present unsolved problems
of major significance, and because they are easily accessible to
investigations, the Folded Appalachians have become classic
ground for geomorphic study.

Sedimentary beds of great total thickness were accumulated in a
geosyncline situated to the west of an oldland, Appalachia. These
originally flat-lying strata were compressed into open folds during
the Appalachian Revolution. The major drainage from the
Folded Appalachian mountain belt, as then formed, appears to
have been from the southeast toward the northwest. This direction is transverse to the axes of the folds. The inference is that
extended consequents from Appalachia were able to persist against
the rising folds; that is, their courses became antecedent.

Davis in a classical paper accounted for an original northwestward flow of the Pennsylvania drainage by fitting consequent
courses upon, and off, the slopes of the newly risen fold mountains.

Both the antecedent and consequent explanations are discovered
to be somewhat inadequate when it is attempted, in harmony with
the assumptions made in their application, to account for the
reversal of an original southeast to northwest transverse drainage
to the northwest to southeast flow-direction which now prevails.
It has therefore been proposed that the drainage of the northern
section of the Folded Appalachians was *ab initio* from the northwest to the southeast. The contention is that the flow was consequent on southeastwardly inclined dip slopes of overturned
folds and thrust faults. These structures have since been completely destroyed by erosion so that the present stream courses
were superimposed on the open folds underlying the thrust structures. The presence in Triassic sediments, deposited along the
Atlantic coast, of materials derived from far western sources is
held to be conclusive evidence that the southeasterly courses were
established immediately after the Appalachian Revolution.

The marked alignment of successive water gaps in the courses
of major transverse streams across numerous, close-spaced, resistant ridges, as exemplified by the Susquehanna River, is thought
by some geomorphologists to indicate a general, rather than local,
superimposition. These students postulate widespread submergence and deposition of a thick sedimentary cover on a peneplaned
Folded Appalachian surface, followed by uplift and superimposi-

tion of extended consequent streams (with sources in the north-west) from the sediments on the underlying, truncated fold structure.

Even Davis was constrained to resort to a limited application of the superimposition sequence in rounding out his analysis of the Pennsylvania rivers. But it was suggested early, and much evidence has been marshaled since in support of such interpretations, that the present-day transverse streams of southeastward flow are neither reversed antecedents, nor consequents, nor superimposed. Instead, the southeast streams are represented to have been originally short water courses, descending by steep gradients to the Atlantic, from a north to south divide extending along the eastern side of the Folded Appalachian belt. By achieving successive piracies, through headward erosion, these short streams have been able progressively to divert and replace (not reverse) the former northwestward drainage.

The evolution of Folded Appalachian drainage has not been comprehensively and finally explained. But the forms produced by dissection of the unit in the last great, and in minor, recent, part cycles of erosion are of themselves geomorphically significant and afford the clues which should eventually evoke an adequate general theory of Folded Appalachian topographic development.

BIBLIOGRAPHY

CLASSICAL

Hayes, C. W. and Campbell, M. R. (1894) *Geomorphology of the Southern Appalachians,* National Geographic Magazine, Vol. 6, pp. 63–126.

Willis, B. (1895) *The Northern Appalachians,* National Geographic Society, Monograph 1, No. 6, pp. 169–202. Also in *Physiography of the United States,* American Book Company, New York, 1896, pp. 169–202.

Davis, W. M. (1899) *The Rivers and Valleys of Pennsylvania,* National Geographic Magazine, Vol. 1, pp. 183–253. Also in *Geographical Essays,* Ginn and Company, Boston, 1909, pp. 413–484.

Davis, W. M. (1903) *The Stream Contest Along the Blue Ridge,* Bulletin Philadelphia Geographic Society, Vol. 3, pp. 213–244.

Chamberlin, R. T. (1910) *The Appalachian Folds of Central Pennsylvania,* Journal of Geology, Vol. 18, pp. 228–251.

RECENT

Renner, G. T., Jr. (1927) *The Physiographic Interpretation of the Fall Line*, Geographical Review, Vol. 17, pp. 276–286.

Fridley, H. M. (1929) *Identification of Erosion Surfaces in South Central New York*, Journal of Geology, Vol. 37, pp. 113–134.

Ver Steeg, K. (1930) *Wind Gaps and Water Gaps of the Northern Appalachians*, Annals of the New York Academy of Sciences, Vol. 32, pp. 87–220.

Ashley, G. H. (1930) *Age of the Appalachian Peneplains*, Bulletin Geological Society of America, Vol. 41, pp. 695–700.

Johnson, D. W. (1931) *Stream Sculpture on the Atlantic Slope*, Columbia University Press, New York.

Cole, W. S. (1934) *Identification of Erosion Surfaces in Eastern and Southern Ohio*, Journal of Geology, Vol. 42, pp. 285–294.

Wright, F. J. (1934) *The Newer Appalachians of the South, Part I, Between the Potomac and the New Rivers*, Bulletin Dennison University, Vol. 34, No. 13, Science Laboratory Journal, Vol. 29, pp. 1–105.

Wright, F. J. (1936) *The Newer Appalachians of the South, Part II, South of the New River*, Bulletin Dennison University, Vol. 36, No. 6, Science Laboratory Journal, Vol. 31, pp. 93–142.

Meyerhoff, H. A., and Olmsted, E. W. (1936) *The Origins of Appalachian Drainage*, American Journal of Science, Vol. 32, pp. 21–42.

Miller, B. L. (1937) *Geophysical Investigations in the Emerged and Submerged Coastal Plain, Part II, Geological Significance of the Geophysical Data*, Bulletin Geological Society of America, Vol. 48, pp. 802–812.

Thompson, H. D. (1939) *Drainage Evolution in the Southern Appalachians*, Bulletin Geological Society of America, Vol. 50, pp. 1323–1356.

Rich, J. L. (1939) *A Bird's-Eye Cross Section of the Central Appalachian Mountains and Plateau: Washington to Cincinnati*, Geographical Review, Vol. 29, pp. 561–586.

Stose, G. W. (1940) *Age of the Schooley Peneplain*, American Journal of Science, Vol. 238, pp. 461–476.

Thompson, H. D. (1941) *Topographic Analysis of the Monterey, Staunton, and Harrisonburg Quadrangles*, Journal of Geology, Vol. 49, pp. 521–549.

Chapter Seventeen

FAULT–BLOCK MOUNTAINS AND TOPOGRAPHY RESULTING FROM FAULTING

Introduction. With few exceptions (of which the Jura Mountains are the outstanding example) the relief of regions made up of multiple folds is not an intact or exhumed manifestation of the structural units that compose them. Instead, the visible mountain forms are commonly the product of degradation and dissection processes acting on broadly upwarped areas of the fold structures. In brief, they are second, or third, or n + 1 cycle mountains.

In dome mountains the existing relief is much more generally a direct expression of the initial uplift. The height of such mountains, their outlines, and their slopes are the immediate product of the endogenic force that made them. The relief developed on their surfaces by the subaerial processes is conditioned by the uplift and the nature of the rock cover that the uplift affected.

At sites where diastrophism has consisted of the breaking and differential movement (faulting) of blocks of the earth's crust, the existing relief, not uncommonly of mountainous proportions, may, as is regularly the case with dome mountains, be the immediate result of the tectonic action. It may, on the other hand, be second- or later-cycle relief, to be attributed primarily to subaerial processing, as is generally true of the topography in regions of fold structure.

Whether the forms observed at specified localities are directly the result of fault movements, or whether the presence of the breaks affects the relief only indirectly, is often a matter for controversy between competent observers. The point at issue is, in effect: Have movements on fault breaks been sufficiently recent, of such magnitude, and rapid enough to permit them to get expression as surface relief in competition with the subaerial gradational processes? In the past, geologic opinion has been inclined to deny this possibility, but since then more careful study and the application of new criteria have led to the conclusion that relief of large proportions is directly owing to fault movements.

From the viewpoint of the structural geologist and that of the stratigrapher the complexities of faulting are almost innumerable. With the geometrical methods required for the solution of the underground and outcrop problems to which these complications give rise the geomorphologist is little concerned. The stratigrapher or structural geologist may find it profitable to test the interpretations he makes, on the basis of measurement and computation, by giving attention to the probable geomorphic consequences, modifying or revising his first-formed conclusions if these are found to be inconsistent with the topographic evidence.

The geomorphologist's business is rather with the sites where the fact of faulting has, either directly or indirectly, significantly determined or influenced relief. In other words, his science applies at places where the geomorphic evidence of faulting is discernible in the existing prospect rather than where the breaks can only be discovered by the retrospective approach.

Nature of Faulting. The surface in which a fault break occurs is called the fault plane, if single; the fault zone, if the break is distributed over a number of generally parallel planes. The differential movement of the blocks separated by the fault may be up, down, horizontal, oblique, or rotatory. It is the up-and-down movements chiefly that find relief expression. The distance that two points, previously coincident in the plane of the fault, are separated by the movement is called the displacement; the vertical component of the displacement is the throw.

The measure of displacement, especially of the throw component, may be thousands of feet, or only a fraction of an inch. The great displacements are probably never achieved in one movement. On the other hand, large displacements may be accomplished in geologically short periods by a number of successive small movements. Although faulting gets its greatest expression in relief where both the displacement and the unit blocks involved are large, lesser displacements may significantly guide weathering, stream, and other processes.

Fault-block Mountains. The most characteristic occurrence of relief because of faulting is that where the dominant movement is up or down, or both up and down, and the blocks involved are tilted. This statement implies that the fault break is terminated at its two ends either by dying out, by passing into a flexure, or by cross faults. The fact of tilting indicates that at least one of the fault breaks, the principal fault, is not vertical. It has, however, commonly a high angle, so that reference is made to high-angle faulting (Fig. 207). A high-angle fault is usually also a normal, or gravity fault. In normal faulting the hanging-wall ("overhanging") side of the fault, has moved down with reference to the foot ("underlying") wall. This relation indicates an extension of area

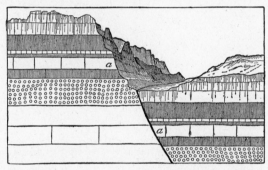

Fig. 207. HIGH ANGLE, NORMAL, OR GRAVITY FAULT
Foot wall on the left, hanging wall on the right.

in the region of faulting. From the fact of extension in area it may be inferred that a general condition of tension or of relaxation from compression initiated the faulting.

If the tilted block is sufficiently large, the throw component of displacement of great magnitude, and the movement so fast that the discordance of level brought about by the faulting is not eliminated by subaerial degradation so rapidly as it develops, a *fault-block mountain* results.

The exposed, steep, fault face and crest of the upthrown block of the principal normal fault then compose a *fault scarp* of first magnitude (Fig. 208). If the block is terminated at the ends of the principal fault by cross faults these will be marked by lesser scarps. The gentler inclination at right angles to the main fault scarp is called the *back slope* of the tilted block.

FIG. 208. FAULT BLOCK MOUNTAIN, DEEP SPRING VALLEY, CALIFORNIA

The straight fault-line trace shows dimly at the base of the steep slope; triangular fault facets are conspicuous. The upper reaches of the valleys are wide and open; the lower ends are gorges.

Criteria for the Identification of Young Fault Scarps. It is stated above that geologists have in the past been averse to the concept of block mountains as the direct product of faulting. The preferred interpretation has been to consider them the result of exhumation by the action of differential weathering and erosion. It is pertinent, therefore, to inquire how a recent fault scarp of mountain height may be recognized.

If the fault scarp is very new, or has recently been affected by further displacement, the rocks on the face of the scarp, especially near its base, may retain the frictional markings, slickensides, resulting from movement on the fault plane. The fault scarp is terminated at the bottom by the fault line. The fault line is the trace of the underground continuation of the fault plane. Where movement has occurred within the last few tens, or hundreds, of years the fault trace may extend across talus (Fig. 209) and alluvial fans built up over the fault line, and be manifest in small, secondary scarps in the gravel accumulations. The underground break in the plane is a fissure through the rocks that commonly permits the escape of hot water upward from depth. Such emergence, as hot springs, is a frequently remarked phenomenon at the base of young fault scarps. These hot waters commonly carry much mineral matter in solution. In eastern California (Deep Spring Valley, Inyo County) deposition of such mineral matter by precipitation consolidated alluvial-fan gravels and cemented them to the fault face. Renewed movement carried a wedge of this cohering gravel up on the fault face to an elevation 30 feet above the present emergence level of the spring. Outflows of lava are also of frequent occurrence along the trace of recent faults.

In fault blocks of considerable elongation the fault-line trace, that is, the line of the base of the mountain front, is characteristically straight or gently curved. The line is in effect "simple." In this respect the base and crest lines of recent fault scarps differ markedly from those of weathering escarpments (Figs. 35, 88, 107, 156). The latter are commonly interrupted by strong salients and large embayments and may be outlined by pronounced curves. It is not, however, safe to place too much dependence on straightness of crest and base line in assigning a faulting origin to a scarp front.

Fig. 209. RECENT FAULT SCARP CUTTING ACROSS TALUS, DEEP SPRING VALLEY, CALIFORNIA

The steeper declivity at the base of the mountain slope, at the left of the picture, is a newer part of the fault scarp resulting from further movement on the fault plane. The heavy load of the intermittent stream in the small valley has built up the alluvial fan steeply so as to bridge across the new declivity. Note that the valley widens out toward its head.

374

The crest line of a fault scarp is only by coincidence dependent on or related to structure. Fault-plane breaks can and do traverse any and all kinds of structure. Weathering escarpments are normally governed by structure.

Conclusive evidence of the verity of origin by uplift from fault displacement of fault-block mountains is had from the phenomenon of the **louderback,** named for G. D. Louderback who first appreciated its significance. At many sites in the Great Basin

Fig. 210.   LOUDERBACK, CHOCOLATE MOUNTAIN, CALIFORNIA
The lava capping of the back slope of the fault-block mountain shows dimly as a knob at the summit of the fault scarp. The down-faulted lava beds show more clearly at the center of the picture.

region in California and Nevada extensive lava flows were spread across an ancient uplifted peneplain. The upper surface of a wide lava flow is essentially horizontal. But in the localities named the lava cover and the undermass have been broken across by faults. The upthrow side is tilted to form a fault-block mountain; the continuation of the once-horizontal lava sheet extends away from the base of the scarp. The part of the lava cover which remains as a cover on the back slope of the block is the louderback (Figs. 210, 211). It is obvious from these circumstances that whatever may have been the geomorphic history of the undermass it had nothing to do with the elevation of the present ranges. Further, the relief of the mountains cannot be attributed to differential erosion, because degradation since the displacement

FIG. 211. CHOCOLATE MOUNTAIN, CALIFORNIA, LOUDERBACK Shown by Diagram. Drawing by Elizabeth Burckmyer.

has not sufficed to modify greatly, much less to strip off, the louderback lava cappings.

Davis (1930), when suggesting the adoption of "louderback" as a geomorphic term proposed also that the geomorphic history of the Great Basin region should be used to memorialize the work of the famous contributors to its understanding. The "King Mountains," of fold origin, were reduced to the "Powell Peneplain," which was widely covered by lava flows and finally broken up and lifted to form the "Gilbert Fault-block Mountains." This proposal deserves wide acceptance, as it applies to Basin Range structures, both for its appropriateness and for its graciousness, in view of Davis's own noteworthy studies in the same field.

Identification of Old Fault Scarps. Even those who are strongly of the conviction that, in general, the topographic expression of actual fault displacement endures only briefly, and is of minor geomorphic consequence, are disposed to concede the verity and largeness of such endogenic forms with reference to some of the block mountains of the northern Great Basin region of the United States. In these instances the evidence of the recency of the faulting and the competence of the fault displacements to produce the existing great relief, are so clear and compelling as to make any other explanation highly improbable, if not impossible, of application.

But the identification of old fault scarps is not so sure and is often disputed. When slickensides have been destroyed by the action of subaerial processes, louderbacks crumbled away, broken fan deposits at the base buried under further debris, and the face of the scarp has been furrowed by consequent streams, made to retreat, and when the scarp crest is rounded by weathering, then the obvious and undeniable evidence of relief directly and solely originating from fault movement will have largely disappeared. If, in such instances, it is contended that relief from displacement nevertheless persists, further interpretative analysis is essential to a successful demonstration of the proposition.

The old, weathered fault scarp will still have a straight line base and its crest will not be marked by particular structural conditions. Weathering escarpments characteristically show irregularities in trend, uneven fronts, and summit levels determined by resistant capping beds. But a conclusive discrimination is not possible from these differences.

A distinctive feature of old fault scarps is the presence of *triangular fault facets* on the spur ends of the dissected fault face. The western front of the Wasatch Mountains in Utah exhibits this phenomenon very perfectly developed (Fig. 208). The openings of the parallel, consequent stream valleys occupy a considerable portion of the original area of the fault-plane façade, but the ridges between the valleys are terminated by the flat, though roughened by weathering, surfaces of the fault plane.

The triangular form of these facets results in part from the somewhat equal spacing of the consequent valleys (in itself indicative of their fault-face origin), in part from the widening of the valleys at the top by weathering. The triangular form is accentuated where a fault-block mountain is the product of intermittent movement recurring at long intervals, as has been the history of those at the north end of the east side of Death Valley in California (Fig. 212). At such sites what are termed *hourglass*, or *wineglass valleys* develop. (The designation "hourglass valley" has also been used to characterize the pattern in plan of valleys extending without interruption across a former divide, toward which the valley narrows from both directions.) The hourglass, or

FIG. 212. HOURGLASS VALLEYS, EAST SIDE OF DEATH VALLEY, CALIFORNIA

Note the narrow gorge in rock at the lower ends of both valleys. The older alluvial fan (darker shade, built up at the end of the valley on the left) has been trenched, following the most recent uplift, to the depth of the narrow rock gorge.

wineglass, valleys on the fault scarps flare broadly open at their upper ends, that is, have a wide funnel-shaped head, and have a constricted, gorge-form, lower section, the stem of the wineglass, and open on a spreading alluvial fan, the base of the wineglass.

The funnel head is the product of weathering and gully erosion acting without interruption from the time when the fault declivity was first formed (Fig. 209). In the later periods of the existence of the valley the rate of enlargement of its upper part may have been significantly accelerated by the increase in altitude resulting from further uplift (or depression on the downthrow side). The narrow rock gorges at the lower ends are the young valleys notching the new declivities, introduced by the later displacements. If the last movement has been very recent the end of a gorge may be hanging, that is, terminate at a level above that of the surface of the alluvial fan at the base of the scarp. It is even possible that an older alluvial fan will be bisected after a new uplift, because of the high velocity of flow imparted to the water emergent from the valley by the increased declivity introduced there by the uplift. In brief, the hourglass valleys have an older cross-section form at their upper ends than in their lower courses; the complete reverse of the development of a valley under normal conditions. If there are several abrupt changes in the width of the hourglass valleys, each such variation may be considered indicative of a phase of active uplift followed by a period of relative stability. Study of such valleys should provide evidence of the diastrophic history of the sites of their occurrence.

The back-slope summit areas of some of the fault-block mountains situated to the east of the Sierra Nevada in eastern-central California bear traces (v. Engeln, O. D., 1937, p. 336) in the form of beds of ancient river gravels (Fig. 213) of stream courses dismembered by fault displacements. The persistence of these dissevered remnants of former continuous valley lines is almost conclusive evidence that the declivities which cut them off from their earlier extensions have not resulted from a subaerial, differential degradation of the area.

The Sierra Nevada. The Sierra Nevada Mountains of California are probably the largest unit fault block in the world, both with regard to areal dimensions, 400 miles long by an average of 50 miles wide, and to altitude, ranging from 8000 to over 12,000 feet above sea level. The block, as a whole, is tilted gently west-ward. At its southern end it is terminated abruptly on the east by a steep fault scarp (Fig. 214), 6000 feet high, overlooking the Owens Valley. This part is the region known as the High Sierra.

The back slope of the Sierra Nevada fault block is an uptilted peneplain surface. The lesser fault-block ranges of the Great Basin region are, in general, similarly constituted. It appears that large relief from faulting results primarily where a region

FIG. 213. ANCIENT RIVER GRAVELS ON THE SUMMIT, BACK SLOPE, OF A FAULT-BLOCK MOUNTAIN, DEEP SPRING, CALIFORNIA

has previously been worn down to a surface of low relief. Whether there is a genetic relationship in the association of an antecedent peneplain condition with later diastrophism by faulting is un-certain. The earlier deep degradation does insure the exposure of rigid, consolidated rock. If, then, the peneplaned area is broken up into blocks, and these blocks are variously tilted, the relief due to the faulting may be the dominant topographic expression for considerable periods because the resistant rock does not speedily succumb to subaerial attacks.

Fig. 214. SCARP OF THE HIGH SIERRA, CALIFORNIA, MT. WHITNEY SECTOR

The steep, but eroded fault scarp of the east side of the Sierra Nevada block mountain. The smooth areas may be downfaulted remnants of the peneplaned and glaciated back-slope surface. Photograph, copyright, Spence Air Photos.

FIG. 215. FAULT-LINE SCARP, HORNBY BAY, GREAT BEAR LAKE, CANADA

The scarp extending diagonally across the center of the picture appears to mark the contact between two unlike Pre-Cambrian formations. The one on the left has yielded more to degradation, fluvial and glacial, and the line of faulting is thus brought into relief. The fact of notching of the scarp by the stream at the center of its length, and the development of subsequent drainage at the base of the scarp support the fault-line scarp interpretation. The large lakes on the left appear to be the plunge-pool developments of a glacial melt-water drainage. Royal Canadian Air Force Photograph.

It is asserted (Callaghan, E., 1939), on the basis of careful field study, that the fault-block mountains of the Basin-Range province have resulted from the breaking up of a once broad arch that had the Sierra block as its western limb and extended eastward from the present Sierra crest.

The great extent and high altitudes of the Sierra Nevada unit provide scope for the development of geomorphic phenomena that could not well get expression on smaller fault-block mountains. The widely developed peneplain surface of the back slope of the Sierra Nevada demonstrates that the present altitudes were acquired by uplift with reference to sea level. The uplift may have been a broad warp, with later collapse, by faulting, of portions of the uparched area. Whether raised to its present height by fault displacement, or owing its altitude to upwarp, the new attitude of the Sierra Nevada block profoundly affected valley development on its surfaces (v. Engeln, O. D., 1937, p. 335). F. E. Matthes (1939) has stated his conviction that the Sierra scarp was produced chiefly by downthrow of the basins to the east, after the range had attained sufficient altitude to maintain extensive glaciers.

On the back slope of the Sierra block those streams which had courses from east to west on the peneplain surface, previously to the uplift, that is, at right angles to the line of the fault scarp, were revived over their whole length by the upwarp, or the uptilt, of the block. The trunk Merced River there is west-flowing. Its small tributaries were left hanging The scale of this hanging-valley relationship was greatly magnified by the differential erosion of the glaciers which occupied the valleys in the Pleistocene ice age. The spectacular waterfalls of the Yosemite (Fig. 84) are the product of these several circumstances (Matthes, F. E., 1930, p. 35).

The directness of the westward flow of the Merced, duplicated by parallel streams to the north and south, indicates that its course is in some measure consequent, that is, influenced by the uplift. The torrential streams that descend the eastern scarp face are wholly consequent. The pre-faulting divide appears to have been nearly coincident with the line of the fault break. Earlier east-flowing drainage was disrupted by the fault displacement. New streams plunged down the scarp face. This face was evidently

never a single declivity.   It jogged at various places.   The drag
of the great uplift (or downthrow) caused subordinate faults and
shelves (v. Engeln, O. D., 1937, p. 338).   The shelves are a large-
scale effect of the same kind as that developed in miniature where
cemented gravels of an alluvial fan cling to a fault face when
further displacement occurs.

The displacement which gave the eastern scarp of the Sierra
Nevada its present high altitude was not achieved in a single,
short-period, great movement.   Instead it required a considerable
time to accomplish, and was probably done by a large number of
successive small shifts.   Meanwhile the plunging consequents
were effectively dissecting the scarp.   As it emerged the scarp was
also attacked by weathering.   It now appears as a steep, but, in
detail, a very frayed, irregular wall with a serrate summit.   It is a
representative, weathered fault scarp.   But the dissection is so
pronounced that early students were hesitant to pronounce it a
fault scarp.

Fault-line Scarps.   It has been emphasized that fault-block
mountains do provide examples of initial, diastrophic relief.   But
the known effectiveness of degradational agencies and the long
erosional histories of many regions gave adequate grounds for
skepticism concerning the survival, over considerable periods of
geologic time, of any relief, short of mountain ranges or plateaus
as wholes, resulting directly from uplift or depression.   It seemed
more reasonable to attribute the majority of the fault-block mountains in the Great Basin country of Nevada and adjoining states
to differential erosion, than to account for their existence and
strong relief by fault movements.

According to this interpretation, if a declivity resulted from the
original fault displacement, it disappeared completely by subaerial
degradation very shortly after its erection.   Later a general uplift
of the region of faulting, by warping or otherwise, brought about
renewed degradation.   Then if the rocks on two sides of a fault
line differed greatly in resistance the weaker formations on the
one side were reduced in altitude much more rapidly than the
stronger ones on the other side.   Thus a sharp declivity would be
created at the fault line.   If the weak rocks were on the downthrow side of the fault the new declivity would be a *resequent
fault-line scarp;* if on the upthrow side, an *obsequent fault-line*

scarp would be developed (Figs. 75, 215). The obsequent fault-line scarp would face in the opposite direction from that of the original fault scarp; if indeed, such a scarp ever existed.

Despite the entirely rational premises of this argument, fault-line scarps are probably neither so numerous nor so prominent as has been asserted by some geologists. However the great north-south extending scarps that border the Colorado Plateaus on the west, such as the Grand Wash Cliffs, 4000 feet high (Fig. 107), and Hurricane Ledge, are probably correctly interpreted as fault-line scarps. The flow of the principal drainage directly transverse to these scarps and the fact that cappings of lava flows bridge the fault plane without louderbacking attest the validity of this view. So also does the vast length of time that must have been available to permit the great recession of the east-to-west-line weathering escarpments, Vermilion Cliffs, White Cliffs, Pink Cliffs, in the same region. But the northern end of Hurricane Ledge is a true fault scarp. There fault movement has louderbacked the lava cappings (Davis, W. M., 1924, pp. 171–172; Huntington, E., and Goldthwait, J. W., 1903). The east slope of the present Teton Range of the Rocky Mountains is primarily an exhumed fault-line scarp (Fryxell, Horberg, and Edmund, 1941).

Fault-line scarps of less magnitude occur in the Connecticut River valley. Mt. Tom and Mt. Holyoke are small ridges of trap rock, in form replicas of the much larger fault-block mountains of the Great Basin region. But the steep scarp faces of the Connecticut Valley occurrences are definitely fault-line scarps. In common with the crystalline rocks of the rest of southern New England, the tilted and faulted sedimentary layers (with interbedded lava sheets) of the Connecticut Valley belt, were first peneplaned, then uplifted. Since the uplift the Connecticut Valley area has again been degraded to an erosion surface only little above base level. But as the faulted lava sheets were much more resistant to sub-aerial processes than the sandstone country rock, they were made to stand out in relief and now present steep fault-line scarps on one side and relatively gentle back slopes, determined by the top surface of the lava beds, on the other (Fig. 216).

Horsts. Where the principal fault face is inclined, as is commonly the case with fault-block mountains, the displacements at right angles to the major break may be readily absorbed by lesser cross faults or even by a monoclinal flexure. If, however, the

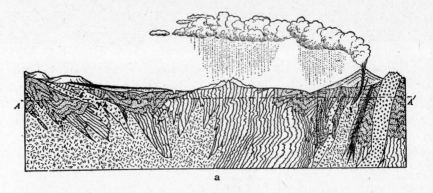

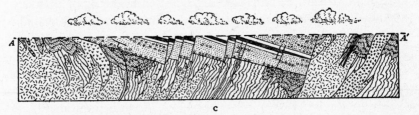

Fig. 216. SECTIONS ACROSS THE CONNECTICUT RIVER VALLEY AND THE
IN ITS TOPOGRAPHIC HISTORY

These diagrams show how this area got its present topographic features
by faulting and degradation.

Diagram (a) shows the conditions when the Appalachian Mountains were
volcanic activity. Volcanic ash settles down in quantity over the area that is
deposits of sediments in a basin formed by later downbending. The line

Diagram (b). Volcanic activity has ceased but meanwhile there have been
block mountains. Erosion tends to bring the more resistant (black) lava

Diagram (c). A long period of no land movement follows, during which
peneplain at about sea level altitude.

Diagram (d). A slight uplift comes next. Rejuvenated streams and
relief to form the block mountains in the valley, and only slightly modified
present conditions. The differences in elevation shown by the diagrams
After Joseph Barrell.

principal break is vertical and its throw one of great magnitude,
the cutoff adjustments are not easily achieved by a bend of the
rock. The cross faults that should, instead, result will tend to be
vertical. If this is the case the yield at the back of the block,
parallel to the principal fault, should be either by a sharp flexure
or, more probably, by faulting. In effect a block bounded by
faults is then lifted above its surroundings and, as such, is referred
to as a *horst*.

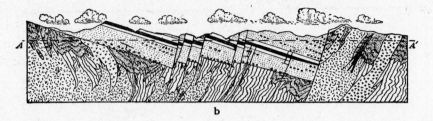

b

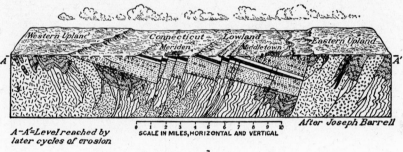

A–A'=Level reached by
later cycles of erosion

SCALE IN MILES, HORIZONTAL AND VERTICAL

After Joseph Barrell

d

NEIGHBORING UPLANDS OF CENTRAL CONNECTICUT AT FOUR DIFFERENT PERIODS

with reference to rock origin and structure, and to the changes in elevation

being uplifted. The rocks are being bent and contorted and there is much
now the Connecticut Valley. There are also lava flows (not shown) and
A–A' may be thought of as having an altitude only slightly above sea level.
further movements of the rock masses by faulting and the formation of
layers into relief.
degradation slowly, but rather completely, reduces the whole surface to a

weathering wear down the less resistant rocks, leaving the lava layers in
uplands on either side of it on the ancient, strong rocks. These are the
seem low but this is only because the horizontal and vertical scales are equal.

The Harz Mountains (Fig. 217) in Germany well represent the
horst phenomenon. Their northern terminus is a sharply defined,
steep fault scarp or fault-line scarp. Streams wander toward this
scarp over a gently undulating, peneplain surface, which constitutes
the interior upland of the mountains. Most of the peneplain is
on weak rocks, shales, but an extensive granite mass, the Brocken,
famous as a literary site, rises above the general level as a monadnock. A similar intrusive mass lies athwart the course of the Bode
River at the edge of the northern scarp. The Bodetal, well known
as a scenic region in Germany, is a gorge cut by the stream across

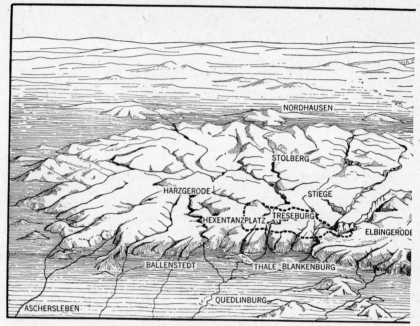

FIG. 217. THE HARZ MOUNTAINS, GERMANY, A HORST

The dashed lines enclose areas of intrusive rock which have a monadnock stones. The northern scarp is much frayed by erosion and the plain at its

this resistant barrier. It is a narrow cleft with great potholes in its bottom, indicative of the manner of the downcutting. The geomorphically important relations of the Bodetal are that the stream flows placidly over a gentle gradient in a widely open old valley on the uplifted peneplain surface and then plunges, via the gorge, over the edge of the scarp. Because of its superior resistance to erosion the inner border of the granite intrusion has functioned as a local base level to preserve the upper Bode in its peneplain characteristics. The breaks and uplifts on the other sides of the Harz horst were nearly enough of the same throw as that on the north to permit the Bode to continue its flow without change on the uplifted surface. The continuity of the upland surface across the outcrop of diverse rocks indicates that the Harz block was not exhumed by differential erosion, that the northern border scarp is a fault scarp and not a fault-line scarp. The frayed edge of the scarp and the presence of very weak recent rocks in front of it are, on the other hand, evidence for its interpretation as a fault-line scarp.

The Harz is one of a number of similarly uplifted units; the

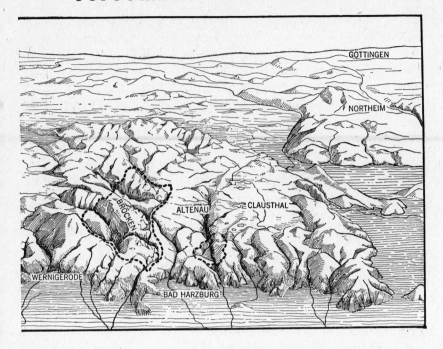

aspect. The remainder of the peneplaned upland is on shales and sand-
base is over weak recent sediments. Drawing by Elizabeth Burckmyer.

Thuringian Forest is another, in this general area. These others
are not such perfect horsts as the Harz but like it are lifted above
the surrounding lower lands. The Germans call such an assemblage of raised blocks a *schollenland*.

Massifs. Akin to horsts are the areally more extensive, and
structurally less simple, elevated, ancient, geomorphic units known
as *massifs*. The Spanish Meseta (Fig. 218), the Central Highlands
and Brittany in France, and the Laurentian Highlands of North
America are characteristic examples. Throughout the geological
ages these regions appear to have had the tendency to rise. At
times they were worn to low relief and perhaps transgressed by
the sea, as were the Central Highlands of France in relatively recent geological time, but always they have been again lifted up.

In general their areas are blocked out and cut off from the
surrounding lands by great fault displacements. In places, however, the declivity which affords the descent from the peneplaned

uplands to the lower lands is itself a warped peneplain surface. This type of intersection of two peneplain surfaces is referred to as a *morvan* (Fig. 219), from the type locality of that name in France. It has been said that a morvan is not in itself a land form but is, rather, the *problem* of the intersection of two peneplains. In the United States the intersection of the Piedmont

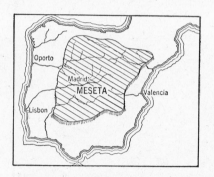

FIG. 218. THE SPANISH MESETA, A MASSIF

The representation is diagrammatic. Drawing by Elizabeth Burckmyer.

Province with the Fall Zone peneplain at the eastern border of the former is a morvan relationship.

Rift Valleys. Strictly speaking, "horst" is a geologic term and refers to the structural relations of the block rather than to its relief. The corresponding geologic word for a block that is depressed in relation to the surrounding rock units is *graben,* from the German word for "trench." The topographic basin that results from graben faulting is a *rift,* or *rift valley.* Rift valleys may develop along a single fault break, especially if the fault is one on which there has been recurrent movement. The San Andreas Rift in California (Fig. 220) along the fault of the same name is an example. Such rifts are also referred to as *earthquake rifts* (Fig. 221). The San Andreas Rift extends for many miles as a succession of linear valleys, narrow lake and pond basins, sags in slopes, and cols across ridges. These topographic effects are partly due to the displacements, partly to the readier yield of the shattered and ground-up rocks in the fault zone to weathering and subaerial erosion than that of the unaffected rock alongside.

It is demonstrated geomorphically that fault-block mountains and horsts are actually uplifted with reference to sea level, in that their upland surfaces are commonly of peneplain origin. It is difficult to show that a graben block, between two parallel faults,

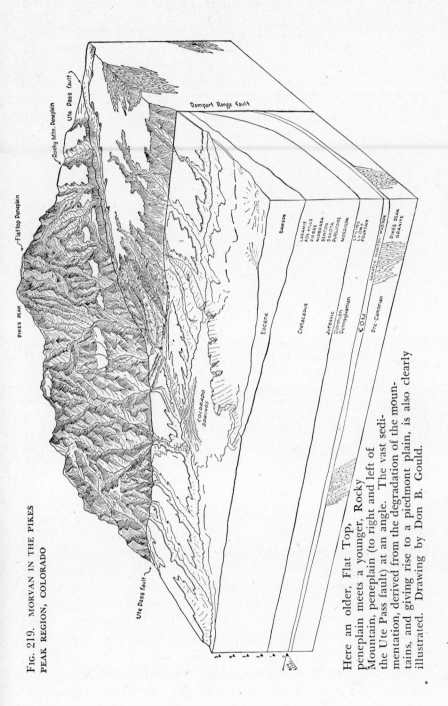

FIG. 219. MORVAN IN THE PIKES PEAK REGION, COLORADO

PIKES PEAK

Flattop Peneplain

Rocky Mtn. Peneplain

Ute Pass fault?

Ute Pass fault

Rampart Range fault

COLORADO SPRINGS

Eocene

Cretaceous

Jurassic

Permian
Pennsylvanian

€OM

Pre-Cambrian

DAWSON

LARAMIE
FOX HILLS
PIERRE
NIOBRARA
BENTON
DAKOTA
PURGATOIRE
MORRISON

LYKINS
LYONS
FOUNTAIN

SAWATCH MANITOU-MADISON

PIKES PEAK
GRANITE

Here an older, Flat Top, peneplain meets a younger, Rocky Mountain, peneplain (to right and left of the Ute Pass fault) at an angle. The vast sedimentation, derived from the degradation of the mountains, and giving rise to a piedmont plain, is also clearly illustrated. Drawing by Don B. Gould.

has sunk while the adjoining areas remained at rest (Fig. 222). Both the adjacent blocks may have risen leaving the graben area behind.

Small scale grabens of recent development are attributed to the faulting that occasioned the great Alaskan earthquake of 1899. This direct association of the graben, or rift feature, with differential movement of rock units, permits the inference that the large depressed block, that extends across the island of Capri

FIG. 220. RIFT VALLEY, SAN ANDREAS FAULT, SOUTHEAST FROM PALO PRIETO PASS, TEMPLAR RANGE, CALIFORNIA
Photograph from Spence Air Photos.

(Fig. 223) in the Mediterranean, bounded on each side by vertical walls, is of exactly similar origin. Lake Tahoe, at the angle of the boundary line between California and Nevada, occupies a basin created by the subsidence of a block, 200 square miles in area, between the main Sierra Nevada on the west and the associated Carson Range on the east (Reid, J. A., 1911, p. 106). The most famous graben is that of the upper Rhine Valley (Fig. 224). In this instance it has been established with certainty that the land to the north of the graben rose. The Hunsruck heights, on the west, and those of the Taunus, on the east of the Rhine, are the south-facing scarps of a cross fault and an uplifted block which cuts off the Rhine rift at its north end.   The Rhine gorge, which separates the Hunsruck and Taunus heights, is held to be ante-

FIG. 221.   EARTHQUAKE RIFT, DETAIL, NEAR MAMMOTH, CALIFORNIA
   As these rifts look immediately after movement on the fault break. Photograph from Frashers, Inc., Pomona, California.

cedent.   It is inferred that the Black Forest, east, and Vosges Mountains, west, on the two sides of the Rhine graben were uplifted at the same time.   This left the Rhine to wander over the floor of the graben, and gave it the task of cutting across the

rising mass blocking the graben on the north. The flat floor of
the graben is 20 miles wide and 200 miles long. It is composed
of alluvium, glacial deposits, and recent marine sediments. From
the presence of the marine beds it may be inferred that if the rift
area was not actually depressed it remained at a low altitude when
the blocks which bound it rose.

The Scottish Lowlands exhibit the characteristics of a graben in
diagrammatic perfection. They are bounded on the north and
south by long parallel scarps, the trace of well-defined faults. It
is, however, inferred that the present scarps are fault-line scarps.
Originally the site was one of graben depression, but thereafter
the whole region was reduced to a near-peneplain stage. The
existing relief is the product of differential erosion following a
general upwarping of the peneplaned area. The weaker rocks of

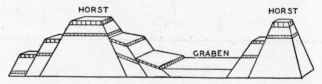

FIG. 222.   CONVENTIONALIZED DIAGRAM OF A GRABEN AND HORSTS

the Lowlands, stratified beds of Paleozoic age, have been again
degraded almost to sea level while the crystallines of the adjoining
blocks still retain summit surfaces at the altitudes acquired by the
upwarping of the peneplain. The Caledonian Rift, which like
the Lowlands also extends across the whole width of Scotland, is
a fault-line trace. It is, however, so narrow that the graben
concept seems inapplicable. Further, the depression, as such, is
almost certainly the result of differential erosion, partly by stream
action, partly by glacial action. It is perhaps best classified as a
rift, in origin similar to the San Andreas Rift, that is, developed
on a shatter belt resulting from fault movement.

The famous Death Valley (Fig. 225) in California has been
called a graben. It cannot well be ascribed to differential erosion
because it is a closed basin and its floor is below sea level. The
east side of Death Valley is a steep fault scarp (Fig. 230), the Tele-
scope and Black Mountains. The west side, however, is in part
formed by the long back slope of the tilted Panamint Mountains
block (Fig. 233). A sedimentary infilling of great thickness blan-

FIG. 223. DEPRESSED BLOCK, GRABEN, AND FAULT SCARP, ISLAND OF CAPRI, ITALY

kets this back slope and levels the bottom of the valley. In eastern
United States the basin of Lake George at the border of the Adi-

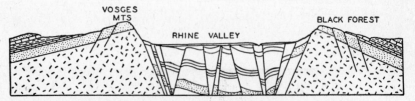

FIG. 224. GENERALIZED DIAGRAM OF THE RHINE VALLEY GRABEN

rondacks is probably a graben that has been somewhat rejuvenated in its topographic aspects by differential glacial erosion
along the axis of the trough.

FIG. 225. DEATH VALLEY, CALIFORNIA, FROM THE FAULT SCARP ON THE EAST SIDE
The view looks down on the deepest part of the valley.

The region commonly cited as the scene of most impressive
rifting is the Great Rift Valley of eastern Africa. The origin of
its remarkable features is an actively disputed topic. According

to the graben concept the depressed area sinks, or remains behind while the adjoining blocks rise.

Unless the parallel bounding fault planes are perfectly vertical it is readily appreciated that there is difficulty in providing a hole into which the depressed block may sink, or where it may remain while the adjacent units rise. If the planes of the opposed faults are of the inclined normal type, resulting from tensional stresses, their dips are toward the downthrow area between, and outline a wedge-shaped block. Any tendency toward foundering of such a block is stopped in the fashion that a tapered cork closes the

FIG. 226. THRUST FAULT, TOWANDA, PENNSYLVANIA

The force of the thrust, from right to left, would act to depress the foot wall on the left. This thrust fault has a low angle.

neck of a bottle (Fig. 222). This difficulty is met if it is conceived that the faulting involves a measurable sundering of the upthrow sides. The possible circumstances for such pulling apart are suggested by Taber (Taber, S., 1927) in an experiment with a block of wood cut to conform with inclined normal faulting and floated in water. The central wedge sinks and the side blocks tilt up. This representation presumes that the rifted blocks are in isostatic adjustment with the underlying, mobile sima.

The completely opposed view is that the grabens are produced by compression. In that case the breaks are thrust faults, with the bounding fault surfaces diverging with depth, and with movement of the border blocks inward toward the central wedge, which is then literally forced downward (Fig. 226). Overhanging fault scarps would be produced, but the overhang would have only a transitory existence, because secondary faulting, rock falls, and weathering would eliminate the forward thrust of the crests. On the other hand, steep back slopes away from the crests are suggestive of thrust. This interpretation is vigorously advocated by Willis (1936) for the East African Rift valleys and, by implication, applies to all items of the great linear series of rifts in Asia and Africa, including the Dead Sea, part of the Red Sea, and the African lakes Tanganyika and Nyassa, as well as many less well-known basins in that region. The rift valley is then more appro-

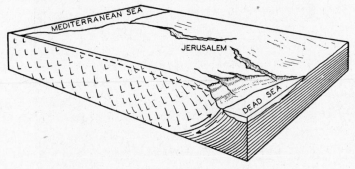

FIG. 227. THE DEAD SEA, AS A RAMP VALLEY

The high angle thrust fault on the left of the Dead Sea is matched by another similar fault, opposed as to the direction of the thrust, on the right side. After Bailey Willis.

priately termed a ***ramp valley*** (Wills, B., 1928). The chief idea of the ramp concept is that in a domed upwarp, resulting from compression, parallel, high-angle, thrust faults will develop, with the inclination of the fault planes opposed as to direction. In these circumstances the hanging-wall side of each fault will ride up and toward its counterpart. In so doing the two upthrust units exert a downward component of force on the wedge-shaped block which is the foot wall common to both faults. This wedge is depressed (Fig. 227). In its downward motion it induces basal melting by pressure and shear. Escape of the melt, by flow at depth, permits further subsidence of the central unit. It is presumed that the paired, opposed faults strike with the crest line of the upwarp.

SUMMARY

The initial diastrophic relief resulting from movement of blocks of the earth's crust by displacement on fault breaks is topographically preserved at many sites.   This conclusion was formerly much attacked but is now generally accepted.   Various criteria applied to fault-block mountains afford evidence that their fault-scarp declivities are the surface expression of the actual fault-block movements.   It is somewhat more difficult to discriminate between old fault scarps, produced by many times repeated small movements, and fault-line scarps which are brought into relief by erosion acting differentially on unlike structures on opposite sides of an ancient fault break.   However, such evidence as the presence of triangular fault facets suffices for identification of weathered fault scarps; the existence of rock differences on opposite sides of a fault, adequate to promote markedly unequal erosion, for the recognition of fault-line scarps.

Where normal faulting results in tilted fault blocks the displacement at right angles to the principal fault may be absorbed in lesser cross faults, or in a monoclinal flexure.   If the fault movement is in a nearly vertical plane the emergent or depressed block needs to be bounded by comparatively great fault breaks on all sides.   Horsts, massifs, and rift valleys result from this type of displacement.   As in the case of the tilted blocks the geomorphic expression of such tectonic units may be diastrophic or erosional.   For the greatest example of this kind, the Great African Rift, it has been proposed that compressive force ramped up the sides, and that the opposed thrust faults wedged down a central depressed block.

BIBLIOGRAPHY

CLASSICAL

King, C. (1870) *Report of the Geologic Survey of the Fortieth Parallel,* Vol. III, Mining Industry, Washington.

Gilbert, G. K. (1874) *Geographical and Geological Surveys West of the One Hundredth Meridian,* Progress Report, pp. 48–52, Washington.

Le Conte, J. (1889) *On the Origin of Normal Faults and of the Structure of the Basin Region,* American Journal of Science, Vol. 38, pp. 256–263.

Spurr, J. E. (1901) *Origin and Structure of the Basin Ranges,* Bulletin Geological Society of America, Vol. 12, pp. 217–270.

Davis, W. M. (1903) *Mountain Ranges of the Great Basin,* Bulletin Museum of Comparative Zoology, Vol. 42, pp. 129–177. Also in *Geographical Essays,* Ginn and Company, Boston, pp. 725–772.

Louderback, G. D. (1904) *Basin Range Structure of the Humboldt Region,* Bulletin Geological Society of America, Vol. 15, pp. 289–346.

RECENT

Louderback, G. D. (1926) *Morphologic Features of the Basin Range Displacements in the Great Basin,* University of California, Bulletin Department of Geologic Sciences, Vol. 16, No. 1.

Shepard, F. P. (1926) *Further Investigation of the Rocky Mountain Trench,* Journal of Geology, Vol. 34, pp. 623–641.

Taber, S. (1927) *Fault Troughs,* Journal of Geology, Vol. 35, pp. 577–606.

Blackwelder, E. (1928) *The Recognition of Fault Scarps,* Journal of Geology, Vol. 36, pp. 289–311.

Gilbert, G. K. (1928) *Studies of Basin Range Structure,* Professional Paper No. 153, United States Geological Survey, Washington.

Willis, B. (1928) *Dead Sea Problem: Rift Valley or Ramp Valley,* Bulletin Geological Society of America, Vol. 39, pp. 490–542.

Davis, W. M. (1930) *The Peacock Range Arizona,* Bulletin Geological Society of America, Vol. 41, pp. 293–313.

Chapter Eighteen

THE DESERT (OR ARID) GEOMORPHIC CYCLE

Introduction. The sequence of changes in landscape form commonly referred to as the "arid cycle" may be more appropriately called the "desert cycle." The designation desert cycle, however, should not be held to signify that stream processes are inoperative where the desert cycle prevails, still less to imply the complete absence of precipitation and runoff in desert territories. Actually the role of stream processes in the desert cycle is hardly less important than it is in the fluvial cycle. It is, rather, dissimilarity of circumstance and manner of application of fluvial processes that makes unlike the progress of the two cycles, and the forms that result from each.

The desert cycle obtains in deserts. It is a distinguishing feature of deserts that they are characteristically regions of interior drainage. Desert streams singly, or in small connected systems are land-terminated at both their upper and lower ends (Fig. 228). In the fluvial cycle perennial streams flow in unbroken continuity from upland sources to a final discharge of their waters in the sea. That is to say, they reach down to the general base level. By contrast, streams of the desert are characteristically intermittent and end in closed basins with floors that may be at any altitude above or, as in the instance of Death Valley, California (Fig. 225), even below sea level.

Desert Defined. Geomorphically, deserts in their large aspects are basins of initial endogenic deformation not filled (to overflowing) with water. As pointed out above, they are, hence, regions of interior drainage. However, the Nile, the Colorado, and the Indus rivers persist across the full width of deserts and reach the sea. While this fact may be held to invalidate the universal application of the interior-basin concept of deserts, it is significant to

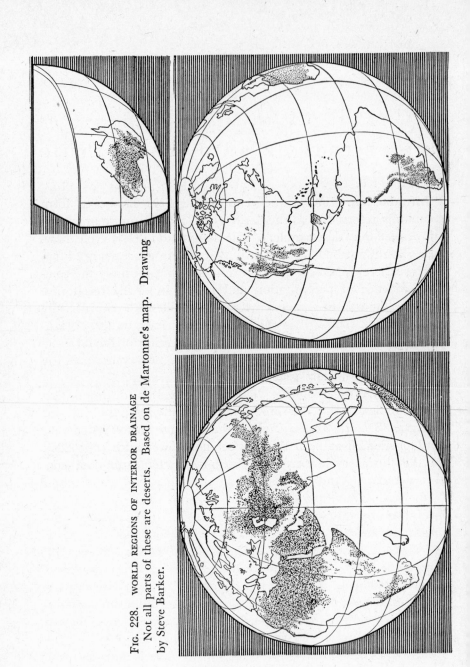

Fig. 228. WORLD REGIONS OF INTERIOR DRAINAGE.
Not all parts of these are deserts. Based on de Martonne's map. Drawing
by Steve Barker.

note that the desert geomorphic cycle is not fully operative in the areas transected by these streams,

Climatically deserts have been described as regions where evaporation exceeds precipitation; or, in relation to their vegetative aspects, as places where precipitation is too meager to maintain a continuous plant cover (Fig. 229). The characterization by plant cover has quantitative significance. There is a gradational transition from humid regions, where the cover of forest or turf is

FIG. 229. SAGE BRUSH AND CACTUS TYPE OF DESERT
The foreground growth is a Joshua Tree. In the Mohave Desert of California. Photograph by John Kirk.

unbroken, to steppe lands with bunch grasses, then to the sage brush and cactus type of deserts, and, finally, to lands almost devoid of plant growth.

It is where the nearly barren and wholly barren areas are also basins of diastrophic origin that the desert geomorphic cycle governs the evolution of the relief.

Reasons for Deficiency of Precipitation. The inadequacy of precipitation that occasions deserts results from several causes.

Tropical deserts occupy parts of the Trade Wind belts. The

constant Trades are normally evaporating winds because they
become progressively warmer as they descend from higher to
lower altitudes and proceed from higher to lower latitudes. The
air of the Trades may have considerable vapor in its composition.
Where they blow first over the sea, then over rising land, very
heavy precipitation results on the windward slopes. But in that
case the regions on the lee side of the uplands are exceptionally
dry. The Sahara and the Kalahari Desert in Africa, the Arabian
Desert, the Atacama Desert in South America and the interior of
Australia are Trade Wind deserts.

Less extreme desert conditions are induced by mountain barriers in other wind belts. Such areas are said to be in a rain
shadow. Thus the Gobi Desert, or Steppe, of Asia resides behind
the lofty Himalaya, and other mountain ranges north of India,
that block the wet monsoon. Outside the tropical regions some
degree of aridity also results from remoteness from the sea. The
vast land mass of Eurasia experiences this effect in its deep interior
parts.

Altogether approximately 30 per cent of the land surface of the
earth is at present under the desert regime, but not all of this
area has interior drainage (de Martonne, E., 1927, p. 402).

Nature of Desert Rainfall. Hardly less characteristic than the
deficiency of precipitation is the nature of the desert rainfalls.
To begin with, the deserts of most extreme aridity (the Atacama
is the driest) do not completely lack precipitation. At a given
place within the very dry deserts there may be no rain for several
years. However, even in such deserts every point probably re-
ceives enough precipitation to have the equivalent of 5 or more
inches of rain annually, if the amount received over a long period
of years is averaged.

Of as great geomorphic importance as the fact of precipitation
in the deserts is the manner of its occurrence. Desert rainfalls
are regularly torrential downpours over a restricted area. Mete-
orologically such rains are presumed to be the result of ascending
air currents. This inference is supported by their tendency to be
concentrated over highland regions either within or at the borders
of the desert. The highlands promote convectional air movement. Because of these circumstances a particular area of the
desert may receive the whole of its 5 inches of "average" annual

rainfall in one terrific downpour lasting, perhaps, less than an hour. If this is the extreme case, it is nevertheless representative of the phenomenon. The result of such precipitation is flood-

FIG. 230. MOUNTAIN VALLEY, WASHES AND ALLUVIAL FAN, DEATH VALLEY, CALIFORNIA
    Looking east from Surveyor's Well. Photograph, copyright, from Spence Air Photos.

flow, commonly very violent, because, as the rainfall tends to center over highlands, the water is immediately collected in well-defined channels and hurried down steep gradients. Where the furrowed uplands join the lower slopes of the basin floors the valley torrents become wide sheetfloods, or cut characteristic wide, flat-bottomed, steep-walled channels, called *washes* (Figs. 134, 230), in previously deposited accumulations of alluvial-fan debris.

Initial Stage.   For an analysis of the desert geomorphic cycle it is not necessary to specify the nature of the structure. Moreover, the initial relief may be any topography other than that of a level plateau or the surface of a peneplain.   But as the desert condition is intimately linked with the occurrence of basined lands, it is appropriate to assume the pre-existence of a wide, depressed area rimmed about with mountain barriers.   Within the general depression there may be local elevations of considerable extent and height, and numerous lesser basins at various altitudes, as in the Sahara, and in the Great Basin country of western United States (Plate V).

Desert Weathering.   Like all rocks subaerially exposed, those of the desert are subjected to the disintegrating and decomposing processes of weathering (Fig. 69).   Desert rock weathering differs from the weathering of humid regions in that solvent chemical action, dependent on the presence of abundant supplies of water, or continuous availability of moisture, is inoperative or ineffective in the desert territories.   The sufficient evidence of this difference is that, when limestone or feldspathic rocks weather in desert areas, the derived waste contains unaltered (relatively) carbonate and feldspar fragments.   In humid regions limestones are completely dissolved and feldspars are wholly decomposed to clayey materials.

Although enough water for complete solution or decomposition is not ordinarily available in deserts, chemical action nevertheless plays a large part in desert weathering.   The desert rocks are occasionally drenched by rain and may be moistened more or less regularly by dew.   Such wetting promotes a subtle but pervading hydration (accompanied by carbonation and oxidation) of the exterior rock material.   The surfaces of rocks exposed in the desert also experience great extremes of temperature difference within a few hours, from excessive insolation alternating with extremely rapid heat loss by radiation.   The different minerals of a rock such as granite expand and contract unequally to a significant degree when thus heated and cooled, with the result that stresses adequate to break down the coherence of the rock are induced.   The chemical processes referred to above tend to facilitate such disintegration by bringing about varying volume changes in the different minerals.   The sum result of these several actions is to cause granular disintegration, especially marked in coarse crystalline rocks, and the accumulation of waste made up of angular fragments of crystal

FIG. 231.   DESERT WEATHERING OF COARSE CRYSTALLINE ROCK, DEEP SPRING, CALIFORNIA

grain coarseness referred to as *grus* (Fig. 231). Grus in turn breaks down to make sharp, fine sand. The grus piles up at the base of ledges and around detached boulders.

The edges of the outcrops and the surfaces of the boulders are regularly rounded off to approximately spherical curves (Fig. 50).

This rounded form is the exterior contour of a shell of rock concentric to an interior solid core. The shell is either visibly or incipiently detached from the main mass of rock. Such peeling of rock is called "exfoliation." It is a moot question whether exfoliation results chiefly from the far greater range of temperature difference experienced by the exterior rock zone than by the inner mass under the extreme conditions of desert heating and cooling, with consquent differential expansive and contractile stresses, or from expansive stresses in the outer shell resulting from hydration and other chemical processes that bring about increases in volume (Blackwelder, E., 1925).

It appears, accordingly, that both processes, the heating and cooling and the slow chemical alterations are each in part responsible for both the granular disintegration and the exfoliation peels which together provide the characteristic and main aspects of desert weathering.

The available evidence indicates that desert weathering is relatively slow. However, the lack of a plant cover means continuous exposure. As time passes the mantle of residual waste could become complete. But this is ordinarily prevented by the erosional processes characteristic of the desert cycle.

The Stage of Youth. A region in the desert cycle has its maximal relief in the stage of youth. Otherwise stated, the relief of the initial endogenic deformation is the greatest relief attained in the desert cycle. All later stages are marked by reduction of the initial relief.

• As soon as a region is subjected to the climatic conditions of the desert, desert weathering of its rocks begins. Waste accumulates. A desert cloudburst occurs. The fine waste, and much coarse stuff as well, is hurtled from the high to the low spots in violent torrents. The phenomenon of rain-gulley erosion on bare slopes in humid lands is here presented a hundred times, a thousand times magnified (Fig. 232). The mountain sides are almost instantaneously gashed with great gutters, channels of consequent stream flow.

In this sequence the summit areas have meanwhile been slightly reduced in altitude by weathering. In larger measure the separate basins have had their floors raised by a fill of waste. A very small basin may temporarily be filled to overflowing with water. But such discharge withers away as it descends into a lower, broader basin. Thus all the waste is caught and held within the desert, and all the streams are separate units with intermittent, short-lived flow. The combined effect of weathering, wash, and fill is to reduce the measure of the initial relief.

It is important to notice, further, that there is very little opportunity for the development of either master consequent or subsequent valleys. The downpour which centers over one area will only by coincidence be centered on the same spot the next time.

Fig. 232.   Consequent stream channels on desert mountain sides, deep spring valley, California

As a result of this random incidence of concentrated stream action the consequent stream channels are maintained at approximate equality of size (Fig. 232). Differences in rock strength and structural variations in resistance have comparatively little significance because the persistently effective differential erosion required to make them manifest is not operative.

Where extreme differences in rock resistance are present, or where the original slopes provide an exceptionally wide drainage area for a single consequent stream, some degree of adjustment to structure may be noted, or a valley of larger than average size may be excavated. These larger channels do not, however, function significantly as master consequents. The secondary drainage tributary to them and to the other consequents is not progressively concentrated in subsequent courses because it flows only intermittently and at random. Competitive development of valleys in relation to structure is precluded. The secondary streams keep to an essentially insequent pattern, "developed under accidental controls of which no definite account can be given." (Davis, W. M., 1894. In *Geographical Essays*, p. 174.)

Stage of Maturity. Continuation of the processes of weathering and of intermittent erosion brings about the progressive filling of the basins with waste. Eventually first one, then another, and so on, of the higher level basins is filled to overflowing with the debris. Further supplies are then washed down into the next lower basin. Or, headwater erosion of a consequent channel on the slope between two basins may lead to the capture of the upper level basin by breaching its rim. Then a rapid dissection of the deposits in the upper basin occurs. If these have, meanwhile, been partially consolidated by cementation, some very fantastic erosion pillars may be fashioned in the course of their removal (Fig. 171).

By these several means, longer and longer continuous slopes are progressively developed from the highest altitudes toward the lowest depression within the desert. If a broad structural basin is accepted as the unit area in which the course of the desert cycle is to be run, the highest altitude will normally be the rimming mountains. The lowest depression does not need to be, and probably will not be, central to the basin. Wherever it is, drainage will extend centripetally toward it and tend to become integrated with respect to it as a focal point. The measure of relief within the desert continues to be diminished. The summits are lowered by weathering and wash; the basin floors are raised by fill. When unbroken gradients are everywhere established from the high places to the locus of the deepest depression, the stage of middle maturity is attained in the desert cycle.

It deserves to be noted that up to the point when the stage of middle maturity is reached, stream processes are dominant in the desert cycle. Their application is different, and their sum effect is other, than in the fluvial, or humid, cycle. But the desert relief up to this stage, no less than relief in the humid regions, is the result of water action.

In the earlier stages of the desert cycle the intermittent, consequent streams are in general shorter than the slopes. Stream action is discontinuous at the lower as well as at the upper ends. The valleys are far larger than would be eroded by an equal volume of perennial drainage on equally steep gradients in the fluvial cycle because the stream erosion of the desert cycle is almost exclusively effected by flood-flow.

The consequent streams cut channels into the steeper slopes, but on emerging from these and spreading over the basin floors they shift abruptly from rapid downwearing to prodigious aggradation. Alluvial fans of impressive size are quickly built up (Fig. 230). The great volume of material in the fans results from the fact that all the weathering waste of the slopes and all the material removed in making the valleys is contributed to their upbuilding. In the humid cycle, by contrast, the rock debris is continuously in process of transportation, at varying rates, down slopes and downvalley toward the sea. The alluvial fan, accordingly, has its greatest magnificence of development in desert regions. The fans in the lower courses of neighboring parallel consequents soon become laterally confluent and are then referred to as *coalescing alluvial fans.* When the coalescence is perfected all around a basin the continuous waste slope at the foot of the mountain declivities is called a *bajada* (Fig. 233).

Not uncommonly a flood-flow of exceptional volume and violence bursts from a canyon mouth. The water may then be competent to tear a channel across the whole width of the previously accumulated fan. Near the head of the fan such a channel may be 50 or more feet deep and hundreds of feet wide. In western United States such channels are called washes, in the Sahara *wadis.* The deeper continuations of washes extending to the mouths of the mountain canyons are called *arroyos.*

The upper surfaces of the desert fans between the washes, that is the surfaces of the undissected portions of the fans, in representative examples are made up of coarse angular and subangular rock fragments so arranged as to make a very smooth floor sometimes referred to as the *desert pavement* (Fig. 234). In origin the material of the desert pavement is the deposit of the less vio-

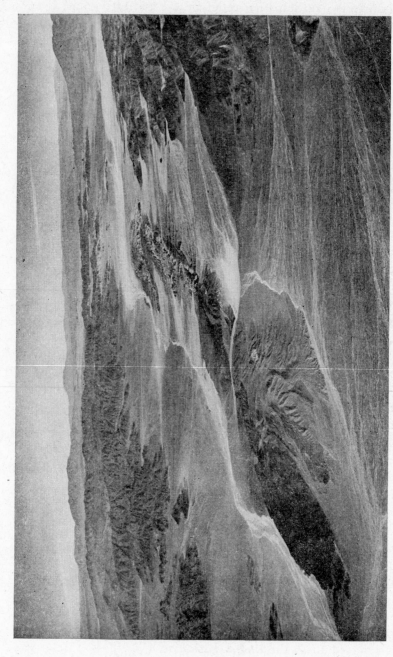

FIG. 233. COALESCING ALLUVIAL FANS FORM A BAJADA, DEATH VALLEY, CALIFORNIA
Looking southeast toward Avawatz Mountains. Photograph, copyright, from Spence Air Photos.

410

lent stream flows from the mountain valleys. Once deposited this water-laid debris is subjected to rainwash and wind-sifting. These processes convey away the finer particles from the surface parts and leave the coarser fragments as a tightly fitting cover. In the Libyan Sahara similar surface sheets, there composed of coarse rounded pebbles, a **pebble armor,** are known as *serir;* in the western Sahara smaller rounded pebbles, tightly packed, consti-

FIG. 234.   DESERT PAVEMENT, DEEP SPRING VALLEY, CALIFORNIA

The smooth surface of the undissected fan is a mosaic of small, angular, rock fragments.

tute the *reg,* which has proved to be a fine surface for automobile travel.

Playas. Flood waters that do not tear out a wash spread over the surfaces of the desert alluvial fans and a large part of their volume filters into the porous deposits. Surface flow may disappear completely before it reaches the outer edge of the fan. Later some of this absorbed water returns to the surface by capillary movement and is lost to the air by evaporation. Some of the underground water emerges at the toe of the fan, and then gives rise to one type of *oasis* (Fig. 235). Floods of sufficient volume to succeed in crossing the full width of the bajada slopes as a surface flow convey clayey sediment to the interior sections of the desert basins. Immediately after a cloudburst a shallow lake of muddy water will occupy wide areas of a central depression. Such ephemeral water bodies are called *playa lakes.* As the playa lakes evaporate they leave the suspended sediments behind, mixed with

FIG. 235. SMALL OASIS UNDER NATURAL CONDITIONS, BENNETT'S WELLS, DEATH VALLEY, CALIFORNIA

Results from emergence of spring water from distant mountain sources. Photograph from Frashers, Inc., Pomona, California.

fine salt crystals. Such deposits commonly build up clay-surface plains of extraordinary flatness, referred to as *playas* (Fig. 236). Playas are characteristic features of many deserts. In the Sahara they are called *sebchas;* in Persia, *kewire;* in Transcaspia, *takyre.* If the percentage of salts in the sediments is high, the flat when dry will have a salt-encrusted surface and is then called a *salina.* The word "salina" is also used to designate a clear-water salt lake (Fig. 237) or a pond that endures between floods in the lowest depression of a basin and is fed by underground percolation.

Playas and salinas have varied characteristics. A basin that still lacks much of the alluvial deposit necessary to fill it commonly has a permanent water-salina, especially if the surrounding mountains are sufficiently high and extensive to afford some perennial stream flow. Although fed by relatively fresh underground water such salinas are kept salty by evaporation at the surface. In Death

FIG. 236.   PLAYA AT BONNIE CLARE, NEVADA

The flat, smooth, hard clay surface is used as an automobile speedway by the local people.

Valley only small, salt-encrusted pools are present. Basins that have been so deeply filled with debris as to have almost level floors are usually dry.

Bolson. A small, intermontane desert basin does not merit designation by a specific term. Where, however, the drainage is centripetal, with gentle gradients toward the low point of an extensive, mountain-girt, alluvium-floored basin, the term *bolson* applies (Fig. 238). In northern Mexico the boundary between one bolson and that of the next is, in places, only a low divide.

If the fill of a bolson site attains a level sufficiently high to permit
overflow occasionally across the lowest divide separating it from
the next lower basin (Plate V), the place may be designated a
semibolson.

Maturity to Old Age in the Desert Cycle. Up to this point
description of the stages of the desert cycle is authenticated by
evidence gained from observation in the field. Much of the
evidence has been collected in the Basin and Range province of
western United States. In general this region is just short of having attained the stage of perfect middle maturity in the desert
cycle. In places the drainage there has been integrated over
wide areas, as, for example, the region that has Great Salt Lake
in Utah for its focal point. In other places of this province basins
remain unfilled and isolated from one another. But it can safely
be inferred that a continuation of the processes currently operating will result in linking up the isolated basins into larger wholes.
One reason why this development to perfect middle maturity has
not been achieved everywhere in the Basin and Range province is
the recurrence of the basin-making, fault-block movements.
Where these shifts have deepened the basins from time to time
their filling or outletting has been delayed. This effect is parallel
to that resulting from interruption of the fluvial cycle by uplift of
the land.

Beyond the stage of maturity the course of the desert cycle is
more a matter of deduction and conjecture. Not all of the inferred steps can be matched by actual occurrences. What is held
to be an end stage may have some other origin; there is no general
agreement in regard to the place in the sequence or with respect
to the interpretation of certain observed phenomena that appear
to belong in intermediate stages.

Once a wide tract of desert has been converted to a bolson it
may be assumed that running water will have only a minor role
in the further modification of the desert land forms. The surrounding mountain barrier will then have been lowered by
degradation and will therefore be much less effective in inducing
precipitation. Smaller quantities of debris will be brought to
the basin because the slopes above its floor will be less steep and
less numerous.

The old age stage in the desert cycle is therefore assumed to

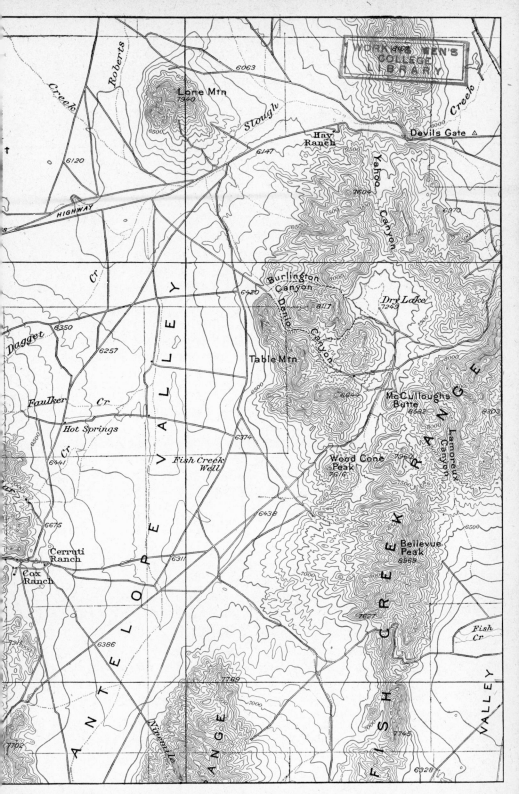

PLATE V. Fault-Block Mountain Ranges, Basins and Pediments. Part of the Roberts Mountains, Nevada, quadrangle map of the United States Geological Survey. Horizontal scale 1/250,000, contour interval 100 feet. Fish Creek Range is a fault-block mountain. Lone Mountain (a born-hardt?) is pedimented over diverse rock types (observations of Laurence Nugent). Antelope Valley is draining its fill to lower basins through Devils Gate.

Fig. 237.   SALINA, SOUTH END OF DEEP SPRING VALLEY, CALIFORNIA.

FIG. 238.   BOLSON: THE CHALCO VALLEY SOUTH OF MEXICO CITY, MEXICO
Cinder cones rise above the level of the bolson plain.   San Andreas Village.

comprise the circumstances attending the modification of bolson plains of alluviation and integrated drainage.

Deflation. Where widespread plains with surfaces composed of fine-textured, dry alluvium are present in desert regions the wind can act effectively as a transporting medium. The vast, level reaches, uninterrupted by plant cover or topographic irregularity, permit the full force of the gusts to be exerted on the loose surface materials. The sand storms of desert areas are a well-known phenomenon. Sand and dust are lifted and conveyed by the wind in sufficient volume to blacken the sky and to cause men and animals caught in them to be in danger of suffocation.

The coarser particles are for the most part driven along horizontally near the ground. Where they encounter any rock projection they exercise a sandblast erosive action. The chief characteristic of such erosion is its undercutting effect. As the wind, unlike water eroding a channel, is not confined to any one line, or even one direction, the erosion and undercutting can take place from all sides. When, by this action, a steep slope or summit mass has been rendered unstable and topples down, the fragments at the base are in turn attacked and reduced. Then the attack on the remainder of the original projection can be renewed. Another characteristic of the sandblast erosion of the wind is its searching differentiation between even slight variations in rock resistance. Resistance in this case is primarily a matter of difference in hardness and degree of cementation. Every little inequality of durability is found out and brought into relief. As a result of undercutting, and of this differential erosive action, wind-eroded rocks in desert areas have commonly very fantastic forms (Fig. 239).

Wind erosion was long regarded as a very potent process in the development of desert geomorphology. More recently competent opinion inclines to assign much less importance to it. Wind erosion undoubtedly functions but probably neither so rapidly nor so comprehensively as was once thought.

In part wind erosion is the self-abrasion of the sand particles that are in motion. By this action coarse sand grains are reduced to the texture of dust. Impacts on rock ledges also wear down the sand grains. Much more material of dust-fineness is available directly from the alluvial deposits. Such dust can be lifted high by minor, upmoving currents in the major forward sweep of the wind. Once aloft, huge volumes of the dust particles can be carried along for great distances and may be conveyed beyond the desert confines.

The erosion, transportation, and exportation effected by the wind, taken together, comprise the general process of *deflation.* As this word was originally applied it referred only to the winnowing out and exportation of the dust. But "deflation" may be used to advantage as the counterpart, in discussion of the desert cycle, of the word "degradation" as used in analyses of the fluvial cycle. Through deflation, thus conceived, the altitude of desert

FIG. 239. UNUSUAL FORMS FROM WIND EROSION, LIBYAN DESERT, AFRICA
After Johannes Walther.

plains is lowered and their substance conveyed beyond the desert territories.

Loess. The dust exported by the wind to regions outside the desert territories, hence to regions in the fluvial geomorphic cycle, is, when accumulated in deposits of appreciable size, called *loess.* Loess has a number of particular characteristics resulting from its origin. Some of these, although geologically important, are not of great geomorphic significance. On the other hand, the extent, surface expression, and dissection-relief of loess deposits are items of considerable geomorphic interest.

Dust from the Sahara seems to be carried chiefly westward over the Atlantic and is therefore lost from view through deposit on the ocean bottom. Sahara dust is also scattered occasionally and thinly over the Mediterranean regions of Europe. Probably dust

from the Arabian, Indian, Australian, and South African deserts
is similarly disposed of. That is, its volume may not be great in
proportion to the size of the source areas; if it is great, it may be
carried out to sea, or it may be widely dispersed over adjacent
lands. In any event, no large deposits of loess obviously derived
from these desert tracts are known. There are extensive loéss
areas in the Pampas country of Argentina. Other marked accumulations occur in the Danube, Rhine, and Mississippi River

FIG. 240. TOPOGRAPHIC EXPRESSION OF LOESS DEPOSITS NEAR FORD, KANSAS
Photograph by H. T. U. Smith.

basins (Fig. 240). The Mississippi loess comes in part from the
Great Plains. The regions peripheral to the Central Asiatic
deserts (Fig. 241), however, are especially noteworthy as sites of
loess accumulation (estimated to cover 230,000 square miles of
surface).

The large, continuous area of wind-deposited loess of China
occurs in the central region of the Hwang Ho drainage system
(Fig. 242). Although the Chinese loess mantles hill and valley
alike, and occurs at altitudes up to 5000 feet, it is primarily a
basin fill. It is said to attain a thickness of 1000 feet in places;
more generally it is 300 to 400 feet deep. These thicknesses are

FIG. 241. LOESS TOPOGRAPHY AND STEEP-WALLED CANYON IN LOESS
In the steppe land of Turkestan, near Bokhara. Photograph by W. Rickmer Rickmers.

adequate to give rise to a gently undulating topography of constructional origin which is the characteristic aspect of a loess plain.
Such a plain may extend undissected over wide territories.

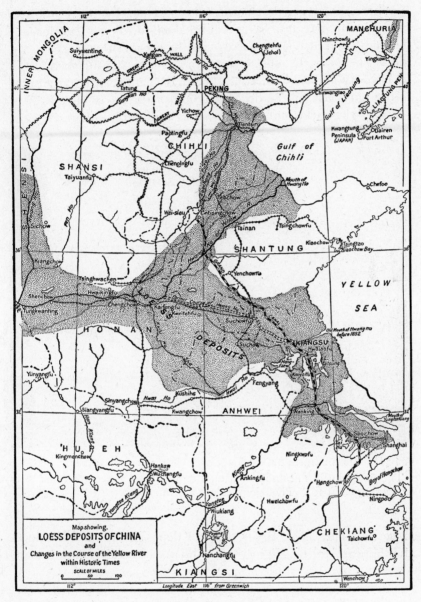

FIG. 242. LOESS DEPOSITS OF THE HWANG HO BASIN OF CHINA
After Collier Cobb.

419

Where, however, the Chinese loess is cut by the erosion of intermittent streams, remarkably steep-sided gorges develop. Though composed of fine particles, in homogeneous masses, the loess, when cut through, stands up in vertical walls because of its porosity and because of a structural characteristic (attributed to the pores left by the decomposition of the lower ends of grass roots, as the surface of the deposit is built up) which gives rise

FIG. 243. LOESS DEPOSIT OVER GLACIAL TILL AT OMAHA, NEBRASKA

The fine-grained, unconsolidated loess stands up as a steep cliff and rests on (dark) glacial till. Photographer not known.

to vertical cleavage. In its original depositional state the loess also appears to be slightly consolidated by calcium-carbonate cement.

Not uncommonly the bottoms of the gorges in the Chinese loess are used as highways. Then the loess, puddled by traffic, becomes a sticky sludge when wet, loose dust when dry, and is again subject to transport by water and wind. Under these circumstances the canyons are in time extraordinarily deepened, the while retaining their vertical walls and narrow width.

Loess deposits not directly associated with existing desert regions, particularly those of the Rhine Basin, and of the eastern side of the Mississippi, probably have glacio-fluvial conditions as their background. At the close of the Pleistocene ice epochs, in particular after the advance preceding the Wisconsin in North America (Würm in Europe), vast tracts of country adjoining the ice fronts were exposed, without benefit of a protective plant cover, to strong downglacier winds. The flood plains of the larger rivers were then the source of great dust clouds, made up of the silt and rock flour of the glacier's detritus (Fig. 243). The earlier ice sheets seem to have wasted under more arid conditions than those associated with the Wisconsin retreat, and it is inferred that the loess was chiefly accumulated during interglacial times. However great quantities of dust are still being brought from glacio-fluvial areas in New Zealand, South Island, to sites where extensive loess deposition took place in the Pleistocene, when the source glacierization was much greater. The circumstances of the New Zealand occurrence afford confirmation of the general interpretation of the river-basin loess deposits as of glacio-fluvial origin, and indicate, by continuance of the deposition to the present, that extreme aridity was not an essential factor in such development. R. J. Russell (1941) is convinced that the loess of the Lower Mississippi Valley is the product of leaching and alteration of Pleistocene flood-plain silts and clays, and suspects the validity of the hypothesis of eolian origin for the loess of other regions.

Dunes and Erg.   At particular sites in deserts the sand grains that are moved along close to the ground collect in characteristic accumulations called *dunes.*   It is usually said that a dune is started by the presence of some obstruction, a plant (Fig. 244) or rock outcrop, in the lee of which the sand piles up. But it may well be that irregularities of the wind currents suffice of themselves to cause deposits of sand to build up at certain spots. Then there are places where rapidly disintegrating sandstones, in projecting masses, furnish a large volume of sand grains to particular courses of the wind. In the line of this supply dunes start. Once begun the dune-heap tends to be maintained, to increase in size, to take special forms, and to migrate.

The free progress of additional sand brought by the wind is stopped when the windward side of an incipient dune is encountered. The nuclear hummock is a windbreak. But the wind is nevertheless competent to roll grains up the relatively gentle slope formed by deposit on the windward side. Thus the size and height of the dune are increased. At some limiting height, governed probably by the volume of the sand supplied and the average force of the wind, further material is swept over the crest, and, encountering the calm area immediately behind the dune, falls down the leeward side (Fig. 245). The leeward slope is therefore as steep as the angle of repose of the loose sand permits, and may be even steeper than that if a wind eddy is effective.

Isolated dunes have ideally the **barchane** (from Turkestan, variously spelled **barchan, barkhan**) form, in outline that of a

Fig. 244.   DUNE BUILDING UP BEHIND SAGE BRUSH, DEEP SPRING VALLEY, CALIFORNIA

lunar crescent. The windward slope is the convex side; the horns point down wind. The barchane is highest in the center; the surface, as well as the outline of the windward slope, is convex. The lee slope tends to be concave because a back eddy of the wind acts to hollow it out. Barchanes are held to be the elementary dune form and are inferred to be the product of a moderate supply of sand and moderate wind velocities. A nucleus starts, builds up to the equilibrium height, then develops the characteristic barchane shape by migration. Grains are moved from the base to the top and dropped on the lee side without being immediately replaced at the starting point. Thus the dune as a whole is shifted piecemeal down the wind. The crescent form develops because, with a uniform force of wind approaching the dune, the sand must be moved over a longer course and to a greater height at the center than at the sides. The particle by particle migration of the dune therefore proceeds more rapidly at the ends, and the characteristic barchane, sickle form results. Where many partial barchane forms are aggregated in an exten-

FIG. 245. WINDWARD (LEFT) AND LEEWARD (RIGHT) SIDES OF A DUNE, WEST OF SYRACUSE, KANSAS
Photograph by H. T. U. Smith.

sive dune tract, the arcuate crests make knife-edges called *sifs* in the Sahara (Fig. 246). More massive summits above the general level are *oghurds*.

With diminishing sand supply or stronger winds a barchane may experience a *blowout* (Fig. 247); that is, a hollow is eroded in the central highest section of the windward side. In time the barchane may be completely bisected by this process and give rise to parallel dunes greatly elongated in the direction of the prevailing winds. Blowouts are regularly a feature of shore dunes in humid climates where the dune mass tends to be fixed by vegetation.

The origin, generally speaking, of longitudinal dunes is not a fully solved problem. They appear to be the forms character- istically present in desert interiors, (Libyan, Sahara, and Australian deserts) where strong, steady winds prevail, while the barchanes are desert border forms in areas of weak and shifting winds. At some sites complicated, intersecting systems of dunes develop.

The barchane type of isolated dune migrates most freely; longitudinal dunes remain nearly fixed in position; in the first instance

FIG. 246. EXTENSIVE TRACT OF BARCHANE DUNES AT YUMA, ARIZONA
The prevailing wind is from the left. The knife-edges of the dune crests are characteristic sifs. The picture also illustrates the development of gassi. Photograph, copyright, from Spence Air Photos.

accumulation seemingly dominates, in the second the wind has erosive effectiveness. In the Sahara long sand-free passages between dunes, called *gassi,* are apparently kept clear by the sweep of the wind (Fig. 247).

The popular idea that deserts are vast expanses of sandy waste gets support from bolson occurrences in the American West, interior Mexico, the eastern Persian and Tibetan deserts. The further conception that these sandy tracts are prevailingly sand-dune regions is, however, greatly in error.   It is said that only one-ninth of the Sahara is occupied by dunes.

Nevertheless, wide regions, called erg in the Sahara, **koum** in Asia, are continuous dune tracts.   The Libyan erg extends over an area as great as that of Texas.   Curiously, these great ergs seem to remain absolutely fixed in position.   It is suspected that those in the Sahara constitute only a mantle of sand, with heights and depressions related to an underlying rock topography which anchors the erg as a whole.   The surface forms of the dunes

FIG. 247.   BLOWOUTS ON DUNES ON THE EAST SHORE OF LAKE ONTARIO, N. Y.

change, but the shift of the sand is only back and forth within the area of the erg.   The great erg regions seem, further, to be remainders of earlier, vast, stream-transported, bolson deposits or to be derived from such accumulations.   If so, inner moisture may assist in keeping them areally stable.   Or it may be that shifting winds prevent the transfer of the sand beyond a limited circle.

Hammada.   In the deductive analysis of the desert cycle deflation is considered to be the dominant process after maturity, assuming maturity to be marked by the integration of drainage over a wide bolson area.   Under those circumstances the wind can sweep unhampered across the flat reaches of waste.   It piles up dunes, it whips up ergs. Through the attrition they experience in the sandstorm and in the sandblast the sand grains are worn to dust. The dust is winnowed out and conveyed beyond the desert. Thus the desert surface is slowly lowered. In consequence of such lowering bedrock surfaces are here and there exhumed.

The exposed bedrock areas immediately become the sites of active sandblast attack. They are undercut (Fig. 239) and truncated or horizontally abraded. Where steady winds blow, particular forms such as the *yardangs* of the central Asiatic deserts develop. These are long, weirdly undercut rock ridges separated by passageways through which the wind rushes as in a chute. If the rock is easily eroded, a shallow depression may be excavated in its surface. Although it has been conjectured that some of the deeper rock basins of the Sahara are the product of wind erosion, it is more probable that these larger hollows are of endogenic origin, perhaps enlarged and modified by wind action.

It is inferred that, normally, a shallow, wind-eroded depression would be refilled with debris (washed by rain from adjoining areas covered by waste) before it could be dug very deep. Once such interchanges are being made the stage of maturity gives over to that of old age in the desert cycle. The previously integrated drainage is progressively dissevered, as one after another of the shallow basins develops and collects the local drainage. Presumably the rock floors of the margins of the basins would be first exposed because there the cover of waste would be least thick. However, the stage of shallow rock basins alternating with waste-covered, flat divides — the topography appropriate to such dissevered drainage — does not seem to be represented by any actual occurrence. Perhaps the wash of waste so generally keeps the basins full that the flatness of maturity is never destroyed. Some of the bolsons of New Mexico explored by boring are reported to have only a very thin cover of waste over a rocky floor (Keyes, C. R., 1908, p. 66).

In this manner rock surfaces nearly level and covered with only a thin veneer of debris are progressively extended over wider and wider areas. As the material is washed back and forth the less resistant fragments are gradually reduced to dust and exported. Eventually only a pavement of flints, cherts, quartzites, and the like obdurate rock stuff remains. The pebbles composing the surface are commonly facetted by wind erosion to the characteristic *dreikanter* shape. The desert has become a broad expanse of level rock floor, thinly and incompletely covered with these *lag gravels.* Such is the deduced end stage of the desert cycle — desert leveling without base-leveling.

Unlike the inferred preceding stage, which should exhibit shallow basins separated by flat rock divides, but which does not seem to be representatively developed as a natural occurrence, numerous extensive regions of desert rock floor are known. In the Sahara such widespread areas of flat, bare, rock floor are called *hammada* and there appear as a topographic element in marked contrast with the erg, or sand desert. The hammada development is also present in the Atacama Desert, in inner Australia, and in southwest Africa. It is, however, very much an open question whether the flat rock floors of the desert region, anywhere, were actually wrought in accordance with the deduced succession of the desert cycle as outlined above. The scheme is rational — the idea, that a rock plain could be produced, thus, at any altitude and independent of any fixed base level very intriguing. But hammada has many aspects, and even where the case for leveling without base-leveling best applies, there are very puzzling phenomena.

Over wide areas on both sides of the Nile, and in the interior of the Sahara where the rocks are flat-lying beds, there are level surfaces of bare rock, or rock thinly veneered with coarse debris. Presumably these regions never had a more irregular relief. What is seen there is the product of a leveling down by wind erosion of tableland areas to some particular resistant bed, that is, a species of stripped plain is developed. A residue of refractory stuff from the formerly overlying, in general less durable, rock masses, may, of itself, constitute the protective mat that prevents further reduction in level. In the Arabian Desert such hammada plains at different levels are separated by escarpments. These Arabian hammadas cannot well have acquired their platform-step relationship by wind erosion, although the surfaces of each of the flats may be of such origin.

Inselbergs and Bornhardts. The translation of the German word *inselberg* is "island mountain." The English phrase "island mountain" could be understood to refer to any isolated peak. In geomorphology the German "inselberg" has a more restricted application. To be an inselberg the mountain must rise from a wide expanse of plain or plateau surface. Many volcanic cones and divers other summits could, even with this limitation, be referred to as inselbergs.

"Inselberg," however, was originally used to designate a genetically distinctive feature. And the landscape in which this feature was prominently developed was appropriately called an *inselberg-landschaft*. The later application of both these terms to designate the occurrence of isolated peaks of varied origin makes it desirable to seek a new word to specify the phenomenon "inselberg" in its original meaning. For this purpose the term *bornhardt,* after Bornhardt, who first described inselbergs, has been suggested.

At the place of their most representative occurrence, which is on the plateau uplands of East Africa, bornhardts are isolated summits ranging from some tens of feet to a thousand or more feet in height. Typically the bornhardts consist of gneiss, and rise directly from a floor of gneiss. The transition from the level plateau surface to the steep slopes of the base of a bornhardt is so abrupt as to constitute the most perfect of knicks. A residual red clay covers the base of the African bornhardts; the gneiss plain is thinly mantled with yellowish and grayish brown sands and pebbles. But below this sand mantle the rock plain is found to have an essentially level surface. The bornhardts exhibit an islandlike emergence (Plate V) from the rock plain. Bailey Willis (1936, p. 117) lists the characteristics of bornhardts in the type region as follows: they have bare, domelike summits; their forms reflect the internal rock structure; their slopes steepen at the base; no talus is present.

Except that the bornhardts are seemingly composed of the same rock as the plateau surface, they could be considered monadnocks. Then, however, the level upland surface would need to be interpreted as a peneplain. If it is a peneplain it has an extraordinary perfection of development and preservation despite its present high altitude. The knick feature and the occurrence in semiarid and desert regions are further difficulties with the facile monadnock and peneplain solution.

Passarge and Davis were of the conviction that this type of level upland, together with its bornhardts, as seen in the Kalahari Desert, is the end product of the desert cycle of erosion — desert leveling without base-leveling. In the Kalahari, the bornhardts are made up of resistant granite, quartzite, and other durable rocks; the plains of truncated gneisses and schists (Davis, 1905, p. 310). The rocks of the plain are not deeply weathered and the alluvial veneer observed to be present is concentrated in shallow depressions hollowed into the rock floor. Removal of the unconsolidated debris would expose a rock surface only slightly more irregular than the perfection of level plain that meets the eye. It has been suggested, further, that the sharp knick at the base of a bornhardt is the mark of the eventual supremacy of deflation over fluvial action in the end stages of the desert cycle. Waste exportation by wind proceeds until an almost level rock plain is produced. Then, with alluviation at a minimum, the mantle of debris at the base of the bornhardts is also attacked, and finally removed, by the deflative process.

Curiously, however, no undercutting at the knick line is reported. Moreover, the occurrence of typical bornhardts is not confined to desert regions. Stone Mountain in Georgia, previously referred to as a monadnock, can qualify as a bornhardt (Fig. 32). Indeed it has been argued that a warm, humid climate is the essential circumstance requisite for the isolation of bornhardts. Under such conditions rock decay proceeds far more rapidly in gneisses and schists than in granite, so that granite intrusives in time are made to stand out in bold relief without the development of a waste cover. Their side slopes, representative of the form of the intrusive mass, then make an angular intersection with the surrounding plain developed over the gneissic rock.

A direct, genetic relationship between bornhardt occurrence and the sequences of the desert cycle has not been established. On the other hand, bornhardts composed of the same rock substance as the plain above which they rise are likewise inexplicable as the result of differential rock decay in a warm, humid climate. It has been suggested, therefore, that such bornhardts mark sites where, at higher levels, resistant rock was present and functioned to promote the isolation of residual heights, monadnocks. By reason of the presence of summits so engendered a stream pattern is established which thereafter persists. But long enduring continuance of general degradation eventually reduces both the bornhardt sites and the surrounding lowlands to levels deeper than that of the downward extension of the resistant rock. Then bornhardt heights, originally monadnocks, and encircling plain present themselves devoid of their initiating structural credentials. A variation of this hypothesis is that degradation completely strips off a former continuous cover of weak rock which was originally thinner over the sites of the bornhardts than elsewhere. These sites, accordingly, are converted to summits composed of the underlying durable rock exhumed before the weak cover over surrounding areas is destroyed. The emergent bornhardts then govern the pattern of the stream system which accomplishes the remainder of the denudation. The bornhardts in either case persist as relief features. The initiating conditions have been eliminated from the setting but the bornhardts remain because of their divide-site relationship to the drainage pattern. In the German terminology, what had been härtlinge (true monadnocks) become fernlinge (residual divide heights). However, it must be confessed, that these sequences or other theories of exhumation from under a cover, and elaborate theories of climatic change, are not adequate, singly or jointly, to reconcile all the observed phenomena of bornhardt occurrence.

Desert Domes. In the discussion of the desert cycle, as heretofore outlined, the assumption was made that the mountains of the desert borders and desert interior were rapidly uplifted by diastrophic action, and so attained sufficient altitude and sharpness of slope to insure their dissection by consequent streams. These streams excavated steep-walled valleys of normal, downward erosion. The consequent drainage may even have been perennial in high altitude, headwater areas, because of heavy and regular precipitation induced there by the mountain heights.

If, instead, the uplifts are conceived to be broad, low, and slow, and to be restricted to the confines of the desert basins, the erosional circumstances are altogether different. The slowly upheaved units will have low initial relief and will experience only the desert type of precipitation, namely cloudburst downpours very irregularly distributed in space and time. Davis (1938) maintained that the movement of drainage over the surface under these conditions will be in the nature of *streamfloods* and *sheetfloods*.

Streams in humid regions have high and low water stages, but their variations in volume take place more or less gradually. The drainage resulting from desert cloudbursts may follow inbranching channels comparable to an ordinary stream system, but, unlike normal drainage, arrives almost instantaneously at the flood stage, and is very shortly loaded to capacity with sediment. These desert streamfloods subside as rapidly as they rise, and terminate within short distances from their point of origin by spread and

FIG. 248.   IDEALIZED DIAGRAM OF DESERT SHEETFLOOD FLOW
After W. M. Davis.

insoaking. In the long intervals between downpours the sides of the valleys excavated by the streamfloods are continuously attacked by weathering processes. As a consequence such channels are widened faster than they are deepened. If, on the other hand, the initial relief is not of sufficient measure to confine the flow of the desert downpours to definite lines, the drainage at once becomes a sheetflood (Fig. 248) of enmeshed, bifurcating channels, through which the water moves in pulsating rushes, rising and falling in turn, as the way is blocked or cleared by deposit or transport of the enormous load of debris the surges carry.

Prolonged exposure to the activities of the desert streamfloods and weathering, and of sheetfloods, brings about the development of convex domes that have extremely uniform and smooth slopes and which may be called *desert domes* of downwearing. Cima Dome (Fig. 249), in the Mohave Desert of southeastern California, is a magnificent example. Its perfection of regularity derives from its homogeneous, granitic lithology. Domes of heterogeneous composition have surfaces made up in detail of low, rounded

FIG. 249.   CIMA DOME, MOHAVE DESERT, CALIFORNIA
View from the north. The knobs are of metamorphic rock, more resistant than the coarse granite of the smooth slopes of the dome. Photograph by Eliot Blackwelder.

knobs, but in their broader aspect conform to the convex-dome profile, and are similarly the products of downwearing by weathering, streamfloods, and sheetfloods.

Such domes may be regarded as a particular development of the old-age stage of the desert cycle. Their summits are progressively flattened because there the sheetfloods are most efficacious in erosion. When the flash flow of a sheetflood starts on the upland tracts, it is not immediately loaded to capacity with sediment; accordingly it has energy for active downwearing of the summit areas. The domes are, therefore, a broad-scale phase of the process of desert leveling without base-leveling, as the end stage of the desert cycle is approached.

Desert Pediments. In the Great Basin region of western United States it is found, in many instances, that what appear to be bajada slopes at the bases of mountains bordering and rising out of bolsons, are in reality slightly inclined rock plains thinly veneered with fluvial gravels (Plate V). This phenomenon is particularly in evidence in the southern part of the Basin where diastrophic movements, restricted to that region, do not seem to have occurred since far back in the geologic past.

Such rock floors are called *desert pediments.*

Desert pediments have been much studied in the field following the appearance of a classic paper by W. J. McGee (1897) entitled *Sheetflood Erosion.* McGee contended that the general effect of desert sheetflooding is to carve base-level plains. In regions where drainage has a continuous downslope to the sea, this may be true without further qualification. McGee (1897, pp. 91–92) reported wide tracts, 5 miles or more distant from the mountain base in northwestern Mexico, Sonora, to be planed rock surfaces. In traveling across these areas the wheels of his wagon were half the time grinding harshly over bare, flat, granite rock.

Where, on the other hand, drainage is to an aggrading playa the presence of flat, pedimenting rock floors is not so directly explicable. Numerous investigators have sought evidence that would serve in the formulation of an adequate explanation of such occurrences. Their researches have made available certain facts of observation that appear to be significant. It is noted that the transition from the flat pediment floor to the mountain slopes is abrupt, a knick-line. The pediments incline 7 degrees or less, the mountain sides 35 degrees or more. The knick-line is commonly straight along the mountain front, but the rock floors do extend up the embayments of the mountain-valley emergences. Where the sides of such embayments meet the valley floors the same abrupt change of slope as that seen along the uninterrupted mountain front is in evidence (Fig. 250). There are no sharp changes in level between the floor of one embayment and the next. The pediments are developed, if not without exception at least more regularly, on the scarp side of fault-block mountains that have remained stable for a long period after their upheaval.

(The back slope of the uplifted block meanwhile experiences the downwearing erosion of streamfloods and sheetfloods leading to the production of convex domes.)   The pediments attain greatest perfection at the base of homogeneous granitic masses.

In accordance with these observed conditions the development of desert pediments around the borders of aggrading basins may be inferred to follow a particular sequence.   The fault-scarp face of a granitic block mountain (after the erection of the mountain by diastrophic movement) retreats by weathering or backwearing in successive parallel planes of a certain, unvarying degree of

Fig. 250.   PEDIMENT FORMATION BY BACKWEARING AND BY LATERAL PLANATION

At the far left of the diagram a fault-block mountain is shown.   This is reduced by backwearing and sheetfloods, center, or by lateral planation and streamfloods, right.   After W. M. Davis.

declivity.   H. A. Meyerhoff (1940, p. 251) proposes to call such a plane of retreat, with its fixed angle, the gravity slope and have it correspond to the German "böschung," or "steilwand."   Bryan (1922, pp. 42–46) showed that certain homogeneous rock types, in particular granite, weather into rounded boulders and small grains, grus, with no fragments of intermediate size.   Once this process of boulder formation by weathering is established over the whole surface of a slope-face its further backwearing will take place at a constant declivity.   This result follows because as the fine debris around a boulder, exposed on the outer surface of the slope, is washed away, and the boulder, deprived of support rolls down, another boulder of the same size, requiring the same angle of repose for its retention at the surface, is ready in the subsoil to take the place of the one which succumbed to gravity (Fig. 251). As the conditions for the subsurface production of the boulders and for maintaining their stability remain constant, the angle of slope also remains constant. The slope is always graded at a particular angle, yet continuously receding. Retreat of slopes at a constant angle may also occur under favorable circumstances with other rocks in a humid climate (Fig. 252).

At the base of the receding slope sheetfloods sporadically convey the accumulating debris towards the low point of the aggrading playa or bolson. The sediment is made to travel fan-shape outward, much as the stream from a fire-hose nozzle directed against

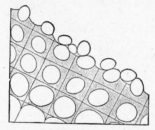

FIG. 251. BACK WEATHERING OF A GRANITIC MOUNTAIN SLOPE
The chemical weathering agencies penetrate along the joint planes. Wash and creep remove the fine weathering waste. The boulders deprived of support roll down. As the process continues the slope retreats at a constant angle. At the base of the slope the boulders disintegrate to grus. After W. M. Davis.

a paved street hurries and rolls loose fragments ahead of its spreading current. A feather edge of detritus is always present at the base of the mountain slope; this cover of alluvium becomes progressively thicker toward the center of the playa, and the level of the rock floor declines under it. Meyerhoff proposes to call this the wash slope and finds it to be the equivalent of W. Penck's haldenhang. Kesseli (1940) defines the haldenhang as the talus-covered part of the rock slope at the foot of the gravity slope. The wash slope then is the gentler slope that results from the weathering of the haldenhang; both its talus cover and its rock floor.

As the pediment floor is widened by backwearing of the gravity slope, not only parallel to the mountain front, but also laterally along the sides of the embayments, the supply of weathering waste available to the sheetfloods is progressively diminished. They may, therefore, develop an increasing erosive competence, which will be further enhanced, when, by deflation, the previously aggrading playa has its level lowered and steeper surface gradients develop toward its center. Thus the ultimate development of a flat rock floor across the whole width of a bolson may be en-

FIG. 252.   RETREAT OF A GRAVITY SLOPE AT A CONSTANT ANGLE IN A HUMID CLIMATE

Slope of Cayuta Creek gorge, Central New York. The rock is thin-bedded sandstone and shale in alternating layers. The sandstone weathers to small sharp fragments, the shale crumbles.

visaged; a condition perhaps actually attained in certain bolsons in New Mexico where borings reveal only shallow alluvial fills in the central areas (Keyes, C. R., 1908, p. 66).

It should be added that some investigators are of the conviction that desert pediments are the product primarily of lateral erosion by streamfloods emerging from the mountain canyons. These floods are asserted to be constantly engaged in narrowing and blunting the spurs between neighboring valleys, so that by the combined action of many streams on many spurs the mountain front is made to recede and a wide pediment to develop at its base. The absence of any declivities of the cut-bank type, even of only obscure development, to indicate the action of lateral cutting, at sites where pediments are characteristically present, tends to invalidate this concept (Fig. 250).

SUMMARY

Appreciation of the fact that deserts are characteristically regions of interior drainage is the primary requisite for studies that have as their purpose the attainment of an understanding of desert geomorphology. Interior drainage, further, is commonly the earmark of areas that have been converted to basins by diastrophic action, and the desert regime prevails where precipitation is of insufficient volume to fill such diastrophic basins to overflowing.

A deficiency in water supply is indicated by the circumstances of interior drainage. Nevertheless the desert cycle, like the fluvial cycle, is operated by running water. However, the course of the desert cycle differs from that of the fluvial cycle. In the desert cycle relief is greatest initially (youth), and diminishes steadily to the end stage of desert leveling without base-leveling. From youth onward original desert highlands are reduced in elevation by weathering and wash; basin floors are raised in elevation by alluvial aggradation. Only consequent valleys develop because rainfall is sporadic in space and time, and of the cloudburst type. In middle maturity all drainage is integrated over wide bajada slopes to the lowest depression of the desert basin. When this stage is attained the topographic unit is called a "bolson."

In late maturity and old age deflation becomes dominant. Wind action erodes projecting rock masses, builds dunes and transports great volumes of dust beyond the desert confines. Some of the dust exported by the wind from the desert basins is lost to sight by coming to rest on the sea floors, or by being widely dispersed over adjacent humid lands. In certain areas the dust is, however, accumulated in concentrated deposits called "loess." Geomorphically loess has the particular characteristic of standing up in vertical walls though composed of unconsolidated material of very fine texture.

Flat hammada surfaces of bare rock are developed by the combined erosive action of the wind, streamfloods, and sheetfloods. The altitude of such rock floors is unrelated to the sea as a base level and has far greater perfection of flatness than that of the peneplains of the fluvial cycle.

Isolated rocky summits, bornhardts, rise abruptly above the level rock floors. Bornhardts appear to be the last remnants of former elevated areas reduced to small dimensions by the concurrent backweathering of the surrounding slopes. They differ from the monadnocks of the fluvial cycle in that they are not necessarily the topographic expression of more durable rock masses. Convex desert domes are the product of prolonged sheetflood erosion on broad areas of low upwarp within the desert. Desert pediments develop by the backweathering of slopes and the sheetflood erosion at the base of fault scarps.

BIBLIOGRAPHY

CLASSICAL

Desor, E. (1864) *Le Sahara, Ses Différents Types de Deserts et d' Oasis,* Bulletin Société Sciences Naturel, Neufchatel.

v. Richthofen, F. (1882) *On the Mode of Origin of Loess,* Geological Magazine, New Series, Decade II, Vol. 9, pp. 293–305.

McGee, W. J. (1897) *Sheetflood Erosion,* Bulletin Geological Society of America, Vol. 8, pp. 87–112.

Passarge, S. (1904) *Die Kalahari,* D. Reimer, Berlin.

Davis, W. M. (1905) *The Geographical Cycle in an Arid Climate,* Journal of Geology, Vol. 13, pp. 381–407. In *Geographical Essays,* Ginn and Company, Boston, pp. 296–321.

Keyes, C. R. (1908) *Rock-Floor of the Intermont Plains of the Arid Region,* Bulletin Geological Society of America, Vol. 19, pp. 63–92.

Lawson, A. C. (1915) *The Epigene Profiles of the Desert,* University of California, Bulletin No. 9, pp. 25–48.

Bryan, K. (1922) *Erosion and Sedimentation in the Papago Country, Arizona,* Bulletin 730, United States Geological Survey.

Walther, J. (1924) *Das Gesetz der Wüstenbildung,* 4th. ed., Quelle & Meyer, Leipzig.

RECENT

Blackwelder, E. (1925) *Exfoliation as a Phase of Rock Weathering,* Journal of Geology, Vol. 33, pp. 789–806.

de Martonne, E. (1927) *Regions of Interior-Basin Drainage,* Geographical Review, Vol. 17, pp. 397–414.

Berkey, C. P., and Morris, F. K. (1927) *Geology of Mongolia,* G. P. Putnam's Sons, New York.

Blackwelder, E. (1931) *The Lowering of Playas by Deflation,* American Journal of Science, 5th Series, Vol. 21, pp. 140–144.

Johnson, D. W. (1932) *Rock Planes in Arid Regions,* Geographical Review, Vol. 22, pp. 656–665.

Cressey, G. B. (1934) *China's Geographic Foundations,* McGraw-Hill Book Company, Inc., New York.

Blackwelder, E. (1934) *Yardangs,* Bulletin Geological Society of America, Vol. 45, pp. 159–166.

Gautier, E. F. (1935) *Sahara, The Great Desert,* Columbia University Press, New York.

Chapter Nineteen

THE GLACIAL GEOMORPHIC CYCLE

Foreword. Some of the statements in this chapter may be thought dogmatic to a degree not warranted by well-established knowledge of the phenomena accounted for. Such presentation is defended on several grounds. In part it represents a consensus of informed opinion on disputed questions. In part the author states his own preference or interpretation on controversial topics. Space limitations preclude setting forth conflicting theories in full. Further, as the processes of glaciation are much less directly observable than those of the fluvial cycle, elucidation of glacial forms must be much more regularly by inference and deduction. What is printed here properly serves only as an introduction to the further study of the many fascinating problems of glaciology.

Introduction. Extensive areas of the earth's land surface are mountain regions at altitudes above the snow line (Fig. 253). In these territories precipitation regularly falls as snow. In consequence such mountain areas are drained by glaciers instead of by rivers. Glaciers consist of snow converted to ice chiefly by crystal growth that results from the compaction due to successive additions of more snow at the surface, and from internal melting and refreezing of the accumulation. When ice of sufficient depth (200 feet is perhaps the minimal thickness) has been built up, the mass begins to move. Like fluvial drainage the "flow" of mountain glaciers is confined and directed by rock-hemmed channels. Like rivers, although not in the same manner, mountain glaciers erode the floors and sides of the valleys they occupy. Glaciers also transport and deposit the debris worn and broken from the parent rock. In view of these circumstances it has proved conducive to understanding of the geomorphic changes wrought by mountain glaciers to relate such developments, by comparison and contrast, with forms resulting from stream action.

Plateau glaciers originating on level uplands in polar latitudes, and glaciers of continental dimensions now existing in polar regions (and at lower latitudes in the immediate geologic past) function more or less independently of rock topography. Their movement is an outward spread from a center of accumulation; not one down a slope. Snowfalls, annually in large excess of losses by melting and evaporation, eventually create a pile of such thickness that the ice at the bottom of the mass yields laterally because of the pressure to which it is subjected. By con-

FIG. 253. SNOW LINE ON FUJIYAMA, JAPAN
Photographer unknown.

tinued growth and movement glaciers of the plateau and continental types overtop and engulf all former rock relief and become, of themselves, the geomorphic expression of the areas across which they extend.

The rock topography of the regions occupied and traversed by plateau and continental glaciers is not, however, preserved unaffected by ice action. Where such ice masses existed for a long time and then melted off, the glacially occupied areas are found to have a unique geomorphic aspect, which is inferred to be the result of glacial processing.

Because the action of mountain glaciers is governed by rock topography and that of plateau and continental glaciers is not so controlled, except in the marginal zones, the glacial geomorphic cycle needs to be considered in two parts, first for mountain glacierization, then for plateau and continental glacierization.

MOUNTAIN GLACIERIZATION

Initiation of Mountain Glaciers. If it is assumed that without regional climatic change, a mountain range, by diastrophism, or a volcanic peak, by accretion, has been raised to altitudes above the snow line it follows that the summit areas in both instances will be permanently snow-capped. The snow cover will not, however, be uniformly thick. It will lie deeper than average in all hollows and depressions, while very steep slopes may be bare rock (Fig. 254). Snow blows and avalanches from the sites where it is unstable to the basin sites, which thus become the focal points of incipient glacierization.

On volcanic peaks initial irregularities of accumulation of the volcanic materials will, chiefly, give rise to the hollows available for snow collection. As the disposition and form of such depressions follow no well-defined pattern, the glacierization, that is, their occupation by glacial ice, that results from their accommodation of adequate quantities of snow is correspondingly sprawly. Indeed, the glacierization of volcanic peaks may well be regarded as representative of the infantile stage in the glacial geomorphic cycle. High, isolated volcanic peaks are geologically of recent erection and their summit areas are commonly too new and too small to have well-established, large, glacial systems.

Although mountain ranges may be raised so slowly that large rivers are able to survive and to maintain antecedent courses athwart the axis of the uplift, lesser drainage is commonly disrupted by such diastrophic movement. Then consequent streams develop valleys as the upheaval takes place. The principal high altitude hollows, ranged along the divides, are accordingly, the valleyheads of these streams (Fig. 255). These hollows become the sites for the beginning of glacierization when the mountain areas have been lifted to sufficient elevation above the snow line to insure a considerable excess of snowfall annually over the amount lost each year by melting and evaporation.

FIG. 254.   UNSTABLE SNOW MASSES, SUMMIT OF MONT BLANC
Photograph from Ad Astra-Aero, Zurich.

If the incidence of glacierization results not from a new uplift but from climatic change, that is, to lower regional temperatures at a given altitude, the ice drainage takes possession of the head-

Fig. 255.   SIERRA MADRE, NEAR LAKE CHAPALA, JALISCO, MEXICO

A young mountain range with consequent streams and valley-heads suitable for mountain glacierization.

water reaches of well-established, previously existing, stream-eroded valleys. It has, in fact, been stated that all mountain glacierization is fitted to and conditioned by preglacial relief. So put, the assertion is perhaps too comprehensive, but the basic idea is valid.

To sum up — mountain glaciers begin as snowbanks collected in the hollows (resulting chiefly from earlier stream erosion) distributed along the summit-level divides.

The Glacial Cirque.   The longitudinal profile of a normal stream valley is a concave curve steepening rapidly at the head-waters.   Mountains in the late-mature stages of the fluvial erosion cycle, exhibiting broadly convex summit areas, have stream-valley heads with only slight topographic expression.   The little rills which join to make a mountain brook peter out in a shallow

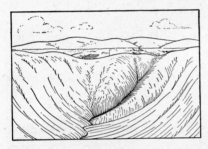

Fig. 256.   FUNNEL-TOP FORM OF NORMAL STREAM-VALLEY HEAD
After W. M. Davis.

basin near the summit level.   The terminations of deep mountain valleys regularly have the form of a bisected funnel top (Fig. 256). In very pervious rock, valley heads of nearly vertical steepness may be present.   There strong springs at the base of the declivity tend to bring about undermining and collapse of the headwalls. In the second and third cases there is a sharp transition from a steep to a less steep slope at the base of the valley head and the beginning of the axial profile of the valley.   But in all three cases the combined slope of the valley head and the axial profile is always forward and downvalley.

With the incidence of glacierization the streamhead hollows are converted to *glacier cirques.*   Around the lower edge of the permanent snowbanks which first occupy the hollows the process of *nivation* acts.   Nivation consists of alternate freezing and thawing around the fluctuating margin of the snow accumulation. Such frost weathering disintegrates the rock and melt-water seepage removes the debris. A border depression is created and tends to be enlarged and deepened

When the snow attains a certain thickness, the measure of which varies with the steepness of the underlying rock slope of the earlier valleyhead and nivation-formed basin, it begins to slide, probably because of a decrease in the cohesion of the bottom layers. The snow mass has not yet attained glacier status but its sliding abrades the rock bed over which it moves. A further deepening of the hollow results. Continuing increase in thickness

Fig. 257. BERGSCHRUND, PALISADE GLACIER, SIERRA NEVADA, CALIFORNIA

converts the lowest portions to glacier ice and glacial "flow" begins. Then the whole snow and ice mass, now a true glacier, moves away from the rock on its upper side and a *crevasse* opens there, the *bergschrund*, or *randspalte* (Fig. 257). Fragments of rock are detached in the pulling away and included in the head-wall of the glacier. Freezing and thawing in the rock wall behind the bergschrund loosens more rock fragments (Fig. 258). Further snowfalls and avalanches refill the bergschrund, further movement reopens it, and still more rock is removed. Meanwhile glacier movement greatly accentuates the abrasion of the rock floor. Because such erosion is most effective under the thickest ice, which necessarily occurs remote from its lower terminus, the glacier progressively digs itself down into the rock. The rate of erosion is much affected by the rock structure.

The joint action of these different processes results in the development of the glacier cirque. The glacier cirque is so distinctive as a geomorphic form that it is identified by a specific word in many languages, thus *kar, corrie, cwm, botn, caldare, oule, zanoga*. These foreign terms are occasionally used in English when the reference is to the occurrence of glacier cirques where these words are used.

Glacier cirques attain particular prominence in mountain landscapes when, through deglacierization of the site, they appear devoid of the ice fill to which they owe their existence. The empty cirque has a headwall nearly vertical in its upper part (Fig. 259), changing abruptly to a less precipitous slope at the bottom. The upper wall is rough from the quarrying erosion of the bergschrund; the gentler slope below is smoothed by glacial grinding. The transition line between the two slopes apparently marks the depth to which the bergschrund crevasse extended. The form of the cirque basin is that of an amphitheater, or better, in ground plan outline, that of a horseshoe. The floor of the cirque has a reverse slope, that is, downward from its outer edge toward the headwall. The rock

FIG. 258.   BERGSCHRUND, DETAIL, PALISADE GLACIER, SIERRA NEVADA, CALIFORNIA

The freezing and thawing is indicated by the icicles within the crevasse. Photograph by Ted Rust.

basin thus created commonly cups a *cirque lake,* which overflows across the bedrock barrier on its lower side.

Cirque Recession.   It is clear that the development of a glacial cirque converts pre-existing streamhead funnels into an unique type of basin.   Although it is sometimes difficult to make a sure discrimination between a glacier cirque and unglaciated valley-

FIG. 259.   GLACIAL CIRQUE IN THE ALPS AT INNSBRUCK

heads when a large accumulation of talus is present, the fact of a flat or reversed slope terminating at the base of a nearly vertical rock wall is the most dependable criterion for cirque identification.   At some sites the flats of the cirque floors extend over wide areas.   In Europe the concept of a *kar-,* or *cirque-niveau* (Fig. 260) has, in consequence, had a considerable vogue.   The idea is that the level of the cirque floors represents the uneroded

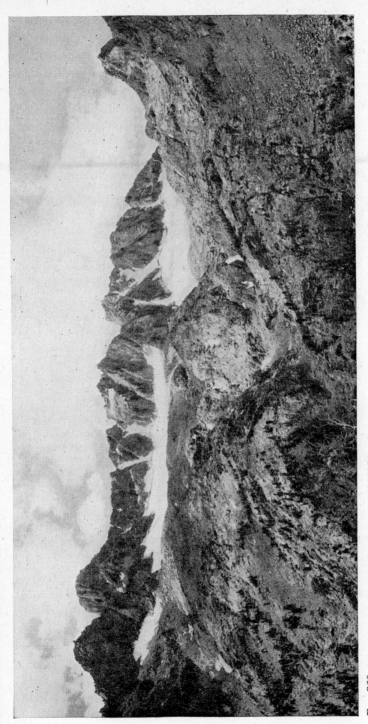

FIG. 260. KAR-NIVEAU, SIERRA NEVADA, CALIFORNIA

The generally flat area at the level of the glacier ends is the kar-niveau. The steep declivity in the foreground of the picture is the trough headwall. Note the bergschrund and the cirque headwall. The mountains are dissected to the fretted upland stage. Photograph from Frasher's, Inc., Pomona, California.

portion of a strath surface developed by a preglacial graded drainage system. Protected by ice, it escaped weathering and fluvial erosion during the period of glacial occupation, while its continuations beyond the ice borders were deeply incised. But the cirque-niveau exists at places where the former extension of a stream-valley system is impossible. Also, its altitude with reference to sea level declines regularly with increase of latitude, a circumstance that would be extraordinarily coincidental for a

Fig. 261. COMPOUND CIRQUES, HIGH SIERRA, CALIFORNIA
Fretted upland summits. Photograph, copyright, Spence Air Photos.

series of stream-valley floors in regions remote and unassociated, but is entirely appropriate to the glacial erosion concept of cirque origin.

The breadth of the cirque-niveau is, however, indicative of the progressive recession of the cirque headwall. When, from close approach to the crest line of a mountain divide, the head of an original cirque of horseshoe outline is no longer supplied with the quantities of snow it received at first, the side walls recede at a greater relative rate, and a *compound cirque* (Fig. 261), somewhat resembling a three-leaf clover in pattern, succeeds the earlier simple unit form.

Cirque formation is not confined to a single valleyhead. All sites that have a sufficient elevation above the snow line are involved. Thus the original summit surface of a mountain area is progressively consumed by cirque development. As the bites made by the ice erosion are circular in form the outlines of the unaffected portions of the preglacial surface resemble that of a biscuit dough remnant after the biscuits have been stamped out, and is referred to as a *grooved upland.* This is the stage of youth in the cycle of mountain glaciation. If it is sought to establish the origin of cirques as the result of glacial erosion by specific, unmistakable evidence, the obvious interruption of the earlier slopes by the cirque hollows, in the biscuit dough remnant stage, should be adequate to the purpose.

With continuation of cirque erosion preglacial upland surfaces of mountains are eventually completely consumed. Then the glaciated mountain ranges acquire the knife-edge and sharp-peak aspect that was once considered the normal topographic expression of "lofty" mountains. The Germans, laboring under this misapprehension, have, indeed, made the empirical categories "plains lands," "hill lands," "middle height mountains," "lofty mountains" (*Flachländer, Hügelländer, Mittelgebirge, Hochgebirge*), a basic classification of regions. It is now well understood that lofty, cirque-indented, sharp-ridged (French, *arête*), and sharp-peaked ranges such as the Alps and the Caucasus Mountains in the Old World, and Alaskan mountain regions, such as the Fairweather Range in the New World, are the product of glacial sculpture. The stage then attained is that of maturity in the cycle of mountain glaciation and is referred to as a *fretted upland* (Fig. 261), from its resemblance to the irregularities of scroll-saw patterns in wood.

Horns. On late mature mountains composed of massive rock, having domed summits, and on volcanic cones, the normal drainage pattern is one of streams flowing radially outwards. Cirque development is correspondingly divergent. By cirque recession and lateral enlargement a narrowing and sharpening of the central residual area of the mountain surface is brought about. The result is an imposing pyramidal form, the *horn peak* (Fig. 262), which is a dominating feature in glaciated mountain landscapes. The type example is that of the Matterhorn in the Alps, but other horns in the same region, and many sharp peaks in other maturely glaciated mountain areas, are of the same origin.

Cols. Mountain ranges are made up of long and short ridges that have their major slopes in two directions from a divide line. Cirque glaciers originate in the valleyheads of streams that di- verge from the crest lines. The cirques developed in parallel valleys on one side of a ridge tend to merge laterally and give rise to a broad kar-niveau. Commonly the structural circum- stances which lead to the development of a drainage hollow on

Fig. 262. HORN PEAK, GIANT'S NEEDLE, MONTANVERT, SWITZERLAND
The sharp ridges are characteristic arêtes. It may be noted that the cirque erosion is still in progress. Photograph by R. S. Tarr.

one side of a ridge are continued across its summit so that initial valleyheads on the two sides may be directly opposed. This rela- tionship gives rise to a saddle, or col; if eroded sufficiently it be- comes a pass, across the range in the fluvial erosion cycle. When cirques recede to the condition of complete intersection at such a site a *glacial col* is produced. Such cols are outlined in cross section by the hyperbolic curve which results from the intersection of inverted cones, and this distinctive curve makes them con- spicuous features on a mountain skyline.

Where a deep saddle existed before glacierization the area of deepest snow accumulation in the hollow will not necessarily be over the preglacial summit section. Glacier movement may then be across the former divide site. The erosion resulting from such transverse flow of the ice may suffice to convert the saddle to a glacially produced pass (Fig. 263). The same sequence can follow the creation of a col by the intersection of cirque heads. Some of the remarkable passes across formerly glaciated mountains find

Fig. 263. PASS LEADING DOWN TO THE VALLEY OF ISFAHAN IN WESTERN IRAN

A col deepened and widened by the erosion of a transverse glacier. Photograph by Ernest Schoedsack. From the motion picture "Grass" by permission G. P. Putnam's Sons.

their explanation in such circumstances. Nearly all the passes of the Alps were in a greater or less degree glacially fashioned or modified by transverse ice movement.

Valley and Trough Headwalls. The lower termination of a cirque is characteristically marked by a steep rock declivity, the *valley* or *trough headwall* (Fig. 260). The valley headwalls occur where glacial occupation of the summit areas has never gone beyond the cirque glacier stage. The level or reversed-slope floor of the cirque basin interrupts the steep terminal curve of the profile of the stream valley below the cirque. The lower portion of this stream profile persists, and acquires greater steepness after glacierization of the stream-valley head. In the case of converging cirque glaciers the volume of ice, from increasing intensity of glacierization, eventually overfills the cirque basins, and, at their joint outlet, pours, as a combined, thick ice stream, into the linear lower section of the main valley. At the junction point the downward erosive action of the single concentrated ice stream on its bed is abruptly greater than that of any one of the converging cirque glaciers on its bed. The originally steep longitudinal profile of the valley below the cirque basin is, in consequence, made precipitous and increased in height. After glacial modification of the main valley beyond this point, the valley headwall so developed becomes a trough headwall (in German, the *trogschluss*). While the ice is present the trough headwall is the site of the *ice fall* regularly present where the transition of a single cirque glacier, or the merging of cirque glaciers, to form a trunk ice stream takes place.

The Glacier Trough. A cirque glacier may attain sufficient volume to spill over the rock lip of its basin. It is then a *cascading glacier.* The ice stream that results from the combining of converging cirque glaciers in sufficient volume to continue downvalley for appreciable distances is a *valley glacier* (Fig. 264).

It is the consensus of informed opinion that mountain glacierization has been without exception fitted to a preglacial relief. Valley glaciers invade and modify valleys made by stream erosion. Precipitation preglacially conveyed away as water, is, after glacierization, drained off as ice. Mountain streams flow at the rate of *3 or more miles an hour;* valley glaciers move at rates from *3 to 50 feet a day.* It follows that the depth, or better, the cross-section area of a valley glacier must be vastly greater than that of a water current handling the same quantity of precipitation. A valley glacier fills the former stream valley from side to side and to depths of 3000 or more feet. It may even overtop the secondary divide between one valley and its neighbor with a parallel course. If, in such case, the neighboring valley is not glacier occupied, or occupied by a glacier of less thickness, a *diffluence glacier* results and by its erosive action carves a distinctive type of pass across the lateral dividing ridge.

The rate of downward erosion by a water stream is primarily dependent on the velocity of the current. As the velocity of movement of valley glaciers is very small, and its variations extend only over a narrow range, it is clear that the processes of valley-glacier erosion and the rate at which they act must be governed

Fig. 264.   VALLEY GLACIER OCCUPYING AND MODIFYING A FORMER STREAM VALLEY

by other factors than those which determine the effectiveness of stream erosion.

The attritional erosion of glaciers results from the pressure, that is, the weight of the ice on its rock bed. The thicker the glacier the greater is the pressure. The pressure and erosion are not reserved to the axial line of the glacier; they operate on the sides as well as on the bottom of the valley. As in the case of water streams the rock debris carried along in the bottom layers of glaciers is used as the tool of abrasion. Unlike water streams glaciers also erode by plucking. The ice wedges, spalls, and pulls loose small and large fragments of bedrock. The volume of rock removed by the plucking action probably far exceeds that eroded by grinding.

In every respect the erosion effected by a valley glacier is much greater, absolutely, than that achieved by a mountain stream of the same annual volume. Moreover, glacial erosion is very little affected by gradient. In consequence of these circumstances the V-form of a mountain-stream valley in early maturity is changed by valley-glacier erosion to that of a **U-shaped trough** (Figs. 85, 263). The glacial trough has a relatively broad, flat floor and steep sides. It should, however, be added that the sides are not

Fig. 265.   GLACIER STAIRWAY, CROSS WALLS AND PATERNOSTER LAKES, IN GLACIAL TROUGH OF THE NORTH FORK OF BIG PINE CREEK, INYO COUNTY, CALIFORNIA

vertical like those of the arms of the capital letter U. Rather they flare at the top to make a typical trough form. This form is almost unmistakable and is the characteristic earmark of former glacier occupation of valleys now clear of ice.

The Glacier Stairway and Paternoster Lakes. In the mature stage of its conversion from a stream valley, the reaches of level floor of the glacial trough are separated by nearly vertical acclivities, *cross walls,* which range from a few feet to hundreds of feet in height. These steep ascents are the risers of the *glacier stairway* (Fig. 265), also referred to as a *cascade,* or *giant stairway.*

The treads of the glacier stairway commonly have a gentle reverse slope. When a valley with a glacier stairway is cleared of ice the treads are in part occupied by *rock-basin lakes,* arranged as are beads on a string, hence *Paternoster lakes.* The water drainage descends in cascades over the steep risers. (Cotton, C. A., 1941.)

Although they have their general features in common, glacier stairways result from different conditions, applying either independently or jointly in a single trough. Variations in the steepness of the gradient of the originally water-eroded valley tend to be accentuated by the plucking action of the ice on the steeper declivities. The steps thus created are caused to recede by continuance of the same erosive action, and in the course of the recession the treads with reverse slopes are created. Inasmuch as the thickness of a valley glacier increases with distance from its lower terminus, up to the site of the trough headwall, and its erosive effectiveness is directly governed by its weight, upglacier points should regularly be eroded at a greater rate, and the reverse slope of the treads follows as a consequence. Incidentally, the reverse slope brings about a progressive increase in the height of the acclivities.

In accordance with this principle (a duplication of the effect that obtains where the converging cirque glaciers give rise to the trough headwall) the point of junction of a tributary with a main glacier is not uncommonly the site of a steep declivity in the bed of the trunk glacier. In explanation of this development, the *law of adjusted cross sections* is invoked (Fig. 266). Given that the surfaces of the joining glaciers are at the same level, that the width of the main valley is not abruptly increased below the junction point, and that the rate of motion of the main glacier is not greater below than above the junction—and all these conditions are met in numerous instances—it follows that there must be an abrupt increase in depth of the main valley to accommodate the volume of the combined ice streams at the place where they join. Thus there is introduced a step in the profile of the rock bed of the trunk glacier.

Hanging Valleys. It may be assumed, because of the relation between altitude and average annual temperature, that in the course of a progressive glacierization the snouts of large and small glaciers in a given region will descend to approximately the same

To illustrate the law of adjusted cross sections. Where the Rhone Glacier now descends over a cross wall it was formerly joined by another glacier from the right. The volume of the combined glaciers occupied and excavated the deeper trough of the middle ground. In the foreground the Rhone River is engaged in excavating and lengthening a gorge in the bottom of the glacial trough. A readvance of the glacier could widen this gorge to a glacial trough and the remnants of the floor of the older trough would then be albs. Photograph from Wehrli-Verlag, Zurich.

FIG. 266. RHONE GLACIER, SWITZERLAND

458

altitude. The first junction of a tributary and main glacier will therefore be effected at a time when the rock beds over which they are severally moving meet at grade. As the rock step which later develops at such glacier-junction points cannot be instantaneously created there must be a period during which the surface gradient of the trunk ice stream above the junction is flattened, and its rate of movement slackened. However, the rock-step declivity-producing conditions are meanwhile operative and, by definition, the trunk glacier is greater, that is, thicker, than the tributary. Hence as glacial erosion rates are positively and mainly

FIG. 267.   HANGING VALLEY, RIGHT, CASCADING GLACIER, LEFT, NUNATAK FIORD, ALASKA

The relation of these features to the main glacial trough, Nunatak Fiord, is clearly shown.

governed by ice thickness, the trunk glacier, markedly below, and appreciably above the junction point, deepens its trough more rapidly than does the tributary glacier. The accordance of grade of the valley bottoms brought about by stream erosion is, in consequence, destroyed, the tributary valley becomes a hanging valley (Fig. 267). Thus initiated, the discordance in level of the two rock floors must continue to increase as long as the valleys are glacier-occupied. In time the volume of the tributary glacier may come to be thrust into the surface levels of the trunk glacier, as has been observed in Alaska; indeed the surface of the main glacier may sink so low that the tributary must cascade to join it. The discordance is always abrupt; the tributary keeps its floor

gradient unbroken to the line of the wall of the main valley, perhaps even projecting beyond that line as a *bastion* (Fig. 268).

Deglaciation makes visible the discordance in level of the rock floors of the two valleys. Its measure will depend on the degree of difference in size of the erstwhile glaciers and on how long the glacial occupation lasted. With these factors governing there is no regularity in the altitudes at which the hanging-valley lips appear along a given glacial trough, or, generally, within a glaciated district. The hanging valleys do not betoken a rejuvenation from uplift.

Immediately water drainage is restored, gorge cuts are stream-eroded across the lips of the hanging valleys. Such clefts are deepened and extended upstream most rapidly where the differences in level between the main and tributary valleys are greatest. There is, hence, a tendency to restore the accordant junction relation of the water streams at a uniform rate, greater height fostering more rapid cutting.

Truncated Spurs. Even when they flow down rather steep gradients water streams tend to follow somewhat sinuous courses. Concurrent downward and lateral erosion produces alternating, overlapping spurs. Until the open valley stage of free meandering over a flood plain is attained, overlapping spurs persist as a characteristic feature of stream-eroded valleys.

The difficult, deep, slow, mass movement of an invading valley glacier is wholly unlike the shallow, nimble flow of the water current it supersedes. The ice is guided by the tortuous curves of the existing valley, but it also tends to overtop the opposing spurs. With increase in thickness of the glacier the spurs are more and more completely enveloped by the ice. They are then subject to grinding abrasion on the up glacier or *stoss side* and to plucking on the down glacier or lee side. The spurs are narrowest and have least bulk at their lower ends. The abrasion and plucking of the ice acting concurrently quickly eliminate these slender tips. Once the spur ends are even slightly truncated the slicing lateral erosion of the ice stream becomes effective over the whole of the surface so developed, and by this process the truncated face is rapidly enlarged. It becomes a *truncated spur* (Fig. 269). In these ways all the spurs are progressively eliminated. When their complete removal has been brought about the glacier follows a nearly straight-line course, suited to its pseudosolid nature, downvalley. The water-eroded valley has been converted to a glacial trough. However, even an ice stream is in some degree susceptible to and capable of a swinging flow (Fig. 270). The valley glacier does not proceed in a perfectly straight line. The curves of its movement are long and easy but

FIG. 269. TRUNCATED SPUR, SIX MILE CREEK, NEW YORK
The steep declivity on the far side of the valley is the end of a spur truncated by the ice of the Pleistocene glacierization.

that side of a valley reach against which the glacier current impinges is regularly *oversteepened.*

Albs. In the Alps and in other regions now supporting glaciers but of earlier more intensive glacierization, and in regions of former mountain glacierization, the high, nearly vertical sides of glacier troughs are commonly surmounted by a flat, or gently inclined, shelf (Fig. 266). This shelf has no great width but nevertheless intervenes as a distinctive feature between the steeper mountain slopes above it and the abrupt declivity extending from its lower edge to the trough floor. The shelf is called an *alb* and albs are the sites of many small Swiss highland villages and farms.

It has been asserted that the albs are evidence of the ineffective-
ness of glacial erosion. The argument is that the upper surface
of a valley glacier is a local base level for weathering and fluvial
erosion. Because of the presence of the glacier these processes

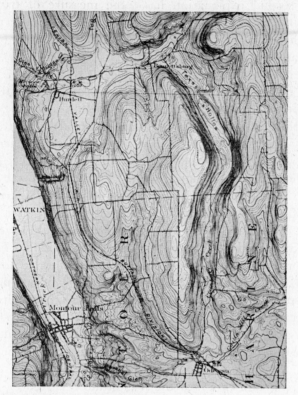

FIG. 270. TEXAS HOLLOW, NEW YORK
The sides of the valley, a glacial trough and through valley, are oversteepened by the swinging flow of the ice current.

could not further reduce the level of the land surface there. But
they were able to develop the flat which is now the alb. This
reasoning overlooks the necessity of accounting for the excavation of the glacial trough to its great depth and width.

Another explanation of albs is that they are the mark of a
sharp and great difference in rate of erosion by different parts
of a valley glacier. At the lateral margins of the glacier the ice
is thinner and moves less rapidly than at the center. There is,

further, a critical line at which the thickness of ice becomes such that motion is abruptly and greatly accelerated. The albs are represented to be the product of the ineffectual erosion of the thin marginal ice; the glacial trough that of the active central current.

If this second explanation has some measure of truth it is because the best theory of alb formation incidentally provides for the differential erosion postulated. The production of albs is not to be attributed solely to the action of glacial erosion. Rather they appear to be the mark of two periods of glacial occupation separated by a period of fluvial erosion of considerable duration. During the intervening time of stream action a V-valley of significant width and depth is cut into the broad flat bottom of a previously glacially excavated trough. The second glaciation is fitted into the V-valley but overfills it. The V-valley is converted to an inner, deeper glacial trough. Remnants of the bottom (perhaps slightly modified by the marginal scour of the second glacier) of the earlier higher level glacial trough persist as albs. The sides of the first glacial trough have meanwhile been caused to recede and be made less steep by weathering action. This two-cycle theory of the origin of albs has been objected to on the ground that the albs are remainders of the floors of preglacial late mature stream valleys, not of earlier glacial troughs. Why the glacial trough should be incised so sharply below a portion of the valley floor is then a difficult question. Renewed mountain uplift is also implied in such an explanation, because the present altitudes and gradients would not correlate with broadly open late mature stream valleys at the sites of alb occurrence.

Stages in the Glacial Geomorphic Cycle. The glacial geomorphic cycle is inferred never to have been in effect to an end stage. There has been speculation about the possibility of terminating a mountain glacierization by having glacial erosion lower the mountains levels so much as to extinguish the ice streams by reason of the higher temperatures that would prevail at the lower altitudes resulting from such complete demolition by glacial erosion of the former greater heights. Without accepting this theoretical possibility as the necessary conclusion of the glacial geomorphic cycle in mountains, it is to be noted that recognizable stages of the progress of the glacial cycle may be observed.

Incipient glacierization takes possession of preformed hollows. The hollows are reshaped to be cirques, the cirques compounded, horn peaks and cols sculptured. These are the glacial geomorphic forms of youth to maturity. There is, to be sure, some confusion here between intensity of glacierization and progress in a geomorphic cycle. But as glacierization involves a substitution of the glacial cycle for the fluvial cycle, and as it requires time to accomplish the substitution, the concept of the degree of substitu-

FIG. 271.   GALIANO GLACIER, ALASKA
Maturity in the erosion of a glacial trough.

tion may, not too inappropriately, be bound up with progress in the cycle.

Young glacierization and young glaciation go over into regional maturity when the main valleys of a mountain district are fully occupied by trunk valley glaciers fed by numerous tributaries. At this stage the summit regions are bound up in what the Germans call an *eisstromnetz,* that is, a network of snow fields and glacier currents that leaves only the higher peaks to project above the encompassing ice as **nunataks.** As downward erosion by the trunk glaciers proceeds differentially, that is, at a higher rate, tributary glaciers are left hanging as cascading glaciers at confluence sites. It appears that meanwhile the originally numerous steps in a glacier bed are being progressively telescoped into fewer greater units, and that these larger declivities in turn recede toward the trough headwall that terminates the lower side of the cirque basin. The trough headwall itself does not stay put. Between it and the cirque headwall there is a race in respect to rate of recession. In youth the advantage is with the cirque headwall, but with the beginning of lateral development and compounding of the cirque basins trough headwall retreat attains ascendency and eventually overtakes and merges with the cirque headwall. This terminus may be regarded as the close of the stage of maturity and appears to have been realized in the case of the Galiano Glacier, Alaska (Fig. 271). The head of the Galiano Glacier is fed by a group of cascading glaciers that stream down the full height of the mountain slopes. Further, the trunk Galiano seems to have attained a low uniform gradient over all its length. In Switzerland the Lauterbrunnen Valley (Fig. 85) exemplifies the same stage as displayed by a now glacier-free trough. This flat-floored U-valley extends without interruption by acclivities to the very base of the Jungfrau and Breithorn peaks.

Piedmont Lake Basins and Fiords. It should be noted, however, that glacial erosion is not conditioned by a profile of equilibrium or grade. In other words the sea surface as a general base level does not apply to the glacial geomorphic cycle. While mountain glaciers, like streams, move downslope under gravity, downward erosion by the ice does not cease when, by recession and merging of declivities, as described, the downhill gradients have been almost completely eliminated; the circumstance indicated above to mark the close of the mature stage. Thereafter the ice moves chiefly by virtue of a pressure head and surface gradient developed within the glacier mass itself. The larger valley glaciers of the Alps have maximal thicknesses of from 2000 to 3000 feet. From such thicknesses, just below the *reservoir* area (Fig. 272), there is a decline to zero thickness at the terminus of the **dissipator** tongue. The thickness differences and surface gradient and the pressure differences are maintained nearly constant by snow supplies in sufficient volume at the head to offset the decline in thickness due to movement and wastage toward the lower terminus.

As the weight of overlying ice chiefly determines the rate of glacial erosion, it is clear that downcutting will continue as long as the ice moves. Also, the downward erosion will be most rapid where the ice is thickest and will cease completely where it ends. It follows that once level-floored maturity is attained, continuation of erosion will bring about the excavation of rock basins because of the differences in erosion rate. This effect is especially

FIG. 272. RESERVOIR AND DISSIPATOR AREAS OF VALLEY GLACIERS

Gaisberg and Rotmoos Glaciers, Bavarian Alps. Photograph from Verlag Lohman and Aretz.

prominent in the piedmont belt of mountains where glacierization was sufficiently intensive to project the ends of the ice tongues beyond the mountain front. Escaping from the confinement imposed by the mountain-valley walls, the glacier spreads laterally and experiences a great decline in thickness within a short distance. The marked difference in erosion rates these relations permit conduces to the excavation of especially well-defined rock basins. The Swiss-Italian Lakes (Fig. 273) on the south side of the Alps are outstanding examples of basins of this origin.

In Alaska and Patagonia mountain glaciers now descend to sea level. During Pleistocene times these *tidal glaciers* (Fig. 274) were far more extensive in both regions. Soundings in the channels where the glaciers once ended in great ice cliffs show increase of depth landward from the terminal sites. Here are rock basins glacially excavated below sea level. They are closed at the seaward end by a distinct rock sill at shallow depth, beyond which the descent to the deeper ocean waters begins. These, now sea-invaded, basins, which commonly extend inland between nearly vertical rock walls of great altitude, are *fiords* (Fig. 275). Their

FIG. 273. LAKE LUGANO, SWITZERLAND—ITALY

origin from glacial erosion has been much disputed. It is asserted that the fiords are due to sinking of the land. But adjoining fiords differ greatly in depth, a circumstance imcompatible with the land-sinking theory of their origin. But even if there has been submergence due to land sinking, the fact of the barrier sill and the increase in depth landward are conclusive proofs of the development of fiords by glacial processes. Soundings at the front of the Muir Glacier, Alaska, which has experienced a great retreat since it was first mapped, make it clear that its tidal end was not floating when the glacier had its farthest extension.

FIG. 274. NUNATAK GLACIER, ALASKA. A TIDAL GLACIER

The depth of water in the part now evacuated is so great that the above-water ice cliff would have been much higher than it was if the ice had been buoyed up at its terminus. Any conceivable included load of rock debris in the glacier would be inadequate to increase the density of the tongue sufficiently to offset the buoyancy of the ice floating in salt water. The ice at the front was evidently in contact with the floor of the rock basin of the fiord. That the pattern of a fiord system fits to the tectonic

Fig. 275. NAERO FIORD, NORWAY
Photograph by Axel Olsen.

fracture lines, joints, and faults of a region is appropriate because the fiords are the glacially enlarged and overdeepened valleys of a stream-eroded, lineamented landscape. Diffluence glaciers account for seemingly anomalous cross channels.

Surface Features of Valley Glaciers. Although, strictly speaking, the surface features of valley glaciers are not geomorphic items, because, like whirlpools or ripples in a water current they are transitory features and a part of process rather than of structure, such phenomena in the ice streams are sufficiently conspicuous and permanent to deserve notice as landscape items.

Ice falls at the trough heads have been mentioned. The glacier there is broken by great *transverse crevasses* induced by the tension to which the ice is subjected in passing over the declivity. Because of differential melting and evaporation of the disrupted mass great snow-ice *pinnacles* or *seracs* rear up at such sites. When slender pinnacles are bent over at the top they are called *nièves penitentes.* Because of the faster movement of the center of the ice than that of the sides, *lateral crevasses,* extending up glacier at approximately a 45 degree angle are regularly present. If a valley glacier spreads sideways in its lower sections, because it has emerged from between confining trough walls, the resulting tension on the surface ice causes *longitudinal crevasses.* In the terminal portions of the glacier the unclosed remainders of these various types of crevasses criss-cross to produce a veritable maze of fissures.

Where melt-water in the lower end of the glacier finds entrance through crevasses to subglacial courses, broad, circular depressions develop on the ice surface; these are called *moulins.* The subglacial water courses fed by the moulins commonly collect to emerge at the front of the ice in a single large stream from an *ice cave.* Such subglacial and marginal drainage has many interesting aspects (v. Engeln, O. D., 1911).

Weathering debris showered down on the glacier from the valley walls rising above its surface gives rise to *lateral moraines* along both margins of the ice stream. Where two valley glaciers join, one lateral moraine from each is contributed to the formation of a *medial moraine.* Huge boulders, especially if tabular in form, hurtled from beetling cliffs and coming to rest far out on the ice stream give rise to *glacier tables.* The protection afforded by the rock block preserves the ice under it from melting as rapidly as the clear ice roundabout, so that, in time, the block is reared on an ice pedestal which may be 6 feet high. In similar fashion, isolated patches of finer fragments give rise to *debris cones.*

The widespread, flat, or gently concave areas of accumulation constitute the *snow fields* or *nèvès,* and terminate at the *nèvè line,* below which the *glacier tongue* or dissipator, composed of solid ice, extends, with a markedly convex surface, to the *snout* or terminus of the ice stream. Tidal glaciers end in *ice cliffs,* which may be 300 feet high and have jagged crests made up of seracs, and from which *icebergs* are discharged or *calved.*

PLATEAU AND CONTINENTAL GLACIERIZATION

Introduction. In high latitudes relatively level upland tracts of moderate altitude will be above the snow line. Snowbanks accumulating on such sites eventually dome up to a thickness sufficient to cause a peripheral yield of the undermasses, converted to glacial ice by the pressure of the overlying layers. In this way *plateau glaciers* are made (Fig. 276).

Some *continental glaciers* have, perhaps, been developed by great magnification of what were originally plateau glaciers. The gradual expansion of an initial ice dome on an area of low relief ultimately enveloped regions extending over hundreds of thousands of square miles. Continental glacierizations may, however, also originate in mountains. Then the beginnings are cirque glaciers, and the ice occupation is extended to lower and lower

FIG. 276. PLATEAU GLACIER, GEIRANGER, NORWAY
Photograph by Axel Olsen.

levels by valley glaciers. When the ice tongues emerge from the mountain troughs and invade the foothill country they expand laterally and eventually these expansions merge at their sides to form *piedmont glaciers*. These, in turn, grow in area and thickness until they fill interrange basins to heights as great as those of the bordering mountains. The focal point of the glacierization is then shifted to the summit of the ice dome. In consequence of this shift the direction of ice movement changes from one divergent from the mountain crests to one outward from the dome center. The mountains in which the glacierization had its beginnings become barriers and the passes through the mountains become the routes of *outlet glaciers* by which the ice of the dome escapes to the sea. These circumstances apply in detail to the existing continental glacier of Greenland, to one that formerly occupied all of Ireland, and in part to the vast present glacier of Antarctica, perhaps three million square miles in extent.

Both the plateau glaciers and the continental glaciers contrast sharply with the mountain glaciers in that they surmount rock relief and, broadly speaking, function independently of rock relief, whereas the mountain glaciers acquire their forms and have their activities guided by topography. Rising to heights of 10,000 feet and covering thousands, even millions, of square miles continental glaciers properly qualify as geomorphic units. Their mass, forms, and altitudes are all inherent. Plateau glaciers, although only in miniature, also fit to such classification.

Description of the continental and plateau glaciers as geomorphic units can be compassed in brief phrases. They are almost smooth ice and snow domes, nearly flat in the central areas, but with progressively steeper slopes (terraced in western Greenland) toward the margins. They are terminated either by division into the outlet glaciers which pour through mountain defiles, or end in broad lobate tongues fitted to the low relief of a plains area.

Piedmont Glaciers and the Ross Shelf Ice. If the plateau and continental glaciers get consideration as geomorphic units, piedmont glaciers and the Ross Shelf Ice also deserve notice on that basis.

A piedmont glacier is an ice plateau spread at the base of a mountain range. Piedmont glaciers are formed by the lateral coalescence of valley glaciers emergent from the mountains. The Malaspina (Fig. 277) and Bering glaciers, Alaska, are the existing type examples of such development. The Malaspina, situated at the base of Mount St. Elias, covers an area the size of the state of Rhode Island (Fig. 278). It is at least 1500 feet thick at the mountain foot, whence it slopes gently forward, with a nearly featureless, flat surface, to a terminal declivity about 100 feet high. Like the plateau and continental glaciers, piedmont glaciers transcend the slight topographic irregularities of the type of areas they cover and have their own surface relief. In form and structure they conform to the geomorphic unit requirements. In the Pleistocene glacial times piedmont glaciers were numerous and of extensive development. The Swiss Plateau, regions at the eastern base of the Andes in Argentina, and at the eastern base of the Rocky Mountains in Montana were occupied by piedmont glaciers then.

The **Ross Shelf Ice** has been referred to as a piedmont afloat. This designation is not a happy one because, despite some resem-

Fig. 277. MALASPINA GLACIER AND MOUNT ST. ELIAS
A piedmont glacier. Photograph by Bradford Washburn.

blance in form and position, and even in origin, to piedmont glaciers, the composition and topographic expression of the Ross Shelf Ice are *sui generis*.

The Ross Shelf Ice is a level, snow-ice plain of low altitude (about 100 to 200 feet above sea level) occupying a shallow embayment of the Antarctic Continent (Fig. 279). It has a front at the sea margin 500 miles long and there rises as a vertical ice cliff from the sea surface. At its sea terminus the Ross Shelf Ice is afloat, but over portions of the 500 miles that it extends inland it rests on the bottom. The Ross Shelf Ice is unlike other glacial forms in composition and in the manner of its accumulation. It consists of névé horizontally stratified so that the fact of annual accretion can be discerned. The Ross Shelf Ice moves out slowly from its inland margin to the sea front, where it is dissipated by iceberg discharge. The Antarctic icebergs, chiefly from this source, are huge tabular masses which may be miles long. In part the Shelf plain is fed by outlet glaciers from the Antarctic

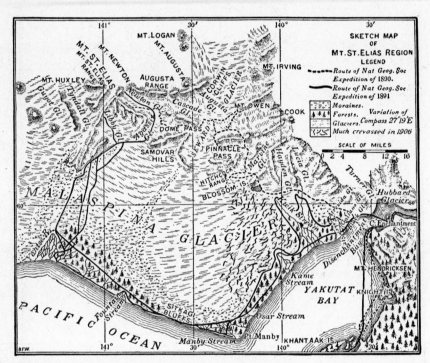

FIG. 278. THE MALASPINA GLACIER
After Israel Russell.

ice dome, in part by overflow (Gould, L. M., 1935) in a broad sheet from an area of plateau glacierization, but its upper section is mainly built up of horizontally disposed snow layers, in part precipitated directly, in part wind-brought. The surface is somewhat diversified by wind-eroded furrows called *sastrugi,* and by crevasses resulting from the drag of the generally floating ice sheet over the higher parts of the bottom where it is aground.

As in the case of the other ice units herein dignified by inclusion in the geomorphic unit category, so with the Ross Shelf Ice, its size, independence of rock topography, and particular compositional and structural characteristics warrant the designation as such.

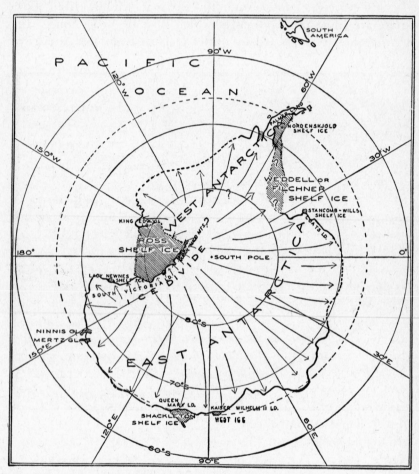

FIG. 279.   MAP OF ANTARCTICA
Shows the location of the Ross Shelf Ice.   After Laurence Gould.

Movement of the Geomorphic Unit Glaciers.   The Ross Shelf Ice appears to be propelled seaward by the thrusts (Fig. 280) of the outlet glaciers and the plateau-ice overflow from the Antarctic interior areas.   In this fact of movement the Ross Shelf Ice, the piedmont, the plateau, and the continental glaciers lose caste as geomorphic units. These ice masses assume the dual role of structural unit and processing agent. Aside from some small scraping of the sea bottom the motion of the Ross Shelf Ice serves merely to swim the unit seawards *in toto*. The other ice

Fig. 280. ANTICLINE IN THE ROSS SHELF ICE

The thrust of outlet glaciers causes uparching and fissuring of the Shelf Ice. After a photograph by Laurence Gould.

masses, however, by reason of their motion profoundly modify the rock bases over which they are reared.

Differential Erosion of Continental Ice Sheets. It is intimated above that the functioning of continental and similar glaciers is unaffected by the topography of their rock bases. It may be said further that with sufficient duration of the continental type of glacierization the rock relief, no matter what its preglacial form, is remodeled to the complete uniformity of an unique glacial pattern. But in its initial onset, and for considerable periods thereafter, the erosional processes of continental glacierization are significantly influenced by the pre-existing topography. The valley systems resulting from fluvial erosion are channels along which the bottom ice moves in greater depth, with more freedom, and at greater speed, than the glacier as a whole sweeps across the intervening divides. There is a great difference whether a valley furrow is parallel to the axis of the main ice movement or lies athwart it. If it is in line with the spread of the glacier the deeper and more rapidly moving ice proceeds to excavate the valley differentially deeper, to enlarge it and to reshape it to a U-trough, precisely as a valley glacier makes over the mountain stream valley of which it takes possession.

It is important to emphasize that such attack is by basal currents of the continental ice. It is also clear that movement is by some form of flow and that the word "current" is definitely applicable. If the surface of the glacier over a site where such differential attack by a basal current had already caused notable overdeepening could be observed, and the erosion were still in progress, no depression would be seen at the ice top to mark the line of overdeepening. Lateral flow within the ice would keep the upper ice surface unaffected and flat. Accordingly, with increase in depth from differential erosion, the pressure and the erosional rate along that axis would experience a continuing increase. It is to this process that long narrow basins such as those of the Finger Lakes of New York (Fig. 281), also the broader one

FIG. 281.   CANANDAIGUA LAKE, NEW YORK

One of the Finger Lakes of Central New York in a rock basin excavated by glacial erosion.   Photograph by A. W. Abrams.

of Lake Michigan and great troughs like Crawford Notch in New Hampshire owe their origin.

Valleys having axes at a greater or less angle athwart the general forward motion are differentially deepened in accordance with the degree of their alignment with such direction of motion. Those at right angles to the main ice movement experience little modification. But whether they are invaded only with difficulty and sluggishly, or freely, the valleys induce some measure of directed current flow in the basal ice. When, after intensive and prolonged glacierization, a region is exposed subaerially it is found to have been grooved and channelled by ice erosion and

FIG. 282.   THROUGH VALLEY, SIX MILE CREEK, NEW YORK

The flat, valley-floor divide is near the center of the picture. From this point drainage goes north to the St. Lawrence, south to the Susquehanna. The upland surface is the Schooley peneplain.   Photograph from Storrs Cole Country Place, Danby Hills, New York.

to have experienced glacial modification in many orders of magnitude.

The measure of differential deepening may be so great as to

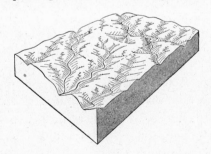

FIG. 283. THE PREGLACIAL TOPOGRAPHY OF THE SIX MILE CREEK, THROUGH VALLEY REGION

Same site as Fig. 282. Shows the preglacial water-parting. The area within the dashed line is shown in the succeeding figures. Drawing by Arthur Robinson.

develop the hanging-valley relationship to a very conspicuous degree. This is true, as a result of Pleistocene glacierization, of the Scottish Highlands region and in the Appalachian Plateau area of central New York State. Attention should be given to

the fact that such creation of hanging valleys is brought about by
the action of divergent bottom ice currents, whereas the same

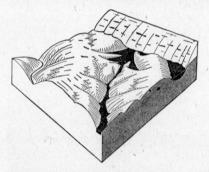

FIG. 284. PONDING OF THE NORTH-
FLOWING PREGLACIAL DRAINAGE BY THE
ADVANCE OF THE CONTINENTAL GLACIER,
SIX MILE CREEK THROUGH-VALLEY SITE

See Fig. 283. Note that the overflow waters have cut a gorge through
the preglacial divide. Drawing by
Arthur Robinson.

phenomenon in mountain glacierization results from the convergence of affluents on, and junction with, a trunk glacier. That

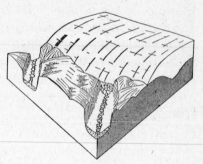

FIG. 285. THROUGH VALLEY, SIX MILE
CREEK, ERODED ACROSS THE DIVIDE AND
GORGE SITE BY THE ICE

Deposit of moraine and outwash to
build up the flat floor of the trough.
Drawing by Arthur Robinson.

hanging valleys are emergent after a region has been subjected
to continental glacierization argues strongly against theories of

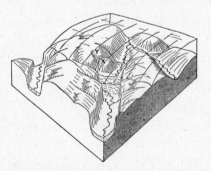

FIG. 286. PRESENT TOPOGRAPHY, SIX
MILE CREEK THROUGH-VALLEY SITE

The hill, X, appears in the left foreground of Fig. 282. The photograph
was taken from hill Y. The ice cover
of Fig. 285 is shown by the skeleton
outline. Drawing by Arthur Robinson.

the preservation of preglacial forms by an ice cover and of a
greater measure of degradation in a given time by fluvial than by
glacial erosion.

One of the most interesting geomorphic effects resulting from the basal erosion of ice sheets is the lowering of, and in some instances elimination of, former water partings. Where such action is carried to completion *through valleys* are created. Through valleys have characteristically a flat floor. The post-glacial water parting commonly resides in a swampy tract at a low summit level in glacial deposits and is referred to as a *valley-floor divide* (Figs. 282, 283). Inasmuch as the overtopping of a preglacial divide involves, during the glacial advance, the temporary ponding of the water drainage (Fig. 284) directed toward the ice front it is not improbable that gorge cutting by overflow of the impounded waters contributes to the first breaching of the rock barrier at the sites of preglacial cols. The forward-crowding ice enters and enlarges the water-cut channel (Fig. 285). Its differential erosional attack is so much facilitated at such a site that the through-valley feature is readily produced (Fig. 286).

Roches-moutonnées Fields. The glacial-erosion phenomena so far discussed are all particular and circumstantial. The universal product of erosive action by glaciers is the *roche moutonnée.* Roches moutonnées appear on the floors of cirques, in the troughs of mountain glaciation and, broadly speaking, over all the areas invaded by continental ice.

The roche moutonnée (Fig. 287) is a knob of rock which regularly exhibits a gently inclined, striated and grooved, smoothed, or even polished slope on the end against which the ice impinged, the onset or stoss end. The long axis of the roche moutonnée, regardless of the structural characteristics of the rock, is oriented in the direction of the ice motion. In sharp contrast with the onset end, the lee end is steep, even precipitous, and regularly has a rough, hackly surface. The irregularities of this surface are intimately related to the structure, chiefly the joint or other fracture pattern, of the rock. It is clear from these characteristics that where the rock slope and mass are opposed to the direction of ice motion the erosional attack is by slow grinding. On the lee end tensional instead of compressional stresses are present. There is considerable observational evidence that the ice at the base of glaciers is at the pressure-temperature melting point. Under these circumstances any local increase in pressure, from differential movement or encounter with an obstacle, causes a portion of the ice to melt, a similarly conditioned decrease in pressure to refreeze such melt-water or to firm the basal ice, and, in either case, cause it to attach itself temporarily to the rock floor of the glacier. The adhesion of the ice to the rock on the lee end, in consequence of freezing due to decrease of pressure, promotes plucking erosion, and the quarried blocks can be moved forward freely as fast as they are detached. The typical roche-moutonnée form is clearly the product of the

Fig. 287. stoss side of a roche moutonnée, fulton chain, adirondack mountains.

combined action of grinding erosion on the stoss end; plucking erosion on the lee slope.

It was long assumed that roches moutonnées represented either residuals of preglacial relief, or were the expression of above-average durability of rock in resistance to glacial erosion. But the occurrence of roches moutonnées where glacial downwearing extends through such great thickness of rock as to make the preservation of any initial relief rather improbable, and the fact of roches moutonnées composed of relatively soft rock standing above harder rocks at their bases prove such assumptions unwarranted and inadequate in explanation of the origin of the knobs.

Rather, the roches moutonnées appear to be the general erosional reflection of the manner of the progress of moving glaciers. They are the impress of glacial action on rock topography made with complete indifference to structure. The energy that resides in the ice so far transcends the measure of all variations in rock resistance that these become a negligible factor. In the large sense, an active, great glacier erodes all rock kinds with equal facility, in effect, at the same rate. The manner of the application of that force inheres in the nature of the glacier motion and it puts its mark, the roche moutonnée, on the rock, no matter what composition or structure the rock may have. It has been suggested (v. Engeln, O. D., 1937, 1938a) that this ultimate roche-moutonnée development reflects an occulted undulation in the mass progression of the glacial ice, but the correctness of this inference is vigorously disputed (Demorest, M., 1939) as incompatible with the physics of an ice mass moving at the low speed of a glacier. Even so, the flow motion of the ice, rather than rock structure, appears to be indicated as the causal factor.

The roche moutonnée in its typical, small-scale expression appears in Central Park, New York City, in the valleys of the Adirondacks, in the passes of the Alps, and in vast collections, *roches-moutonnées fields* in the Rideau Lakes region of Canada, over southern Sweden, the Aaland Islands, and Finland. In larger units, not so perfect in form and not so readily comprehended in a single view, the roche-moutonnée form is given to mountains overridden by ice, such as those of northern New England and Norway, and the hills of the glaciated Appalachian Plateau regions (Figs. 26, 288, 292). The roche moutonnée appears as well at the borders of the Greenland ice sheet (Fig. 289) where it may be inferred that ice has been continuously acting on the rock for countless thousands of years. From this fact of observation, and from the occurrences of the roches moutonnées where deep glacial excavation is obvious, it is inferred that a roches-moutonnées field is the end stage of ice erosion. That is to say, a roches-moutonnées field of wide extension, and uniform level, above, at, or below sea level, depending on the altitude and magnitude of the glacierization is the equivalent in the glacial geomorphic

cycle of the peneplain in the fluvial cycle and desert leveling without base-leveling in the desert cycle.

Wide regions in the south of the Scandinavian countries appear to have been ice-sculptured to this end stage (Fig. 290); so also have large parts of the Canadian Shield. It has been suggested that if the loose detritus covering the North German plain

Fig. 289.   ROCHE MOUTONNÉE, CORNELL GLACIER, GREENLAND
The stoss side of a roche moutonnée rock knob appears at the left of the picture mantled with the depositing ground moraine of the bottom ice of the glacier. Photograph by J. O. Martin.

and adjacent glaciated areas were removed, the underlying rock would be found to have the relief of a roches-moutonnées field. Similarly parts of Spitzbergen now under ice may well be eroded to the roches-moutonnées end stage. The pointed mountains which here and there rise above the ice and give the land its name are "monadnock-nunataks," that is, the last residuals of the pre-glacial topography that the ice has elsewhere subjugated.

In brief, the roche moutonnée unit is representative, in miniature, of all the phenomena of glacial erosion. Adequate explanation of its form and occurrence will comprehend all that is significant in relation to the erosive action of glaciers.

FIG. 290. GLA-
CIALLY ROUNDED
ROCK ISLAND OF
THE SKAGERAK
COAST OF NORWAY

486

DEPOSITIONAL FORMS FROM GLACIATION

Introductory. For the most part, interpretation of the geomorphic forms resulting from glacial erosion rests on inference. Only at marginal sites are wholly inadequate, observational glimpses possible of what transpires under the ice.

On the other hand the origin of many of the depositional geomorphic features resulting from glaciation is immediately discernible. These depositional forms are, however, in general much less imposing than those resulting from glacial erosion. It would seem that if the glaciers erode greatly, deposits of the debris they detach and transport should be of comparable magnitude. But in many instances it is the striking forms produced rather than the volume of rock removed that makes glacial erosion impressive. And much of the glacially eroded material is, on deposition, spread so widely that it loses conspicuousness of aspect.

End Moraines. However, as could be expected, the terminus of a glacier is a site at which the debris from erosion is depositionally concentrated. Such accumulation takes place alike at the fronts of cirque, valley, plateau, and continental glaciers. To these deposits the phrases *terminal moraine, end moraine, stadial moraine, recessional moraine* are variously applied. "Terminal" is most commonly used, but may be criticized because of the implication it carries that the deposit referred to marks the outermost position ever attained by the ice. Stadial moraine and recessional moraine are also indicative of particular conditions; end moraine is general and noncommittal, though perhaps more appropriate to deposits associated with ice tongues than wide lobes.

Much of the material in the end moraines of cirque and valley glaciers is derived from rock fragments brought to them by avalanching snow and from weathering of the rock walls that enclose and rear above these kinds of glaciers. This debris commonly rides down on the surface of the ice, the lateral and medial moraines referred to above, and is dumped at the end of the glacier. The material eroded at the ice base is referred to as *ground moraine* (Figs. 140, 289) or *boulder clay* and is extruded from below the glacier at the ice front. It is also probably plastered on in successive layers for some distance back under the margin of the glacier.

It is obvious that the dumped debris cannot be piled up higher than the elevation of the ice front that supplies it. This circumstance would appear to put a sharp limitation on the height to which an end moraine might rise. But as the front of the glacier is constantly riding up on the ground-moraine layers previously deposited, its surface at the terminus is progressively lifted and dumping takes place at successively higher levels. A sharp advance of the glacier front because of increased snow supply in the reservoir area, or from other causes, may occasion a bodily thrust forward of the ice margin and heaping up by shove of material deposited earlier (v. Engeln, O. D., 1938c).

By these several processes end moraines are, in places, built up to ramparts 100, 200, and more feet high. If its volume is chiefly owing to the plastering on of ground moraine, the back slope of the end moraine is usually very gently inclined. The end moraines of continental glaciers having their fronts in regions of low relief are characteristically of this form. The outer slope is steeper, and the moraine appears as a pronounced ridge when viewed from that side. End moraines of valley glaciers are usually steep on both sides and make arcuate walls, convex on the down-valley side, extending across the width of the valley, and are, hence, called *valley-loop moraines* (Fig. 291). Because the volume of material deposited varies from place to place in the moraine, and because buried ice blocks melt out after deposition ceases, the surface topography of end moraines is normally very irregular, having a *knob and kettle,* or *basin,* aspect (Frontispiece and Fig. 292) which is their characteristic mark.

The lateral and medial moraines which are very prominent on the surfaces of some glaciers commonly make a very small showing when they are deposited, because of the final dissipation of the ice, and are of little geomorphic significance. The high ridges they make on the glacier surface are actually in large part ice, protected by the debris from melting down as rapidly as the bare ice.

The end moraine is a stadial moraine, terminal or recesssional, in that the ice front must be maintained in one position for a

FIG. 291. VALLEY-LOOP MORAINE, REYNOLDSVILLE, NEW YORK

The ice-contact side is toward the observer. Postglacial erosion has breached the loop at the left of the picture.

FIG. 292. MORAINIC BELT NEAR SPENCER, NEW YORK

Shows characteristic knob and kettle topography. Glacially oversteepened valley walls in upper left of picture, glacially rounded hills beyond. Photograph by Cecil Robinson.

considerable period to permit its development. It has been found that prominent end moraines of the Pleistocene continental glaciation, like the Baltic Moraine of north Europe and the Salpausselka of southern Finland required from 100 to 500 years for their building. It is remarkable that this degree of equilibrium should have existed. Where the balance between supply and melting was less perfect, *moraine belts* (Frontispiece and Fig. 292) a number of miles wide occur, and are made up of numerous morainic ridges.

Till Sheets. If, instead of even an oscillating halt, the ice front either of a valley glacier or of a continental glacier is caused to retreat steadily, a more or less uniform sheet of glacial debris is spread over all the surface formerly occupied by the ice. This cover is called "deposited ground moraine" with reference to valley glaciers, but in its more widespread development from continental glaciation is known as the *till sheet.*

Till sheets have an undulating surface to which the phrase *sag and swell* is applied. In the Middle West of the United States this type of topography extends unbroken for thousands of square miles. Such a till sheet is a geomorphic unit because postglacial drainage is consequent upon its surface, and because its depth, amounting to hundreds of feet over preglacial valley lines, and up to 100 feet elsewhere, in northern Ohio, for example, almost completely obliterates the rock topography that underlies it. In this sense it may be referred to as a *till plain.* Over wide areas the Pleistocene till plains are undissected. Where shallow stream courses have been cut into them the drainage pattern tends to be dendritic and the lesser channels are commonly insequent.

Despite the regularity and distinctive nature of the topography of the surface of till plains, it is difficult to be precise in regard to their exact origin. They evidently result from slow, steady melting back of the ice fronts; they are chiefly composed of ground moraine. But they also have intercalated sands and gravels. In view of such inclusion of water-sorted materials the term *glacial drift,* still much in use in Europe, is perhaps more comprehensive than "till sheet" for the phenomenon in its broadest expression. In this connection a concept of *dead* or *stagnant ice* of widespread extent as the chief earmark of the wasting of the last advance of the Pleistocene continental glaciers in America has been insistently advocated by one group of glacialists. So also has the idea of *periglacial weathering.* A surficial bed, of considerable thickness in some areas of the till plains, is composed of a coarser, looser material than the normally compact, ground moraine composed of boulder clay. This surficial part is supposed to have been let down from a vast expanse of stagnated ice, wasting in place. Or, on the weathering hypothesis, it represents ground moraine modified by the rigors of a periglacial climate, persisting for a long period after the actual dissipation of the ice.

Drumlins. If a student informed about glacial deposits desires to interest an untutored person in end moraines or till sheets he

Fig. 293.　DRUMLIN AT IPSWICH, MASSACHUSETTS
Photograph by J. S. Gardner.

must first make his audience conscious of the existence of such features. The half-egg, split lengthwise, form of *drumlin* hills (Fig. 293) is however so distinctive that it gets uninstructed popular attention.

Drumlins are composed almost exclusively of boulder clay. They are steeper and broader on the stoss end, that of the ice approach, than on the lee end. The most perfectly developed units taper off to a slender low point at the lee end. The sides of drumlins not uncommonly exhibit modeling in the form of grooves and low ridges owing to ice action. Drumlins range from 25 feet to 200 or more feet in height and average from one-half mile to a mile or more in length. Between one drumlin and the next the ground may be flat or even marshy. Drumlins occur in fields of considerable extent. One in north-central New York State has been estimated to include 10,000 units. Another considerable tract occurs in Wisconsin. Within such a field the drumlins are disposed radially, fan-shape, but are generally offset on successive concentric lines across the radii.

The question of the origin of the drumlins has been much debated. Against the view that they are remnants of a deep till sheet, eroded by a readvance of the ice, is the levelness of ground commonly observed between drumlin units. It is improbable that glacial erosion would act with the uniformity such levelness would imply. There are those who seek to establish a genetic correlation between roches moutonnées and drumlins, or who see in drumlins a further impress of the manner of ice motion. But drumlins are, more probably, depositional forms and, as such, represent sites where the thin ice of the terminal areas of the glacier was incapable of transporting all the boulder clay of its basal layers to the end moraine. It has been suggested that the drumlin sites were the tracts directly under the radial longitudinal crevasses that are regularly developed in a spreading ice lobe. The ground plan patterns of the two sets of phenomena, longitudinal crevasses and drumlins, match and the diminished pressure under a crevasse might well act to inhibit glacial transportation. The incipient drumlin accumulation, so initiated, would further hamper glacial movement and transportation of debris, and thus promote its own building up.

Glacio-fluvial Deposits. Much of the debris transported by glaciers to their terminal areas is subjected to the action of the melt waters resulting from the dissipation of the ice. The waters model it to particular forms and distribute it about the ice margins and more remotely.

Eskers. Where the ice stagnates over wide areas and disappears finally by melting down *in situ,* drainage of large volume may be concentrated in subglacial channels. Even active glaciers regularly discharge melt-waters as a unified flow from an ice cave at the front. In stagnant ice it appears to be possible for a very extended underice tunnel system to develop, and to function undisturbed for long periods. Water, with heavy loads of surficial and englacial rock debris, reaches these tunnels under a pressure head from its source in crevasses and moulins at high altitudes in the glacier. It grinds the transported debris in its high-velocity, turbulent flow, depositing some of it on the floor of the tunnel, the while it erodes its way upward into the ice. The bottom deposition is made general by the large loss of load at the tunnel mouth. This chokes the outlet and compels the subglacial stream to flow at higher levels.

When the ice eventually melts away completely the deposits on the former tunnel bottoms remain as *eskers* or *osar* (Fig. 294).

FIG. 294. ESKER AT MALLORYVILLE, NEW YORK

They are ridges of gravel (Fig. 295), often very coarse, commonly winding, from a few feet to a hundred or more feet high, and from some hundreds of yards to miles long. A given esker may vary greatly in volume and height owing to irregularities of deposition and inclusion of ice blocks which melt out after deposition ceases. The side slopes, originally supported as a prism by the tunnel walls, stand at the angle of repose for the texture of the esker materials. As the water flowed under pressure the course of an esker may be locally upslope.

Eskers that are made up of a series of expansions connected

by a slender thread of deposit, like beads strung far apart, are referred to as **beaded eskers** and are interpreted as a series of deltas made in a shallow lake fronting a retreating ice margin. The rate of retreat is unsteady; the deltas mark a slowing down when material accumulates in quantity at the mouth of the ice cave.

Some deposits resembling eskers may be *crevasse fillings* let down from stagnant ice. This explanation accounts for great

FIG. 295. SECTION THROUGH AN ESKER AT MALLORYVILLE, NEW YORK
Photograph by R. S. Tarr.

irregularities in the topography and volume of the accumulations and for courses completely indifferent to the land topography.

Characteristic eskers are, however, so clearly composed of current-bedded, water-worked materials and are so intimately connected with ice-cave outlet kame and outwash deposits that their subglacial origin is almost certain.

Kames. In view of the manner of their functioning a great concentration of deposition may be expected where esker-building streams emerge from ice caves at the ice front. The pressure-head flow is there suddenly reduced and the debris load is in consequence nearly all dropped. The deposit then formed is a *kame.* A kame is made up solely of water-sorted materials in a very confused, cross-bedded stratification. It has commonly been banked against and upon the glacier front, so that, from later melting out of buried ice blocks, great, dry pits result. The extreme irregularity of topographic expression such pitting gives is the prominent earmark of kame deposits. Probably the accumulation of the kame deposits does much to block the outlet of the esker stream and so to bring about aggradation along its subglacial course. Where a kame is led up to by a long esker the pebbles and boulders in the kame are very perfectly water-rounded and consist almost exclusively of resistant types of rock. However, not all kames are associated with eskers. If crevasse filling with debris brought by surficial melt-water was as common in stagnant ice as has been urged by certain students of glacial phenomena, it is now much more probably represented by kame deposits than by eskers. In accordance with this idea any irregularity in the surface of inert glacier termini could be a collecting site for gravelly debris, and, on the final dissipation of the ice, appear as hummocky kame masses.

Sometimes end moraines are very largely made up of water-modified materials and are, therefore, called **kame moraines.** Such composition may arise from deposition in water bordering the ice front. Again, large quantities of partly water-sorted debris may be built up along the lateral margin of an ice lobe, banked against the ice on one side and a valley slope on the other. Such a deposit is a **kame terrace** (Fig. 296) and usually has flat upper surfaces with a longitudinal downslope toward the position of the former ice front.

Because it is only here and there that cuts have been made in kame terraces it is difficult to be certain that a particular occurrence is correctly interpreted as such.

Outwash Fans. If the slope of the land is away from the ice margin a large proportion of the debris brought to the glacier end by melt-water drainage is carried away by the outflow streams. It is built up into **outwash fans** or **outwash gravel aprons** or **outwash plains** where the land relief is low; into **valley trains** where there are confining valley walls. Outwash fans may be very wide-spread areally; valley trains continue for many miles beyond a glacier front. Glacier outflow streams are almost universally aggrading. Emerging as trunk streams from ice caves deposition in the chan-

Fig. 296. KAME TERRACE AND VALLEY TRAIN, FACTORY CREEK, NEW YORK
The embayment at the center of the terrace is probably an ice-contact form.

nel immediately brings about a bifurcation of the water current. Such division is repeated again and again downstream, so that remote from the ice front the drainage becomes a maze of shallow currents. The waters are also continually shifting. Channels once dry are reoccupied, built up, and abandoned again. Deposit near the ice front is normally very coarse in texture and has a steep surface slope. The materials become finer and finer and the slope more gently inclined with distance from the outlet site. In effect outwash fans are alluvial fans developed by continuous instead of intermittent upbuilding.

When deposition ceases dry channels trace the former courses of the multitudinous currents on the surfaces of outwash fans and valley trains. These surfaces are also commonly interrupted by shallow, semicircular pits and ponds. Where such pits and ponds are numerous the deposit is called a *pitted outwash plain* or a *pitted valley train.* As with other glacio-fluvial deposits outwash fans very commonly bury blocks of ice in the process of their accumulation. If such ice masses remain unmelted until after deposition ceases, the surface of the overlying gravel or sand slumps down when the ice finally disintegrates. Thus pits, characteristically rudely circular in outline, are formed. As their bottoms are commonly below the level of the water table a pitted plain is generally dotted with ponds.

Rich (1941) points out that in hilly regions the downmelting of tongues of ice is limited by the level of the top of the outwash emanating from them. Thus a mass of ice on the valley floors may be deeply blanketed by sand and gravel. When this buried ice finally melts out it leaves the pitted plains and "crevasse fillings" that have been interpreted as evidence of stagnation and "downwasting" of the ice margins.

The Glacial Series. The studies of Penck and Brückner in the Alpine Forelands made clear the existence of a sequence in glacial deposits to which the term *glacial series* has been applied. The site of a pronounced end-moraine development is a median line in front of and behind which a particular succession of types of deposit is commonly observed to occur. Outside the end moraine and on its outer slopes, are kame deposits; beyond these outwash plains and valley trains. Behind the moraine there may be a drumlin field which, if present, grades into a gently undulating till-plain surface. Behind the moraine the materials are ice-deposited; in front of it, water-deposited; the morainic ridges are partly ice-dumped, partly water-sorted materials; an esker ridge may be threaded across the morainic belt. Apparently, also, a topographic barrier in the nature of a back slope toward the ice front tends to stabilize a glacier terminus and to promote the development of the complete glacial series at such sites. Water, at first ponded as a *proglacial lake* outside the moraine, may, in time, be completely displaced by the building up of outwash deposits there. Such a sequence is present in north-central New York with the ragged escarpment of the northern edge of the Appalachian Plateau acting as the topographic barrier.

Regional Effects of Pleistocene Continental Glacierization. The chronology of the Pleistocene glacial period and the ordering of its deposits are topics that belong in historical geology. But the great continental glaciers of that time are significant for geomorphology in that the imprint made by their presence and action on the topography of extremely wide areas is still clearly in evidence. The duration of postglacial time is probably less than 30,000 years.

In the foregoing paragraphs attention is directed to the specific phenomena resulting from continental glacierization, and these descriptions, almost without exception, refer to the relics of the vanished Pleistocene ice sheets. It remains therefore to give consideration to the location and extent of this glacierization and to the regional aspects of the geomorphic effects it produced.

In Pleistocene time world climates changed to average annual temperatures 10° to 20° F. lower than those which now prevail. Why is very little understood. This change to a more rigorous climate was sufficient to bring about the accumulation in North America of two ice domes computed to have altitudes of 10,000 feet, one over the Labrador Plateau, and the other over the Keewatin area of low plains west of Hudson Bay. Why these relatively lowland sites should have become the great centers of ice dispersion is as little understood as the cause of the world-wide refrigeration that initiated the Pleistocene glacierization. The mountain regions of British Columbia, where valley glaciers still exist, was a third great center of ice dispersion called the "Cordilleran." It failed to develop into a dome and did not effect a junction with the ice from the Keewatin center. A lesser icecap seems to have been centered over Newfoundland.

From each of these centers the ice spread radially in all directions (Fig. 297). Its northern extension is not well known. Southward the ice reached the sea from Labrador to Long Island.

FIG. 297. EXTENT OF PLEISTOCENE GLACIERIZATION OF NORTH AMERICA

After R. S. Tarr and L. Martin, *College Physiography,* The Macmillan Company.

Westward from there its farthest margin was along a curving line across New Jersey, Pennsylvania, Ohio, Indiana, Illinois, and broadly speaking, along the course of the Missouri River. The Labrador and Keewatin ice failed of a complete merging in southern Wisconsin and northern Illinois, but joined again farther south. This left an unglaciated "island," the **Driftless Area,** which except for glacio-fluvial valley trains preserves the preglacial topography of those parts.

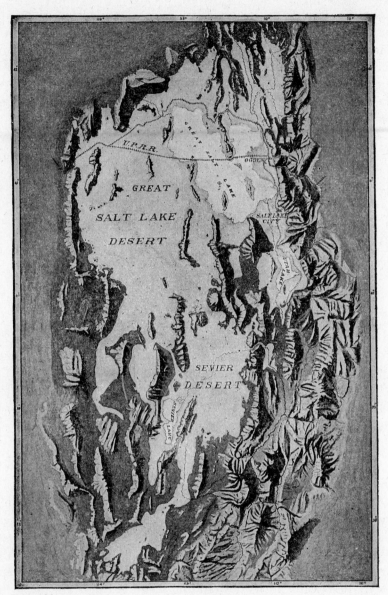

Fig. 298.   EXTENT OF ANCIENT LAKE BONNEVILLE
After G. K. Gilbert.

In Europe the Pleistocene ice was centered mainly in Scandi-
navia, and had its focal point at maximal stages over the Baltic
Sea. Independent domes developed over Scotland and Ireland,

but were eventually merged with the Scandinavian ice by the joint transgression of the glaciers of the full width of the North and Irish Seas. From just north of the Thames River in England the south border of the European ice extended across Belgium, the Netherlands, and Germany into Russia. In the Alps, as in the mountains of British Columbia, an independent ice dispersion center of smaller dimensions was established.

Concerning the extent of Pleistocene ice sheets in other parts of the world much less is known. However, all existing mountain

FIG. 299.   SHORE LINE OF ANCIENT LAKE BONNEVILLE
Photograph by Frederick Pack.

glacierization was then expanded far beyond its present limits and in some instances attained continental glacier characteristics.

In mountainous areas all the effects of mountain glacierization were intensified by the Pleistocene enlargements. The great glacial troughs, deep lake basins and ice-scoured passes character-istic of such districts date from this time. A case in point is the English Lake District made famous by Wordsworth, the landscape poet. Practically all its outstanding scenic features are the prod-uct of Pleistocene glacierization, a circumstance of which the poet shows little comprehension and his commentators hardly more.

In the desert regions of the American West, situated marginally to the ice-occupied areas, basins were water-filled to overflow levels in Pleistocene times. Thus the present Great Salt Lake was, as ancient Lake Bonneville, increased in depth by 850 feet, spread over 20,000 square miles, and overflowed into the Columbia River (Fig. 298). The high and dry shore lines of the extinct Lake Bonneville are conspicuous topographic features (Fig. 299).

The areas uncovered by the dissipation of continental glaciers that radiated from plateau and plain centers are of two distinctive types. Starting from the centers of dispersion the prevailing topographic aspect of the country, over a wide radius, is one of bare rock surfaces, roches moutonnées, lake-filled rock basins, and is a territory occupied by a highly irregular and complicated drainage system alternately expanding into lakes and following rock-walled channels, resulting from ice-scour. This glacial topography has been little modified by fluvial erosion in post-glacial time. This is called the *zone of erosion,* and is well exemplified in the Highlands of Ontario and Labrador regions in North America, by Finland and the uplands of Norway in Europe.

Peripheral to the zone of erosion (in North America in general south of the line of the St. Lawrence and the northern side of the Great Lakes; in Europe, beyond the North and Baltic Seas) is found the *zone of deposition.* In the zone of deposition the glaciated rock topography, and whatever remained of preglacial relief, are commonly smothered under glacial drift of various types. Broadly speaking, the zones of deposition have, in consequence, acquired a plain's aspect. The till sheet which constitutes a large part of the prairies of the Central States is the greatest single expression of this effect, but perfection of levelness is seen where an ice-border lake, Glacial Lake Agassiz, now extinct, extended over wide areas in Minnesota, North Dakota, and Manitoba. During the period of its existence deposits of fine-grained glacial sediments so smoothed its floor that a prospect in this country is like looking over the surface of a calm sea.

The present outlets of the Great Lakes were for a time blocked by the receding ice fronts. Their waters were then held at higher levels and extended over considerable tracts to the south of their existing borders. Lake plains and shore-line developments such as the Ridge Road (Fig. 300), the ancient, higher level, beach paralleling the present shore of Lake Ontario, are features of those areas.

The detailed expression of the drift cover varies considerably in different parts of the United States. New England has a thin and very bouldery soil with many large *erratics* (Fig. 301), rock fragments from distant sources. The mountainous relief of its northern parts yielded an abundance of durable rock material for glacier transport. There is a gradual transition from these bouldery New England fields to the axis of the Mississippi Basin where the glacial deposits are deep and of fine texture, and where conspicuous erratics are much less in evidence.

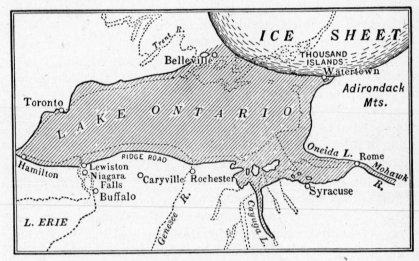

FIG. 300. SITE OF THE RIDGE ROAD, NORTHERN NEW YORK

It was a beach of the higher level of Lake Ontario when the lake overflowed into the Mohawk River.

The border of the ice was everywhere lobate, the farthest advances of the glacier following the axes of depressions in line with the direction of ice motion. In consequence the morainic belts are disposed in great festoons. A sharp transition to a higher altitude, such as that presented by the Appalachian Plateau escarpment, as it extends from north to south across Ohio, if near the ice margins, blocked farther advance of the ice and thus served to define its border over long distances. Where the ice invaded a plateau region in "flood" volume, as in central New York, it eroded differentially and thus operated to heighten preglacial relief instead of, as was normal in the zone of deposition, reducing relief by accumulations of till and outwash.

Postglacial drainage is consequent upon the surfaces created by glacial erosion and deposit, and in many places departs widely from preglacial courses. It is characterized as **disordered** (or deranged) **drainage** (Fig. 44) because of the great irregularities of

FIG. 301. GLACIAL ERRATIC AT THE MARGIN OF THE HARDANGER GLACIER, NORWAY

This one is over ten feet high and has the flat-iron shape which is characteristic of some rock fragments that have been used as grinding tools by the ice. The striations and grooving of its sole are conspicuously evident.

its pattern and the confused intermingling of lakes, gorges, wide-open valleys, waterfalls, and marshes in its make-up. Niagara Falls and Gorge is an outstanding example of the effects of such glacial diversion. A further complication results from the fact that during the Pleistocene glacial period the ice advanced and apparently melted off completely at least twice and experienced wide retreats two or three more times, with long interglacial epochs between. Gorges and other stream cuts made during the interglacial times were partially or completely obliterated by the deposits of succeeding advances.

SUMMARY

Regions that receive an excess of snowfall over snow waste, by reason either of high altitude or high latitude, are drained by glaciers. Glacierization is of two main types, mountain and continental.

Mountain glaciers occupy stream-eroded hollows. Glacial erosion converts these hollows to cirques and glacial troughs. A distinctive feature of glacial erosion is its differential action. In consequence, steep headwalls, rock steps, rock basins, fiords, and hanging valleys are developed. The shelves, called "albs," margining glacial troughs at the top of their steep walls are indicative of two periods of glacial erosion with a period of stream erosion intervening. Stages in the cycle of mountain glacierization are recognizable by distinctive geomorphic developments.

Surface features of glaciers qualify as geomorphic items of the third order of relief because their endurance is more than fleeting.

Plateau and continental glaciers differ chiefly in the matter of size, as both develop by doming, move by lateral spread, and function independently of rock relief. The vastness, homogeneity, and independent existence of continental glaciers entitle them to classification among geomorphic units. Piedmont glaciers and the Ross Shelf Ice have characteristics giving them some claim to similar recognition.

Continental glacierization in its early stages may operate to enhance the rock relief of the territories invaded through differential erosion effected by basal currents. Finger-like basins and hanging valleys then result. The universal product of glacial erosion is the roche moutonnée, which has erroneously been interpreted as a residual of preglacial relief, or an expression of superior rock durability. Instead its form seems to be a reflection of the manner of mass motion of glaciers, for it is imposed on rocks of all kinds and without regard to their structural lines. The roche moutonnée apparently marks the end stage of glacial erosion.

The processes by which the erosional forms due to glaciation are produced are largely a matter of inference; the origin of depositional features from glacial action is more often directly observable. Deposits made by the ice itself are moraines, till sheets, drumlins; those made by melt-water, glacio-fluvial deposits, are eskers, kames, kame moraines, kame terraces, outwash plains, and valley trains. Ice-deposited and glacio-fluvial forms appear in a regular association designated a "glacial series."

Wide regions of North America and Europe, now free of ice, were subjected to continental glacierization in Pleistocene times. Probably not over 30,000 years have elapsed since the final retreat of this ice. Because of the recency of the glacial visitation its regional imprint is preserved almost unmodified in the territories covered. A zone of erosion is differentiated from a zone of deposition. The first is characterized chiefly by bare rock surfaces; the second by a plain's aspect, from deep and smooth drift filling. Postglacial drainage in both zones is highly disordered in pattern and quite unsystematic in make up.

BIBLIOGRAPHY

CLASSICAL

Agassiz, L. (1840) *Etudes sur les Glaciers,* Jent et Gassman, Neuchatel.

Jameison, T. T. (1863) *On the Parallel Roads of Glen Roy,* Quarterly Journal of the Royal Geological Society, Vol. 19, pp. 235–259.

Chamberlin, T. C. (1883) *Terminal Moraine of the Second Glacial Epoch,* Third Annual Report, United States Geological Survey, Washington, pp. 291–402.

Chamberlin, T. C., and Salisbury, R. D. (1885) *The Driftless Area of the Upper Mississippi Valley,* Sixth Annual Report, United States Geological Survey, Washington, pp. 199–322.

Tarr, R. S. (1894) *Lake Cayuga a Rock Basin,* Bulletin Geological Society of America, Vol. 5, pp. 339–356.

Upham, W. (1896) *Glacial Lake Agassiz,* Monograph 25, United States Geological Survey, Washington.

Gannett, H. (1898) *Lake Chelan,* National Geographic Magazine, Vol. 9, pp. 417–428.

Johnson, W. D. (1904) *The Profile of Maturity in Alpine Glacial Erosion,* Journal of Geology, Vol. 12, pp. 569–578.

RECENT

Rich, J. L. (1906) *Local Glaciation in the Catskill Mountains,* Journal of Geology, Vol. 14, pp. 113–121.

Davis, W. M. (1909) *The Sculpture of Mountains by Glaciers,* Scottish Geographical Magazine, Vol. 22, pp. 76–89. In *Geographical Essays,* Ginn and Company, Boston, pp. 617–634.

v. Engeln, O. D. (1914) *Effects of Continental Glaciation on Agriculture,* Bulletin American Geographical Society, Vol. 46, pp. 241–264 and 336–355.

Bowman, I. (1916) *The Andes of Southern Peru,* American Geographical Society, New York.

Hobbs, W. H. (1921) *Studies of the Cycle of Glaciation,* Journal of Geology, Vol. 29, pp. 370–386.

Martin, L., and Williams, F. E. (1924) *An Ice-Eroded Fiord, the Mode of Origin of Lynn Canal, Alaska,* Geographical Review, Vol. 14, pp. 576–596.

Thwaites, F. T. (1926) *The Origin and Significance of Pitted Outwash,* Journal of Geology, Vol. 34, pp. 308–319.

Antevs, E. (1928) *The Last Glaciation,* American Geographical Society, New York, Research Series, No. 17.

Flint, R. F. (1928) *Eskers and Crevasse Fillings,* American Journal of Science, 5th Series, Vol. 15, pp. 410–416.

Matthes, F. E. (1930) *Geologic History of the Yosemite Valley,* Professional Paper No. 160, United States Geological Survey, Washington.

Flückiger, O. (1934) *Glaziale Felsformen,* Petermanns Mitteilungen, Ergänzungsheft No. 218.

Lewis, M. V. (1938) *A Melt-Water Hypothesis of Cirque Formation,* Geological Magazine, Vol. 75, pp. 249–265.

v. Engeln, O. D. (1938) *Large, Sharply Defined Terminal Moraine Ridges,* Comptes Rendus du Congrès International de Géographie, Amsterdam, 1938, Volume 2, Section 2a, pp. 210–213.

Antevs, E. (1939) *Modes of Retreat of the Pleistocene Ice Sheets,* Journal of Geology, Vol. 47, pp. 503–516.

Cotton, C. A. (1941) *The Longitudinal Profiles of Glaciated Valleys,* Journal of Geology, Vol. 49, pp. 113–128.

Chapter Twenty

GEOMORPHOLOGY OF COASTS

Introductory. Just as the shaping of land forms by streams, by wind, and by glacial ice is cyclic, so also is the development of coast lines cyclic, with waves and currents functioning as the dominant agencies. The circumstances of their processing are somewhat like those relating to glacial action, in that direct observation of the underwater changes, as of those taking place under ice, is difficult or impossible. Further, the mechanics of wave and current action are complex, and only imperfectly known. However, there has been much study of coastal geomorphology. The major outlines of its evolution are understood and experimental enterprise, notably in the Netherlands, promises elucidation of particular phenomena that continue to be puzzling.

Configuration of Coast Lines. A distinction is to be drawn between *coast lines* and *shore lines.* By "coast line" is meant the general configuration of the land where it fronts the sea. The "shore line" is the zone of intimate and direct contact between water and land. The *shore line zone* may be a beach or strand at one site, a sea cliff at another.

The broader aspect of coastal geomorphology, referred to as the "coast line," has an epeirogenic or orogenic background; that is to say, its expression is due to continental uplift or depression or to mountain making. Various classifications of coast lines have been attempted on this basis. The major distinction is between a *Pacific type* and an *Atlantic type* (Fig. 13).

In the Pacific type the coast line runs parallel with, and is chiefly comprised of young, fold mountain ranges. The Pacific Basin is ringed by such coasts. The Atlantic type of coast line breaks across the mountain folding it encounters and is, in general, unrelated to structural trends. In this dual classification, coast lines backed by broad expanses of coastal plain are ignored, or referred to the structural trends of their hinterlands.

507

The difference between the two types is real, and is probably of fundamental significance for planetary geomorphology. In the present state of knowledge nothing much further can be said with assurance. However, it seems clear that the Atlantic type expresses fracture and sundering, whereas the Pacific type is indicative of compression and a general tendency to close in on the Pacific Basin. These inferences may eventually be found in complete accord with some modification of the Taylor or Wegener theories of shifting continents, or of elaborations of these, as that undertaken by Du Toit (1937).

Coast and Shore-line Classification.   Shore-line forms are, for particular reaches, matters of detail. But coast and shore lines have also a larger geomorphic aspect which is, in general, based on diastrophic circumstance. Here the distinction is between *coast and shore lines of submergence* and *coast and shore lines of emergence.* It may not, however, be asserted that the one results from sinking of the land and the other from uplift. The difference in aspect may as well be due to change in sea level. If a significant change in sea level is a possibility it might appear that the most recent shift should give a universal uniform aspect to shore lines. But the configuration of coast lines differs in such measure that a change in sea level of a certain amount might affect the shore-line aspect in one place, but not in another. Indeed it is necessary to qualify in regard to coast and shore lines of submergence and emergence by referring, in making a classification, to the dominant conditions. Thus the coast line of the southern Atlantic states of the United States is one of emergence but its shore-line aspect is determined by a succeeding submergence of secondary measure. In this instance the general trend of the coast line results from uplift, but the shore line is embayed because of the penetration of the sea into the stream valleys eroded at the earlier higher stand of the land. As the region is a coastal plain the embayments are relatively shallow.

Broadly considered, coast and shore lines of submergence are initially highly irregular, or *indented* (Fig. 302). The coast lines of northeastern North America and of northwestern Europe are representative examples of this condition. The sinking of the land has been so great in vertical measure, or the rise of sea level so marked, that formerly connected land areas of these regions and the islands of Bermuda (Fig. 303) are separated by marine waters, and the sea penetrates for considerable distances inland at places where there were formerly lowlands or river valleys. The river valleys become drowned valleys (Fig. 118). It is an *embayed coast,* and, by the same token, is a place of many projecting head-lands and outlying islands. By such large-scale sinking the sea margin is brought into contact with land topography, that is, in a general sense, in contact with firmly consolidated rocks. If a period of stability succeeds the submergence, a cycle of shore-line

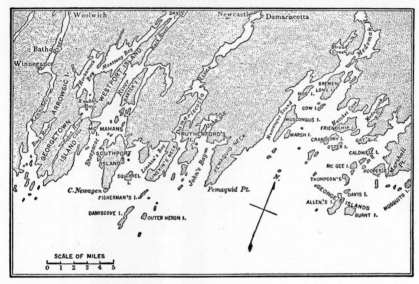

FIG. 302.   INDENTED COAST LINE OF MAINE

evolution is initiated, and carried forward, by marine processes. A sunken coast typically gives rise to the shore line of youth in the marine cycle.

Here again a qualification of the general statement is neces-sary. In the Pacific type of coast line either sinking or uplift can provide a young shore line in the sense that the sea margin is brought into contact with consolidated rock and with topographic forms that are, in origin, independent of marine action. It is true that sinking tends to give a Pacific type of coast greater irregularity of shore line than does uplift. But along reaches where the structural parallelism of the Pacific type of coast line is

FIG. 303. EMBAYED COAST, HARBOR OF ST. GEORGE, BERMUDA
The irregular coast line has resulted from postglacial rise of sea level. Photograph by Henry Head.

510

essentially perfect, shore lines tend to be straight and bold with either uplift or depression.

But, aside from this case, uplift characteristically brings the sea margin in contact with the sea bottom. And the sea bottom, from having been previously a depositional site, can be presumed to have a flat monotonous topography. The new shore line consequently is straight and low. It is not, by virtue of these circumstances, immune from modification by marine action. Like the indented shore line of submergence, it is a new, young shore line. But the cycle of its evolution follows a different order and has a less spectacular progress than that of the shore line of submergence. The shore line of emergence is, in effect, adapted to the sea from the start. Here it may be added that where submergence involves an originally flat low coast the evolutional sequence, from marine action, in many respects resembles that of the shore line of emergence traced across a former sea floor of low relief. The downsinking of the low coast results in submerged, shallow valleys not present on the emergent sea floor. But the development by marine processes is alike in both cases because the submerged valleys of the flat coast are not immediately affected by them.

Waves. The characteristics of stream flow, of glacier motion, and the processes by which these agencies operate to modify land forms are topics regularly discussed at considerable length in textbooks of elementary geology. Wave action is also adequately treated in such books. But waves and wave motion get only passing mention. As such knowledge will not, therefore, be part of the equipment of the student who has had only a beginning course in geology, it is appropriate to include waves and wave motion in this discussion.

The wind generates waves in the surface waters of the sea by friction, by inclined impact, and as the turbulence which regularly develops where moving media of different densities have a plane of contact. In the area where the wind energy is being applied the waves created are *forced waves*. If such waves are of large size they are *storm waves*. Waves encountered away from the site of the disturbance in which they had their origin are *free waves,* and are called *ground swell*. In the open deep sea both forced waves and free waves are *oscillatory waves*. Each mite of water in an oscillatory wave moves in a nearly circular orbit. The diameter of the orbits through which small units at the surface rotate is reflected in the height of the waves in which they are functioning. The *height of a wave* is its vertical measure from trough to crest. Below the surface the size of the orbits decreases rapidly with depth. Eventually a depth of no orbital motion is reached: this is called the *wave base.* The depth of the wave base is equal to the *wave length,* which is the distance between successive wave crests. However, the wave base is sometimes understood as the depth where agitation of sediment by wave action ceases.

The greatest waves are developed in the practically unlimited expanse of the open sea. Such waves are estimated to have a maximal wave length of 600 feet, hence a depth of wave base 600 feet below the surface. This figure is correlated with the fact that the average depth of water at the edges of the continental shelves is also 600 feet. In other words, the continental shelves extend outward to the maximal depth at which sediment can be moved by wave action. With waves of less length the wave base is proportionately nearer the surface. (While 600 feet is the classic figure modern soundings disclose that the depth at the edges of the shelves more commonly ranges between 350 and 400 feet.) (Figs. 15, 20.)

As the wave size increases in height and length, the orbits followed by the water particles increase in diameter. Theoretically each particle operates in a closed circuit: up, forward, down, and back to the starting point. Actually, in forced waves, the wind induces a forward movement, or *drift,* in the surface water so that the return of a specific particle is not exactly to the point from which it started a traverse of the orbit. Also, the wind hurries the motion of the surface particles as they go up and forward to the crest, and retards their downward and backward course. In consequence the waves tend to become asymmetrical, steeper in front, less steep in the rear. *White caps* result when forced waves in the open sea are so greatly steepened in this way that their crests are blown over and fall forward.

Oscillatory waves, forced or free, may approach a shore so steep that the water immediately under the cliff is deeper than the wave base. In that event the lateral components of the orbital motion are eliminated, the wave moves up, then down the wall, and is reflected.

Where, on the other hand, the waves move into water that shallows as the shore line is approached the wave base, at different depths for different lengths of waves, eventually comes in contact with the bottom. From thence onward, toward the shore, the vertical component of orbital motion is eliminated at the wave base, and the water there moves forward and backward in a line along the bottom. This result may be experimentally verified. If a rectangular thin board or metal plate of suitable size is attached at the center of its longer dimension to a slender rod, in such manner that the board can be thrust edgewise to the bottom, at a site where waves longer than the depth of the water are coming in on a beach, it will be found that with the passing of each wave the plate is appreciably and forcibly moved forward and backward. The bather wading into shallow surf is alternately pushed and pulled.

The distorting effect on the orbital motion, complete at the bottom, is transmitted upwards in declining degree as the surface is approached. The normally circular orbits of the surface waters are thus converted to ellipses which are flattest near the bottom. A part of the energy of the wave is consumed in friction with the bottom, but commonly not so much as to compensate for the lesser volume of water involved in the wave because of the decreasing depth. The wave lengths diminish and the wave heights increase so that the waves become steeper.

The frictional retardation, resulting from contact with the bottom, affects the forward motion of the crest of the wave as well as the backward motion of the trough; but not in the same degree. There is more water in the crest of a wave than in the trough, or otherwise put, the trough water is nearer the retarding influence. The velocity of the particles at the crest of the wave is, by comparison, greater than that of those in the trough. This circumstance contributes to a further steepening of the wave front.

Also, when the wave reaches water of approximately the same depth as the wave height, the volume of water in front of the wave is inadequate to provide for the rising and building up of the crest as the wave moves forward. The steepened front of the

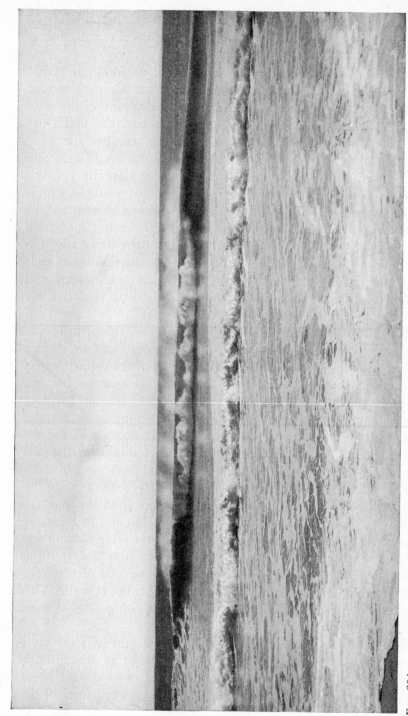

FIG. 304. BREAKER, SURF, SWASH, AND BACKWASH, ATLANTIC CITY, NEW JERSEY
Photograph by William Rau.

514

wave then hollows out. Meanwhile, the wave has been fully built up from behind. Thus the crest of the wave is suddenly left without support and for this reason and because of its forward motion plunges downward toward the shore making **breakers, surf, swash,** and **backwash** (Fig. 304).

If the line of breakers is some distance from the shore line a

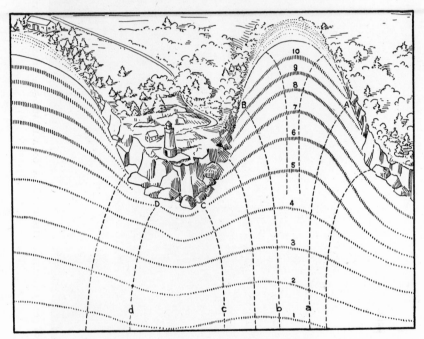

FIG. 305.   CONCENTRATION OF WAVE ENERGY ON HEADLANDS

The wave fronts, a, b, c, d, positions 1, 2, 3 have a parallel approach until they are bent toward the points by the shallowing water off the headlands, so that the energy of the portion of the wave c-d is concentrated on the shore reach D-C, while that of a-b is spread over the shore reach A-B, around the head of the bay. After W. M. Davis and C. A. Cotton.

welter of secondary waves may form and roll in to the beach. Some of these are oscillatory waves reduced in size, others are **waves of translation.** In waves of translation a water particle rises, moves forward, then sinks, without a compensating backward motion. Thus each water unit attains a position nearer shore with the passing of each wave. If large oscillatory waves, ground swell, encounter a shallow reach abruptly, great and regu-

FIG. 306.   FREE WAVES BREAKING AND CONCENTRATING THEIR ENERGY ON A HEADLAND, ISLAND OF HAWAII

lar waves of translation develop. This can occur at the seaward edge of a fringing coral reef, as at Waikiki Beach in Hawaii.

In the open sea, waves advance in straight lines at right angles to the direction of their motion. Forced waves developed by an onshore wind tend to maintain their orientation irrespective of the trend and nature of the shore line. As it can only be by coincidence that the direction of the shore line will be parallel with that of the wave front an *oblique,* or *diagonal approach* of such waves is normally observed.

On the other hand, free waves, not directly impelled by the wind, tend to a *parallel approach* even when the trace of the shore line is very irregular. This results from the fact that the part of the wave which first reaches shallow water is slowed up, so that the part in deeper water, with faster motion, can swing around enough to insure a parallel approach for the whole wave.

The effect of such bending is to direct marked concentration of wave energy on headlands (Fig. 305). An embayment between two headlands will have deeper water along its central axis than that off the points. Opposite the headlands the waves are retarded and their crest lines, because of decreasing velocity and shorter wave lengths, follow each other at shorter distances. The wave fronts are bent and the lines of propagation are focused on the points. The energy of a wave is exerted in the direction of its propagation. By the focusing of the lines of propagation on the headlands the energy of a given section of wave is directed against a shorter reach of shore line in the headland area (Fig. 306) than that of an equal section terminating in the bayhead sites. While forced storm waves are not so much bent, their smashing onset from various directions probably also concentrates more energy on the headlands than on the bay shores.

EROSIONAL DEVELOPMENT OF THE COAST LINE
OF SUBMERGENCE

The Sea Cliff. Where a dissected oldland of considerable relief experiences depression to such depth that an irregular embayed coast, with drowned valleys and exposed headlands, is produced, there is full scope for the processes of the marine cycle to modify the shore line.

When a great storm wave, in complete development, smashes, with undiminished velocity, against a cliff (Fig. 307) where there is deep water directly off-shore, the force of the impact is tremendous. The erosional effect may however be slight because, in this case, the problem of "irresistible force versus immovable body" is resolved in favor of the immovable body. The rock masses which back up the cliff may respond to the shock by tremors, but the net effect is to hurl the wave back on itself. It

FIG. 307.   SEA CLIFF, ISLAND OF HELGOLAND, GERMANY

Note rock fragments at the base of the cliff; sea arch at the point in the distance. Photographer unknown.

is different when human structures are attacked. No matter how securely great concrete walls may be anchored, they are not part of the unit bedrock, hence are frequently pounded to pieces and the fragments, perhaps weighing many tons, tossed far from their original sites by the waves of a single storm.

The cliff does not escape unscathed. Blocks bounded by joint planes may be forced out by the water pressure. These sink to the bottom at the base of the cliff and begin the building up of an underwater talus. Between storms, weathering processes loosen other fragments and these drop and are added to the pile. In time the talus accumulation is so much enlarged that its slopes extend an appreciable distance outward from the base of the cliff (Fig. 307) and its top is near water level. Then the waves are caused to break on the talus. The breaking occurs where the depth of water is slightly less than that of the wave height, for there the full orbital motion of the upper water particles is precluded. The impact of the breaking is a directed blow, unlike

Fig. 308.   WAVE-CUT NOTCH, HOPEWELL ROCKS, BAY OF FUNDY, NOVA SCOTIA
Photograph by William Hayes.

the uniform pressure of the reflected wave. Weathered and joint-separated blocks are broken out. These fragments and the previously accumulated talus material are hurled against the cliff base. Very shortly the cliff will be undercut by a *wave-cut notch* (Fig. 308) which commonly has its median line at the high-water mark.

In little fissured and strongly consolidated rock the notching may proceed to a number of feet back from the cliff face so that there is a considerable overhang. In that case the cliff tends to be maintained as a vertical face because its whole height crashes down when lack of support, from extension of the undercutting, makes it finally unstable. If the land behind the crest of such a cliff rises sharply, the cliff will be increased in height with each successive fall. Between rock falls and renewed notching, the debris of a crash is hammered to pieces by the waves. A structure of inland dipping strata is also favorable to the preservation of steep sea cliffs. At some sites considerable cutting back by wave erosion is indicated by a back slope of the land from the crest

Fig. 309. SEA CAVE, MT. DESERT ISLAND, MAINE
Photograph by Glen Stoddard.

line of the sea cliff. It is then clear that more than one-half of a former hill has been demolished by wave erosion.

If the rock of an initial cliff is cut by close-spaced joints or other division planes, or is weakly consolidated, slumping, *ab initio,* precludes conspicuous notching. The cliff then shortly becomes inclined, the angle of inclination depending on variations in structure. Where a zone of weak material interrupts the face of a generally strong rock cliff a *sea cave* (Fig. 309) will develop because of the differential yield, and may be made to penetrate a number of feet behind the cliff face. However, the more extensive sea caves are usually developed in limestone formations, and are due to the solvent action of the sea water, rather than to wave attack. At places where two sides of a headland are attacked by the waves, a weaker or narrower section may be cut completely through by sea-cave enlargement. The opening so made is called a *sea arch* (Fig. 310). Further wave action and weathering consume the roof of the arch; then the outlying detached portion is a *stack.*

FIG. 310.   SEA ARCH AND STACKS, ISLE OF CAPRI, ITALY
Wave-cut notch shows faintly at the base of stacks.   Photograph by Brogi.

The Wave-cut Platform.   Once an adequate supply of rock fragments enables waves to make an attack on the steep shores of a sunken coast, wave erosion is, for a period, very vigorous. The cliffs are caused to recede rapidly; the *shore line* is one *of retrogradation.* Experiment with waves of uniform size, advancing in unvarying succession and with a fixed water level, indicated that the cutting at the base of the cliff is at the plane of the water surface. It results from the plunge of the wave in breaking. As the cliff is made to recede the waves no longer break at its immediate base. Between the *plunge point* and the base of the cliff a short wave of translation transmits the wave energy and hurls the rock tools. The erosion, so accomplished, makes a narrow, nearly horizontal shelf. As this shelf is widened the force of the wave of translation is more and more dissipated in crossing it. In time this effect would prevent further attack at the cliff base if not offset by other conditions.

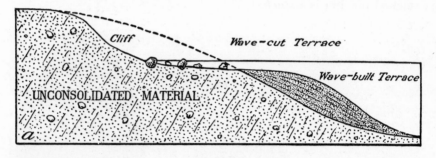

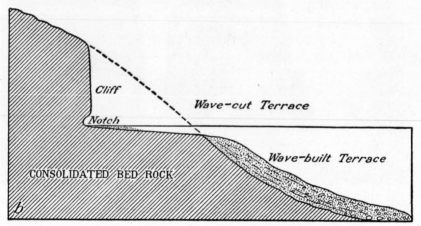

FIG. 311. WAVE-CUT PLATFORM AND WAVE-BUILT TERRACE IN UNCONSOLIDATED (*a*) AND CONSOLIDATED (*b*) ROCK
The dashed lines indicate the slopes before wave erosion modified the coast.

The water brought forward by the wave of translation is moved outward by gravity under the incoming waves, as **undertow**. The undertow is in part hindered, in part supplemented in its outward motion by the forward (impeding) and backward (aiding) motion at the base of the advancing waves. As the handicapping effect of the waves on the undertow is greatly offset by the combined facilitating effect of gravity pull and of wave motion, the seaward direction prevails in the transport of sediment. In shallow water large boulders are readily moved outward. The effect of this movement is to degrade the rock surface over which the transport takes place and to give it a seaward inclination, because the farther out a point on the surface is the longer it will have been acted upon, hence the lower the level to which it will have been cut. The plunge point may, in consequence of such degradation, shift slowly landward in pursuit of the retreating cliff base. The rock shelf that is produced by the combined action of the direct attack on the cliff base and the to-and-fro motion from the undertow and wave base is the *wave-cut platform,* or *wave-cut bench* (Fig. 311).

The Wave-built Terrace. The restored profile of a shore line from the summit of the sea cliff, at any position to which this has been caused to recede by wave erosion, should intersect the original sea bottom at the outer edge of the wave-cut bench. If the initial coast was very steep some remnants of the talus which provided the base for the beginning of the wave attack may still remain on the sea floor at, and beyond, this point. These blocks will then be the nucleus of the *wave-built,* or *shoreface terrace.*

The continued recession of the sea cliff, together with the downward abrasion of the wave-cut bench should bring about a progressive extension seaward of the wave-built terrace—by supplying sediment for deposit at its outer edge. Where the sea bottom descends steeply to great depths such out-building may proceed indefinitely, but increase in breadth in that case will be very slow owing to the ever larger volume of debris required to build up the outer wedge of fill. Experimental studies would serve to test these inferences.

Plain of Marine Erosion. Meanwhile large waves which once, in common with waves of all sizes, broke at the base of the cliff, break at different distances out from the shore line, according to their length, on the sloping surface of the wave-cut bench and wave-built terrace. By such action they contribute to the lowering of their two levels. In turn such deepening permits the continuation of attack at the cliff base and the farther recession of the cliff face. Theoretically a *plain,* or *plane of marine erosion* could be extended indefinitely inland by this system. Such a plain would truncate formations of all degrees of resistance indifferently and its surface would be developed on unweathered fresh rock.

If, however, the level of land and sea remains unchanged marine erosion is, once a broad shelf has been produced, so much slowed up that subaerial degradation will bring about peneplanation long before any vast plain of marine abrasion can be developed. On the other hand, if sinking of the land, or rise in sea level, keeps pace with wave erosion, so that the wave attack at the cliff base is maintained at its maximal rate, the possibilities for widespread marine erosion are great. These are probably the circumstances of the great reduction in area of the island of Helgoland

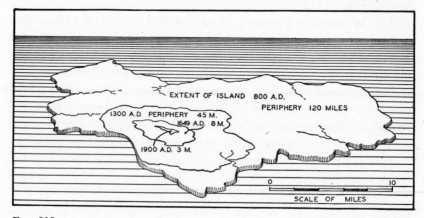

FIG. 312. REDUCTION OF THE ISLAND OF HELGOLAND, IN THE NORTH SEA, BY WAVE EROSION WITHIN HISTORIC TIMES
Drawing by Elizabeth Burckmyer.

in the North Sea within historic times (Figs. 307, 312). At the north end of South Island, New Zealand a level plateau, now 2000 feet above sea level is inferred to be a plain of marine erosion. Its surface is smoothly abraded, unweathered rock on which rest remnants of marine deposits which have a layer of beach pebbles at their base (Cotton, C. A., 1922–26, pp. 388–389). The great marine invasions of the geological past transgressing near-peneplaned lands very possibly achieved similar perfection of widespread marine planation.

An exhumed, ancient plain of marine erosion should have a superimposed drainage system with streams unadjusted to structure; a flat, not undulating, surface; residual summits (former stacks) if present should have sharply defined bases all round; and the plain should be terminated inland by some remainder of a sea-cliff line, or pass under a cover of flat-lying sediments.

The Abrasion Platform.   The base of the greatest storm waves is computed to be at 600 feet depth.   If sediment suitable for abrasive action is available there, some erosion is possible at that depth, and degradation will take place in all shallower waters, because of the backward and forward motion of the water, commonly well supplied with tools, at the wave bottoms.   Except in places where the water beyond the wave-built terrace abruptly attains depths exceeding 600 feet there is a slow reduction of the sea floor by such action.   Thus there is developed the *abrasion platform.*

In the initial stages of vigorous wave attack on a newly submerged coast, with rapid recession of the sea cliff, the supply of debris from wave demolition of the rock, supplemented with the sediment brought by rivers from the land, is normally so great that a prominent wave-built terrace is constructed at sites where the bottom descends steeply.   Where the bottom shelves off more gently, the waste accumulates as a broad, flat deposit.   That is to say, the motion at the wave base, in these circumstances, only suffices to bring about a slow transportation seaward of the waste materials.   There is, apparently, also a period, following the first fury of cliff recession and making of a wave-cut bench, when, owing to the widening of the wave-cut and wave-built terraces, the supply of sediment is too great for the seaward transporting agencies.   In this time the wave-cut bench is temporarily veneered over with debris, so that the wave-built terrace then extends with unbroken upper surface from its outer margin to the beach line. The beach line may actually be advanced seaward by continuous accumulation at the water line.   The shore is then said to be *prograded.*   At the transition point when downward erosion of the wave-cut bench ceases, and before its veneering begins, a *profile of equilibrium,* or *graded profile* is said to be attained. Such equilibrium is not necessarily merely an inversion point; the balance may be maintained over a considerable period.

But at later stages when the effectiveness of the wave attack at the shore line is much diminished and when the relief of the land has been so greatly reduced as to make the sediment supply from rivers very low, *marine abrasion* erodes the sea floor beyond the outer border of the wave-built terrace to produce the abrasion platform. This erosion results from the to-and-fro motion at the base of the greatest storm waves, acting at depths up to 600 feet. It brings about destruction, from the seaward side, of any wave-built terrace. When such removal of the wave-built terrace deposits has been completed the slope of the rock surface of the wave-cut bench merges easily into the similar slope of the abrasion platform so that the two become continuous. It is obvious that very long continued action is necessary to bring about this stage of development.

Continental Shelf. The ultimate resting place of all the sediment (which has meanwhile been comminuted to a very fine texture) is at the outer edge of the abrasion platform in water 600 or more feet deep. The deposit so formed may be called the *continental terrace,* or the *built platform.* The continental terrace and the abrasion platform together constitute the continental shelf (Figs. 15, 20). The continental shelf may become indefinitely wide, but as its outer edge is always at depths of 600 feet or less, the slope of its surface becomes increasingly gentle as its breadth grows greater. Incidentally, the underwater, seaward extensions of the deltas of large rivers bringing fine sediment constitute marked local projections of the continental shelf. Such salients are merely indicative of an exceptionally great supply of sediment locally available for the construction of the built platform. In this overabundance of sediment at particular points the deltaic items anticipate what later becomes a general condition, namely widespread aggradation of the continental-shelf surface with sediment distributed by longshore currents.

EROSIONAL AND DEPOSITIONAL DEVELOPMENT OF COAST LINES OF EMERGENCE

Special Kinds of Emergent Coasts. Emergent coast lines resulting from high-angle faulting, or from the uplift of mountain folds with trends parallel to the coast, have much the same history of development from marine processing as that which the steep coast lines of submergence experience. Deep water immediately offshore insures active wave erosion, the development of a sea

FIG. 313. WAVE-CUT IRREGULAR-ITIES OF A ROCK SHORE, PORT-LAND, MAINE

Photograph by the Long-fellow Gallery.

cliff and of a wave-cut bench. However in both these cases the original, diastrophic coast line will be straighter than that resulting from the submergence of an oldland. Instead of being initially developed, as is true of a submerged oldland coast, on the headlands and salients only, the sea cliff of the faulted and mountain coasts will be continuous from the beginning. In the mountain coast a uniformity of structure may be assumed for considerable reaches. Then the recession of the sea cliff should

FIG. 314.   BEACH RIDGE, NORTH FAIRHAVEN, LAKE ONTARIO, NEW YORK
Photographer unknown.

be similarly regular. But as a fault plane may cut many varieties of rock its originally straight-line scarp will expose all these differences equally to the attack of the sea.

In consequence of differences in the kind of rock, and, more commonly, because of variations in the spacing of joints, the presence of dikes and of other structural characteristics making for exceptional weakness or strength, the uniform battering of the sea will shortly produce many small irregularities in the shore-

Fig. 315.   BEACH AT DAYTONA, FLORIDA

Fig. 316. LOCAL, OR TEMPORARY NIP, BY WAVES, LAKE ONTARIO SHORE
The waves are combing down the material of the higher beach.

line form.   Sea caves, sea arches, stacks, also *sea chasms, blow holes,* and dike ridges appear, together with many small recesses and salients undeserving of specific designations (Fig. 313).   An irregular shore line in this stage is referred to as *crenulate* (Johnson, D. W., 1919, p. 278).   It should be understood, however, that wave attack is incapable of enlarging a recess to the proportions of a bay.   Any salient that attains undue prominence is subjected to increasingly vigorous erosional attack, hence pushed back at a rate superior to the retreat of the embayment.

Shallow Emergent Coasts.   Ordinarily depression introduces a deep-water condition immediately offshore.   Uplift, contrariwise, normally fixes the new shore line on what was an underwater area. Seaward from the new shore line the water becomes unduly shallow.   Wave erosion then takes place seaward of the shore line and there is progradation at the line where land and water meet. Gravel is thrown up by the waves to form successive *beach ridges* (Fig. 314), which may be preserved as the shore is built out, or sand to form a *beach,* ordinarily smoothed out at once to an even slope by wind and wash (Fig. 315).   By such deposition the shore line is progressively moved seaward and a *foreland,* or *strand plain* developed at the land edge.

Meanwhile wave erosion is bringing about an increase in the depth of water offshore.   The combined action of deposition landward and erosion seaward tends to the eventual establishment of an equilibrium.   The bottom slope is steepened by the joint action to the condition of a graded profile.

The sequence set forth above assumes an initial bottom profile sufficiently steep to permit some wave action at the line of contact between land and water.   If, however, the circumstances of the uplift are such that shallow water extends far to seaward all large waves will break a long distance offshore.   The lesser waves produce a low cliff, called the *nip* (Fig. 316), in the weak material of the shore line.   The erosional and depositional processes of large waves operate together to produce a steeper bottom profile in a narrowly compressed zone.   The result is an *offshore bar,* or *barrier beach* (Fig. 317).   The breaking waves erode a trough; the material eroded from the trough is tossed up and deposited subaqueously to form a ridge immediately landward of the

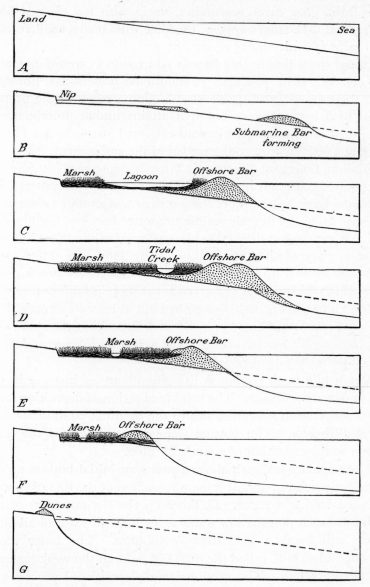

FIG. 317. STAGES IN THE DEVELOPMENT OF AN OFF-SHORE BAR
After D. W. Johnson.

trough. This ridge is built up until it reaches water level. The exceptionally great waves of a storm may then erode the front of the ridge and deposit the sediment so acquired on top of and

FIG. 318. OFF-SHORE BAR, PALM BEACH, FLORIDA
The bridge leads from the mainland across the lagoon to the bar, on which the hotels are located.

531

behind the underwater accumulation, thus duplicating, at an originally subaqueous site, the processes of making and the form of beach ridges. From New York City southward to Florida (Fig. 318) the Atlantic Coast of the United States is fringed with offshore bars formed in this way. These appear seaward of the dominantly emergent, nearly flat, coastal plain province of those parts.

The later history of an offshore bar is one of progressive migration landwards. Wave erosion deepens the bottom immediately seaward of the bar and eats away, "combs down," the front of the bar. The sand tossed up on the crest of the bar is heaped by the wind into dunes or drifted into the lagoon behind the bar. Sediment brought from the land by streams, and marsh growths, also contribute to the filling of the lagoon. Eventually the lines of the bar and that of the shore are made to coincide. After that the former bar will be represented only by some inland moving dunes, while the shore line is again a low cliff like the nip. The bottom profile has been brought to grade.

THE SHORE-LINE CYCLE

Initial Stage. As the shore line takes a new position with either uplift or depression, both directions of shift must be considered initial stages in an analysis of shore-line evolution.

In the case of emergence the new shore line is a former undersea site; hence has in some manner or degree been previously exposed to marine action. It is a place that may be thought of as having already experienced part of a cycle of marine evolution. In other words, either the surface of a plane of marine abrasion or of an offshore or continental terrace ordinarily serves as the site of a shore line of emergence. Orogenic uplift by faulting or folding, the exception to this rule, has the effect of thrusting old rocks into the zone of wave action, and is the equivalent of bringing oldland within the reach of the sea by depression. In view of these circumstances a sunken coast affecting a hilly oldland may be regarded as the representative initial condition in making an analysis of the shore-line cycle. It is logical, also, that the subaqueous marine cycle should follow a course the reverse of that of the subaerial fluvial cycle. The fluvial cycle is initiated

and energized by uplift of the land, so, appropriately, the marine
cycle may be thought of as having its start in sinking of the land.

Youthful Stage.   In the stage of earliest youth a sunken coast
line reflects the features of the previously existing land topography.   Where the strike of the rock structure is at right angles
to the coast, drowned valleys may extend far inland in parallel
lines, each such valley widening toward its mouth.   These valleys
are *rias* and the coast a *ria coast*.   The type site is the coast of

Fig. 319.   Harbor of San Francisco

Galicia in northeast Spain.   Where, in places, the divides between
the parallel valleys are submerged, outlying, rocky islands appear.
Behind them are prominent headlands.   The Maine coast of New
England has this general pattern.   If, on the other hand, the
structure lines run parallel to the coast and streams reach the new
shore line through narrow valleys cut across the ridges, land-
locked harbors result from the entrance of the sea through the
gap to the broader longitudinal valley on the land side of the
barrier.   The San Francisco-Oakland harbor is definitely of such
origin combined with cross faulting (Fig. 319).

The major irregularities due to the former land topography are almost at once augmented by the indefinitely numerous minor irregularities that result from wave attack. Sea cliffs, chasms, notches, caves, wave-cut benches, arches, and stacks are the product of the first intensive wave erosion.

The stage of early youth is, however, of only fleeting duration. The large volume of debris that results from the wave attack, and that from weathering, together with the sediments brought by streams from the land, functions eventually to soften the assault of the sea and to bring about the straightening of the shore line.

Youth to Maturity. The fragments of rock used as tools by the waves are broken and worn in the process of such application. The finely comminuted particles produced in this grinding are in part shifted seaward by the backwash and the undertow. They may come to rest, at least temporarily, in the wave-built terrace. In part they are carried along parallel to the coast by *longshore* (or *littoral) currents.* It is not accurately known in what degree, as to coarseness of texture and as to volume, current transportation is competent to move such material.

But wherever waves impinge on a shore obliquely, even in slight degree, their swash has a partly longshore motion, whereas the backwash is directly down the slope (Fig. 320). In consequence beach gravel, called *shingle* if made up of thin flat pebbles, is continuously drifted in a zigzag course (actually in an asymmetric, curved, parabolic line) along the face of the beach as wave after wave breaks. This process must be observed to realize how efficacious it is with reference both to the size of particles handled and the rate of travel induced.

Where, as on exposed headlands (Figs. 305, 306), wave erosion in the stage of youth is extremely active and concentrated, debris is moved away almost as fast as it is made available. If a bay opening between headlands is wide and the shore line follows an easy curve inland the waste travels from both sides of the salients toward the bay head. As the wave energy decreases, and is dissipated within the bay, sorting of the transported material takes place. The coarsest fragments are dropped immediately in the lee of the tip of the headland. If the bay is large only fine sand is brought to its inmost point where it is deposited to form a *pocket beach,* also called a *bayhead beach.* However, the pocket beaches of small bays may be made up of coarse gravel. In this case the wave energy at the head of the bay is still competent to move the pebbles forward and backward in the *wave mill*. Coarse particles are heaped up in beach ridges, the fine material resulting from the comminution is drawn down into deeper water. The shore line at the head of the bay is rapidly prograded if the sediment supply is ample. Meanwhile the headlands are receding under wave erosion. Thus by prograding of the bayheads and

Fig. 320. diagonal approach of waves and transport of shingle.

erosional demolition of the salients, original indentations are eliminated and the shore line straightened and simplified.

Once the lesser and shallower irregularities have been smoothed out conditions are right for the closing of the larger and deeper embayments. In the case of the deep, narrow inlets, where the shore trends sharply inland immediately in the lee of a headland, wave drift may, from the outset, be incompetent to move debris toward the bayhead. The waste is then deposited tangentially to the headland, which, when so flanked, is termed a *winged head-*

land. More commonly, however, this tendency to close a bay at its mouth, by building a barrier of waste across its width, a *bay mouth bar* (Fig. 321), awaits the elimination, as previously described, of the minor re-entrants. Then long reaches of beach, with an ample content of sediment, are available for the construction. All coarse pebbles or shingle are dropped as soon as such material is carried past the headland, because its transit is effected by swash and backwash on the beach, and the beach, at the start does not extend beyond the headland. The deposit of wave-moved pebbles is supplemented with finer material brought by the littoral current. The oblique propulsion of the water that induces the wave transit may also bring about a strong current motion parallel to the shore where long reaches of straightened shore line have been developed. Such littoral currents may serve to drift immense volumes of fine sediment to the sites of the wider bay mouths. There the longshore currents are checked, by running abruptly into deep water, and the sediment they bring is deposited.

Both processes of shore transport, however, serve only to bring about underwater deposition. If the subaqueous accumulation thus made is to be raised above the water surface it is necessary that storm waves comb down the front of the deposit and contribute part of the sediment eroded to the upbuilding of a ridge along the summit of the fill. The process and the sequence are the same as those involved in the development of an offshore bar. Once the top of the deposit appears at the surface a lateral extension of the beach is created. Then the wave-transit movement of shingle and the longshore drift of finer material can proceed to the new terminus.

A ridge of waste, called a *spit,* is thus made to extend in a straight line farther and farther out across the bay mouth. Spits may be built out from both the boundary headlands of a bay. More commonly, however, there is a prevailing drift of shore material from one direction. This dominant drift seems to be governed by the measure of *fetch* that the wind from different directions has over the water surface. It appears that the quarter from which the wind can travel the longest distance, fetch, across water determines the prevailing drift.

A spit built out from one headland may thus, in time, become

FIG. 321. BAY BAR, FAIR-
HAVEN, LAKE ONTARIO,
NEW YORK
  Photograph by Cecil
Robinson.

a bay mouth bar completely blocking the bay mouth. Or spits may grow from both ends and join in the middle. A voluminous supply of fresh water at the bayhead, or strong tidal currents,

FIG. 322.   TIED ISLAND AND TOMBOLO, MORRO ROCK, ESTERO BAY, CALIFORNIA
Photograph from Spence Air Photos.

may serve to keep an opening free across the bay bar. Such a gap is ordinarily too shallow to interfere greatly with the long-shore drift of sediment. The in-and-out currents thus developed, however, build **tidal deltas** at both the inner and outer ends of the opening. In many instances seepage through the material of the bar functions sufficiently to care for the discharge of land waters and the influx and egress of the tides. Then the bay mouth bar is dry over all its length.

Waste from erosion of the exposed seaward front of an outlying island is drifted along the island's sides and then prolonged as a spit from its rear toward the land. As the presence of the island

FIG. 323.   CUSPATE FORELAND, CROWBAR POINT, CAYUGA LAKE, NEW YORK

shelters the waters behind it from the full force of waves and currents another spit may build out from the land toward the island. When the island spit reaches the land, or when the spits from island and land join, a **tombolo** results, and the island is a **tied island** (Fig. 322). That is, it is tied to the land by the tombolo.

There are instances where two tombolos develop, one from each side of the island. The lagoon between them is eventually filled and a single, very broad bar joins the island with the mainland. The topographic ensemble of Gibraltar is an example of such construction.

Instead of being directed across a bay mouth, wave and current drift may be headed seaward from the end of a coastal salient because of a particular trend of the shore line. Indeed, contributions to the projecting spit, or *cuspate foreland* (Fig. 323) which then develops, may be made from both sides of the headland. If the supplying current is unable to build the end of the spit forward faster than waves or cross currents can push it back or move it sideward the spit becomes a *hook,* or *recurved spit.* Compound hooked spits like Sandy Hook, New Jersey, and the western end of Rockaway Beach, New York, are representative of the dominance of first the one, then of the other, of the competing processes.

Bay mouth bars that have great extension (called *nehrungen* in German) show long sweeping curves concave toward the sea, a form perhaps indicative of the general pattern of swirl flow of the longshore currents. Off the coast of North Carolina the similar long curves of the offshore bars, meeting in cuspate points at Cape Hatteras and Cape Lookout, are attributed to the backward moving portions of great eddies margining the Gulf Stream current (Davis, W. M., 1924, pp. 475–477).

All these constructional developments tend to shorten, simplify, and straighten the broadly and intricately irregular shore line of early youth. The lagoons *(haffs* of the German coast) behind the bay and offshore bars are gradually filled with sand from the sea and sediment from the land. As they become shallow, plants establish themselves and by their growths both contribute to and facilitate the filling, by checking movements of the water. Eventually broad *salt marshes* (Fig. 324) supersede the erstwhile open water. Extensive salt marshes are in part covered by every flood tide, in part only by the greater range of spring tides, in part are completely dry. The ingress and egress of the tidal waters is by mud-walled channels which extend in irregular courses through the marsh.

While the spits, hooks, bars, and tombolos are forming, the headlands and islands are being cut back. As they recede the bars are made to retreat in equal measure by wave attack on their seaward side. After this manner the whole shore is eventually converted to a single, simple line made up of long arcs, gently concave seawards. The coast itself consists of alternately steep (former headland sites) and low reaches (former bay sites). The west coast of Jutland is a good example of such a **graded shore line** in the stage of submaturity. Full maturity is achieved when retrogradation has proceeded to a line beyond the heads of the embayments that originally extended farthest inland. The whole coast is then comprised of eroded cliffs. At this point of development there is coincidence of expression and stage with an emergent coast whose offshore bars and lagoons have been similarly

FIG. 324. SALT MARSH, CAPE ANN, MASSACHUSETTS
Photograph by Samuel Gardner.

eliminated. The low cliffs which re-establish contact of the open sea with the oldland on an emergent coast are designated by the French term *falaises,* of which the coast of Normandy is the type example.

It may be added that the earlier stages of the normal emergent shore line, or the initially low shore line of submergent origin have a very simple evolution. In these cases the initial shore lines are straight; in their youth a nearly continuous offshore bar has developed in front of the shore line; in late youth the bar has been pushed so far shorewards that only shallow lagoon and salt marsh intervene between it and the land. The mature stage is the falaise coast.

In plan the shore line of the mature coast normally consists of gentle, sweeping curves rather than a straight line. While deep bays cannot be opened out by wave erosion, for the reasons set forth above, broad belts of weak rocks yield more rapidly to marine attack than strong ones. The weak rocks are concurrently also lowered more rapidly on the landward side by subaerial processes. Accordingly there is less material to be removed by marine action at such sites. The differential landward retreat of the cliffs these factors induce suffices to bring about the broad, slight inbends needed to provide the curves of the mature shore line.

Old Age. Old age is attained when, by the combined action of marine processes and subaerial degradation, the low continuous cliffs of maturity are reduced to a uniformly low altitude. Then the contact of water and land is a straight line across the surface of a gently inclined plane. The ultimate development is the plain of marine erosion when the land is brought entirely beneath the sea.

Contraposed Shore Lines. In the fluvial geomorphic cycle streams may be superimposed from one type of structure on another. When this happens in the progress of the cycle of marine erosion the shore lines are said to be *contraposed.* Commonly it is a case of flat-lying sediments resting on a base of stronger old rocks having a marked degree of relief. Thus a shore line that has developed to submaturity or maturity in the sedimentaries may suddenly again take on the aspect of youth when the wave attack breaks through the cover rocks. The bared hollows in the old rock then simulate the indentations of submergence; the old divides become the headlands of youth. The further history of such a shore line is, hence, the same as that of a submergent oldland.

Uplifted and Ancient Shore Lines. If, during the stage of early youth of a submerged coast line, the marine cycle is interrupted by an uplift of appreciable magnitude the developed sea cliff and wave-cut platform will be lifted beyond the reach of the waves and become land forms unrelated to subaerial processes. An emergent mountain coast, folded or faulted, will show the same forms if the uplift proceeds *per saltum* with sufficiently long intervals between upheavals to permit wave erosion to make its mark. Part of the Yakutat Bay coast, Alaska, experienced an uplift in 1899 which raised a wave-cut platform (Fig. 25) with a sea cliff (including a sea cave) behind it to an elevation of over

40 feet above tide. Remnants of an earlier uplifted platform were discovered inland at a higher level than that of the 1899 bench (Tarr, R. S., and Martin, L., 1906).

Where they are not thus directly associated with the sea, discrimination between remnants of ancient sea cliffs and benches, on the one hand, and fault cliffs or escarpments between subaerial erosion levels or structural platforms, on the other, is not always easy. Except along a mature or falaise coast the ancient sea cliffs should be discontinuous; they should not be as obviously aligned as is a fault cliff; formations in the bench and the base of the cliff should match but there should not be any indication that the levels of the bench and the top of the cliff are governed by beds having exceptional durability.

Like fault scarps, uplifted sea cliffs possess no structural elements which tend to maintain them against the processes of subaerial degradation. As, further, stream systems are not aligned for the expeditious removal of the waste derived from the crumbling of sea cliffs by weathering action, sea cliffs rapidly degenerate into inconspicuous slopes difficult to discern.

At many sites along sea coasts, and inland, bordering lake shores, there may be observed uplifted, or bared beach lines. Such "fossil" beaches not uncommonly retain their characteristic features for considerable periods. They escape rapid destruction by wash and gullying erosion because of their permeability, which permits underground drainage of precipitation. Such ancient beach levels, where present, afford significant evidence of changes in the level and altitude of the land. Almost without exception "fossil" beach lines are tilted or warped. If horizontality of water surface at the time of their formation is assumed, such warping gives indication of the measure and direction of the land movement. (Rodgers, J., 1937).

Along sea coasts the record provided by raised beaches is difficult to read because of the complex interrelation of changes in land level and eustatic shifts, or changes in sea level. Where they occur in association with existing or earlier bodies of inland water the problem is simpler. If an earlier water body has disappeared by evaporation or sudden change in outlet level, the old beach and cliff lines outline its former extent in undisturbed horizontal extension. The "parallel roads" (beaches) of Glen

Roy, Scotland, which provide a record of the changing levels of a Pleistocene glacial lake, are a classical instance of this kind studied by Charles Darwin.   Hardly less famous are the beaches (Fig. 299) of ancient Lake Bonneville described by Gilbert.   Lake Bonneville disappeared by evaporation and is now represented chiefly by the relatively small expanse of Great Salt Lake.   Lake Agassiz in North Dakota and Manitoba, a one-time vast proglacial lake, likewise has left beach lines to indicate its former extent. The Great Lakes had a complicated proglacial lake history with outlets at varying sites and levels.   Their old shore lines are correspondingly numerous and intricately developed.   They show uniformly, however, a late-glacial and postglacial upwarp toward the northeast.   A particular feature of the old borders of many of these lakes is the presence of a well-developed beach ridge.   These old beach ridges were early utilized as sites for roads because of their levelness and because their slight elevation and permeability provided the drainage conditions necessary to make a highway on them dry and firm.   The Ridge Road of Lake Iroquois (Fig. 300), higher level predecessor of Lake Ontario, is especially well known.

SUMMARY

Coast lines, like other land forms, experience a cyclic development.   Coast lines may run parallel with continental structure, the Pacific type, or across it, the Atlantic type.   Uplift and sinking of the land give rise, respectively, to coast lines of emergence and coast lines of submergence.   The latter are the more significant for shore-line evolution.

Shore-line modification is brought about chiefly by wave action. The depth limit of wave action is about 600 feet.   The maximal erosional attack is made by storm waves on steep headlands of consolidated rock.   This produces the sea cliff and many minor forms, such as stacks and sea caves.   Recession of the sea cliff by undercutting and collapse leaves a wave-cut platform at its base. This is, at first, margined by the wave-built terrace.   Eventually the wave-cut platform and the wave-built terrace are merged into the abrasion platform.   Widespread, ancient plains of marine erosion are theoretically possible but actually improbable.   Continental shelves comprise the abrasion platform, overlain with sediments from progradation, and a built platform, beyond the 600 foot depth.

Steep emergent coasts simulate depressed coasts in their shore-line development. Shallow emergent coasts are characteristically marked by barrier beaches which are made to migrate landward by wave action.

The fluvial cycle is energized by uplift; the shore-line cycle is, appropriately, *per contra,* initiated by depression of an oldland. A young shore line is characteristically highly irregular from alternation of headlands and inlets. Through youth to maturity, erosion and deposition function to smooth out the original irregularities. Maturity is attained when initial salients have been pushed back to a line beyond the farthest bayheads. In old age the line of low cliffs marking maturity is reduced, chiefly by subaerial degradation, to a uniformly low altitude.

Ancient, uplifted shore lines provide records of change in level and altitude of land and sea.

BIBLIOGRAPHY

CLASSICAL

Ramsey, A. C. (1846) *On the Denudation of South Wales.* Memoir Geological Survey of Great Britain, Geological Survey of Great Britain, London, I, pp. 297–335.

Gilbert, G. K. (1890) *Lake Bonneville,* Monograph I, United States Geological Survey, Washington.

Shaler, N. S. (1894) *Sea and Land,* Charles Scribner's Sons, New York.

Davis, W. M. (1896) *Plains of Marine and Subaerial Denudation,* Bulletin Geological Society of America, Vol. VII, pp. 377–398. In *Geographical Essays,* Ginn and Company, Boston, pp. 323–349.

Tarr, R. S. (1898) *Wave-Formed Cuspate Forelands,* American Geologist, Vol. 22, pp. 1–12.

Gulliver, F. P. (1899) *Shoreline Topography,* Proceedings American Academy of Arts and Sciences, Vol. 34, pp. 149–258.

RECENT

Fenneman, N. M. (1902) *Development of the Profile of Equilibrium of the Subaqueous Shore Terrace,* Journal of Geology, Vol. 10, 1902, pp. 1–32.

Goldthwait, J. W. (1907) *The Twenty-foot Terrace and Seacliff of the Lower St. Lawrence,* American Journal of Science, 4th Series, Vol. 32, pp. 291–317.

Cornish, V. (1910) *Waves of the Sea and Other Water Waves,* T. Fisher Unwin, London.

Johnson, D. W. (1919) *Shore Processes and Shoreline Development,* John Wiley & Sons, Inc., New York.

Twenhofel, W. H. (1932) *Treatise on Sedimentation,* 2nd. ed. Williams and Wilkins Company, Baltimore.

MacCarthy, G. R. (1933) *The Rounding of Beach Sands,* American Journal of Science, 5th. Series, Vol. 25, pp. 205–224.

Putnam, W. C. (1937) *The Marine Cycle of Erosion for a Steeply Sloping Shoreline of Emergence,* Journal of Geology, Vol. 45, pp. 844–850.

Thompson, W. O. (1937) *Original Structures of Beaches, Bars and Dunes,* Bulletin Geological Society of America, Vol. 48, pp. 723–751.

Shephard, F. P. (1937) *Revised Classification of Marine Shorelines,* Journal of Geology, Vol. 45, pp. 602–624.

Chapter Twenty-one

CORAL SHORE LINES, CORAL REEFS, AND ATOLLS

Introduction. Reef-building corals live in tropical seas where the waters have a temperature of 68° F. or higher. For their vigorous growth the water must also be free of sediment and of normal marine salinity. They flourish at depths from 15 feet down to 120 feet below the surface. A modern estimate (Ladd, H. S., and Hoffmeister, J. E., 1936, p. 88) is that 200 feet down is the general depth limit for growth of reef-building corals, with 300 feet as a maximum. The little animals thrive best at sites where waves and currents are active.

Such environmental circumstances are available at their optima in the open seas and along the east coasts of the continents. Cold surface currents and the upwelling of cold ocean-bottom waters greatly restrict the areas suitable for reef-building corals along tropical-latitude west coasts. After cold, turbidity appears to be the most important limiting factor for coral growth. This is because sediment clogs the mouths of the coral animals. Also, opaqueness, which results from the presence of sediment, inhibits a symbiotic metabolism that exists between unicellular plants and the coral polyps, a relationship by which the corals derive an adequate supply of oxygen.

A vigorous colony of reef-building corals is competent to maintain itself against strong attack by breaking waves. New settlement is generally on consolidated rock which assures a firm base. Growth proceeds typically by branching from a parent stem upward and toward the surf. Those extensions of growth that reach the level of low tide perish first. (The corals can, however, withstand infrequent short exposures to the air. This makes possible photographs of the upper surface of living coral reefs.) Lateral spread is therefore dominant. Molluscs, echinoderms, and lime-secreting algae in vast numbers live in the spaces

547

between the coral branches. Indeed, while some corals have solid heads, many reefs have only a skeletal framework of coral, their main mass consists of the remains of other lime-secreting organisms. Although the living coral colony is not destroyed by wave attack the reef does suffer fragmentary loss from such assault. The detached pieces are reduced to sand by the wave mill. This sand, together with the hard parts of decedent molluscs, echinoderms, foraminifera, and the like, similarly comminuted, progressively fills in the hollows between the coral stems and branches. Cementation takes place by partial solution and reprecipitation of the calcareous sand of these various origins. The older parts of the reef mass tend, accordingly, to be solidified. Meanwhile talus fragments accumulate at the base of the outer slopes of the reef. As such debris is built up to a sufficient height, and is indurated, a coherent foundation at the appropriate depth is provided for new peripheral colonies. A reef is thus enabled to grow outward over sites where the water was originally too deep for the existence of corals.

The Fringing Reef. Along island and continental coasts that meet the environmental requirements set forth above, reef-building corals will first establish colonies at the ebb-tide shore line. Their growth and spread along the coast and outwards, coincidentally, in time give rise to a *fringing reef.* The continuity of such a fringing reef is interrupted only where large streams from the land either induce too great turbidity or reduce too much the salinity of the ocean waters.

The outer edge of a fringing reef is commonly slightly higher than the more landward portion of its upper surface, known as the *reef flat,* because there the lime-secreting algae (Nullipores) have their optimum growth. The outer edge projects above the surface also because the breaking waves throw up fragments of coral and shell to form a low mound called the *boulder zone.*

Although fringing reefs are of considerable breadth at some places they appear more characteristically as narrow belts along steep shores. At such sites the sharp increase in depth seaward entails the accumulation of an immense volume of talus to provide a foundation for only small outward extension of the living reef. Further, little sediment of fine texture resulting from wave attack will be present along a young, steep shore. The island Sakau

(Fig. 325) of the Maskelyne Islands in the New Hebrides illustrates these conditions. In southern Florida (to the east of the northeast extension of the Florida Keys) a fringing reef has developed along a low emergent coast, but the site is one where there is a minimum of wave action and where there are exceedingly favorable conditions of food supply for coral growth.

ONE MILE

Fig. 325. FRINGING REEF, SAKAU, MASKELYNE ISLANDS
Drawn to scale. Based on a map in R. A. Daly, *Changing World of the Ice Age*. By permission of the publishers, Yale University Press.

Coral Banks.   However, under favorable marine and climatic conditions, as along the Waikiki coast of Hawaii and on the west coast of Barbados a *coral crust* instead of a *wall reef* may develop over wide expanses of shallow flats. The Barbadian occurrence is a coral shelf, which unmarked by a reef, is terminated at its outer edge by a descent to deep-sea depths. It may be inferred that, following an uplift, marine erosion and deposition developed a profile of equilibrium on this Barbadian shore line. Meanwhile coral growth was inhibited because of the turbidity engendered by the processing. But when such action became of minor consequence the waters cleared and coral colonies could establish themselves on the bottom. Only sporadic coral growths occur on the east coast of Barbados where the trade-wind surf is still causing active cliff recession.

Broad tracts of the Bahama banks, with bottoms barely below sea level are covered with white calcareous mud. These **banks** appear to be of continental origin, former lowlands completely truncated by wave action.

A boring (Pirsson, L. V., 1914) made in Bermuda disclosed that this island has a capping composed of consolidated calcareous mud, coral, and calcareous sand 245 feet thick resting on a foundation of volcanic rock. Near Bermuda, soundings show the presence of two flat-topped banks (Challenger and Plantagenet) 10 to 15 miles across, with summits approximately 180 feet below sea level. At the edges of the flat tops of the banks the bottom drops off sharply to depths of 5000 or more feet. It may reasonably be inferred that these submarine banks, and the Bermuda site, are the wave-truncated summits of volcanic cones.

From these examples it is evident that calcareous muds and coral growths have been spread over flat surfaces at various depths below sea level. The leveled surfaces of the deeper submarine banks are presumably the product of wave abrasion. The theoretical ultimate depth for such planation is 600 feet. That would be too deep for the initial colonization of reef-building corals. But the initial planation would be a short distance below the surface and any intermediate depth could be made available by further abrasion or rise of sea level. These circumstances are all of considerable significance for the discussion of the problem of the origin and development of barrier and atoll reefs.

Barrier Reefs. A coral reef, called the Great Barrier Reef, extends, practically uninterrupted, for a distance of over 600 miles parallel to the northeast coast of Australia at a distance of approximately 50 miles offshore. Between the reef and the land the water is shallow, averaging about 100 feet in depth.

On a lesser scale the Great Barrier Reef is many times duplicated by *barrier reefs* wholly or partially encircling many islands of the South Seas (Fig. 326). A representative example is the one about Nairai, Fiji Islands (Daly, R. A., 1934, pp. 218-221) situated 1.5 miles offshore. The water belt, or *lagoon,* between the reef and the shore is 60 to 100 feet deep.

The Coral Atoll. An island ring of coral reef, commonly represented as having a circular outline, but which may be of almost any closed pattern, surrounding a shallow lagoon constitutes a *coral atoll.* The island ring, which is the replica of the boulder zone of the fringing reef, rises only a few feet above sea level, and is, in relation to the diameter of the atoll, very narrow. It is, further, interrupted at one or many places by gaps through which the tide flows and ebbs. All these features are well illustrated by the map of North Minerva Atoll of the Pacific Ocean (Fig. 327).

Atoll reefs and barrier reefs have the form of walls in that the descent from the level of the reef flat into the water is abrupt on both sides. Oceanward the steep slopes go down to the deep-sea bottom. On the inner side the declivities are no less steep but terminate shortly on the lagoon floor. The lagoon floors, almost

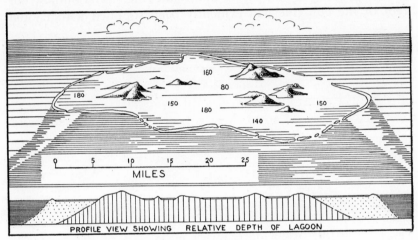

FIG. 326. BARRIER REEF, TRUK GROUP, CAROLINE ISLANDS

Drawn to scale. Depths in feet. Based on a map in R. A. Daly, *Changing World of the Ice Age*. By permission of the publishers, Yale University Press.

without exception, are flat across their full width so that the water over them is everywhere of nearly uniform depth. In the perfection of this development there would appear to be a clue to the origin and history of barrier reefs and atolls. Furthermore, although different lagoons are not of the same depth, the maximum seems to be approximately 300 feet. A search for especially deep lagoons led to the discovery that only a few exceed this depth. This exploration also disclosed that the deeper lagoons tend generally to approach the 300-foot depth.

The lagoon floors are inferred to consist of calcareous sediment derived from the reef wall. There are no, or few, living corals on the inner side of the reef. If the substance of the inner reef is disintegrated by external agencies it is not renewed. It is known that various animals, notably sea cucumbers, bore into and chew up the coral rock. Their collective importance in converting the limestone of the reef to sand and mud is said to be great. In 1937 the ships of an eclipse expedition (National Geographic Society, 1939, p. 381) to Canton Island, an atoll in the Pacific located just north of the equator, found anchorage outside the reef of the atoll on a broad tidal delta opposite the only gap in the continuity of the island ring. The outflow current of the ebb tide had evidently been supplied with enough

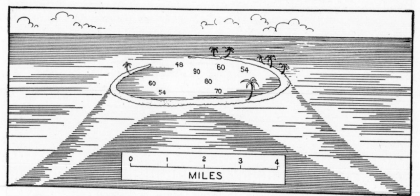

FIG. 327. NORTH MINERVA ATOLL, PACIFIC OCEAN

Drawn to scale. Depths in feet. Based on a map in R. A. Daly, *Changing World of the Ice Age*. By permission of the publishers, Yale University Press.

sediment from the lagoon area to build up a sizeable deposit. The delta had a top sufficiently broad to afford the expedition's ships an ample area of shallow water anchorage, such as was not available anywhere else on the steep outer slopes of the reef. This example affords specific evidence that the activities of the boring animals, together with tidal scour provide an adequate mechanism for (a) lateral enlargement of the lagoon by destruction of the inner side of the reef wall, (b) keeping the wall steep and the lagoon floor flat at a particular level by the continuous removal of the waste.

Darwin's Subsidence Theory of Barrier Reefs and Atolls. The origin and growth of fringing reefs may be learned by direct observation. The presence of the open-water belt between shore and reef in barrier reefs, and of the enclosed, flat-floored and shallow lagoon in the atolls, is, however, a phenomenon not so readily elucidated.

Charles Darwin on the voyage of the *Beagle* in 1842 learned that the reef-building corals could only grow in shallow waters.

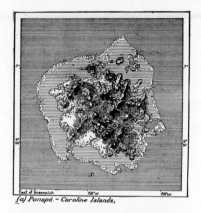

(a) Ponapé. — Caroline Islands,

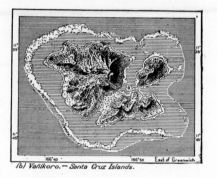

(b) Vanikoro. — Santa Cruz Islands.

(c) Mayotte.—Comoro Islands in Mozambique Chan.

FIG. 328. DEVELOPMENT OF A CORAL ATOLL, ACCORDING TO THE DARWIN THEORY, AS EXEMPLIFIED BY ACTUAL EXAMPLES

A series of maps of two islands in the Pacific Ocean and one in the Indian Ocean that show (*a*) a fringing reef about a sinking volcanic cone, Ponape, Caroline Islands, Pacific Ocean; (*b*) a barrier reef, from deep sinking of the central cone, Vanikoro Island, Santa Cruz Islands, Pacific Ocean; (*c*) an atoll, with the cone sunken almost completely beneath the sea, Mayotte, Comoro Islands, Indian Ocean.

He inferred, on the other hand, that the barrier and atoll reefs were far thicker than the 120 to 150 feet that this limitation of depth on growth would impose. He reasoned that the additional thicknesses indicated a progressive subsidence of the sites of barrier reef and atoll occurrence (Fig. 328, a, b, c). The fringing reef of a slowly sinking island could grow upward and outward as the waters rose and so maintain itself at and above sea level. But as the land behind was progressively submerged the corals on the inner side of the reef would lack food, be troubled by fresh water and turbidity from the land, hence would perish. Thus a moat, growing wider and deeper with time, would develop between the shore and the reef and so give rise to a barrier reef. When the whole island had sunk beneath the waves an atoll would remain. If the sinking should then proceed too rapidly for the upgrowth of the reef a ***drowned atoll*** (Fig. 329) would result. Drowned atolls have been discovered; Penguin and Alexa

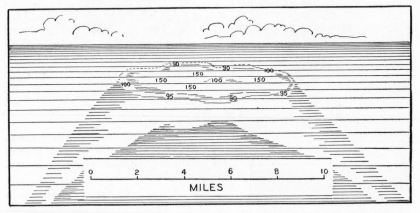

FIG. 329.   DROWNED ATOLL, ALEXA BANK, NORTH OF THE FIJI ISLANDS, PACIFIC OCEAN

Drawn to scale. Depths in feet. The submarine topography perfectly duplicates the reef ring and lagoon of atolls at the surface. Based on a map in R. A. Daly, *Changing World of the Ice Age*. By permission of the publishers, Yale University Press.

Banks, north of the Fiji Islands, Pacific Ocean, are examples. It is also significant that all the Australian coast behind the Great Barrier Reef is embayed and that little progress has been made toward straightening out the irregularities of the continental shore line which have obviously resulted from the drowning of open, late mature, stream valleys. In view of the fascinating nature of the barrier-reef and atoll phenomenon, the perfect simplicity yet adequacy of Darwin's explanation attracted wide interest and approval. James Dwight Dana, on the basis of extensive field studies, also held subsidence to be the answer to the coral-reef problem. But as more and more was learned about the reefs, objections developed. The presence of both a fringing reef and a barrier reef about the same island (for example, Narai Island, Fiji) was deemed anomalous. This difficulty is easily met by assuming stability after a period of sinking and the presence of a moat wide enough to permit waves and currents to supply food to the corals of the fringing reef. But if the theory of long-continued, slow subsidence is accepted, it is necessary to assume that the barrier reefs, and particularly the atoll reefs, are of very great thickness (Fig. 330). Are they?

The Boring Test. If it could be shown (in view of the inability of the reef corals to thrive at depths over 200 feet at the most) that the structure of atoll reefs, in the growth posture, extends unbroken to great depths the Darwin-Dana thesis of subsidence

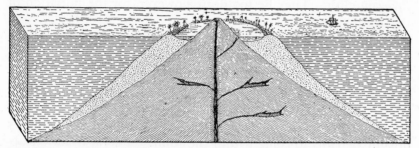

FIG. 330. DIAGRAM TO ILLUSTRATE THE GREAT THICKNESS OF REEF REQUIRED TO SUBSTANTIATE THE SUBSIDENCE THEORY OF CORAL ATOLLS

would be very strongly confirmed. Accordingly expeditions under the auspices of the British Association for the Advancement of Science made a core boring on the atoll of Funafuti, Ellice Islands, in the southwest Pacific. A depth of 1115 feet was reached. But the result was inconclusive because the bore was made at a site too near the edge of the reef. The upper 200 feet of the bore shows the coral skeletons in the position of growth; the core for the rest of the depth is made up of talus fragments. Another boring, at a more representative site, Michaelmas Cay, a coral reef inside the Great Barrier Reef of Australia, passed through coral material to a depth of 240 feet and then struck quartz sand. Assuming that all of the 240 feet thickness represents growth *in situ*, the Michaelmas Cay boring indicates upbuilding from a depth too great for sea level at its present altitude. However, neither boring confirms the idea of a reef's rising from great depths, nor do the two borings finally disprove such a possibility. If the Funafuti boring was too near the outer edge of the atoll to penetrate the full thickness of solid reef-growth coral, the Michaelmas Cay boring may have been too near land to be representative.

The Murray Theory. Flat-topped submarine platforms exist at various depths below sea level. The boring in Bermuda affords evidence, by analogy, that the submarine banks near Bermuda are the truncated summits of volcanic cones. The depths over such banks commonly range between 150 and 300 feet; that is they come within the limits of effective marine planation by wave action. Whether or not the sites were once above sea level, such planation would require a long time, geologically speaking, to accomplish. They lie too deep, however, for the initiation of reef-coral growth.

But if a platform were to be planed off at some depth not greater than 200 feet, coral-reef growth might begin. Sir John Murray held that the submarine banks could originate from submarine volcanic accumulations not built up to sea level. Those which failed to attain quite the height necessary for establishment of the coral colonies might be sufficiently built up by organic detritus to come within the limit. A coral colony established at a central high point would grow upward and radially outward. Then the oldest corals at the center would perish by reaching the surface and by being cut off from food by the newer growth ringed about them. Boring organisms and sea scour would hollow out a lagoon. Thenceforward the reef would grow outward, and the lagoon would expand to develop the typical coral atoll. The same sequence would apply for the conversion of a fringing reef to a barrier reef.

The Glacial Control Theory. The Murray, or *antecedent platform theory,* requires that an extraordinary number of banks be raised or built up to levels within 200 feet or less of the sea surface. The indicated improbability is plausibly met by ascribing the surprising accordance in level of so many banks to marine planation. Extreme areal extension of the level platforms is another easy consequence from prolonged marine abrasion. The remarkable levelness of floor and uniformity of depth of extensive atoll lagoons are also credibly explained. But it remains a great strain on the imagination to visualize such development if it must proceed from initial growth at a central focus and yet provide for an expanding lagoon by decomposition and tidal scour.

In view of this difficulty Daly (1915) contended that the reef-building began at the edges of the submarine platforms. A reef ring of wall form would thus be made to enclose the whole area of a platform from the start. An atoll, any size, would appear *ab initio*. The start according to Daly was made at an average depth of 300 feet because sea level had been lowered in that amount by abstraction of water from the ocean to build up the Pleistocene continental glaciers. From this circumstance comes the designation *glacial control theory*. In accordance with this theory it is further asserted that when sea level was lowered, previously existing coral reefs were first killed by exposure and then destroyed by wave attack. The coral growths are thought to have been prevented from following the sea level in its decline by the turbidity that resulted from the very active wave erosion then in progress. At the lowest level of the sea earlier reefs are considered to have been completely destroyed, and their debris used to smooth up the surfaces and extend the areas of the platforms. When sea level rose again, with the final melting of the Pleistocene ice masses, turbidity was checked. Beach sands may then have been lithified by cementation and thus afforded splendid attachment areas for the coral "larvae" newly settling on the platforms and thriving especially at their edges. The barrier and atoll reefs, according to this view, are "crowns" built up on submarine platforms, shelves, and banks, as sea level rose in post-glacial time. They must, therefore, be youthful, that is, narrow, and not massive. Their foundations should be at a depth not greater than 300 feet. Where reefs of exceptionally great width occur, as in the Banda Sea between Celebes and New Guinea, it is held that the corals were able to maintain themselves against all the vicissitudes of the Pleistocene glacial climate by virtue of a particularly sheltered location, one of exceptional warmth and freedom from severe wave attack.

Uplifted Coral Reefs. The glacial control theory is very satisfying in certain of its aspects. But as even the author of the theory is unwilling to commit himself to the thesis that the general planation of the shallow banks to the depth of 300 feet took place during the limited time of the Pleistocene, the widespread occurrence of the banks at this approximate level in the coral seas remains a problem. It is also difficult to account, under glacial control of sea level, for the unmodified embayed coast of northeastern Australia behind the Great Barrier Reef, particularly as some of the embayments indicate submergence much greater than 300 feet. The drowned atolls make a special difficulty for the glacial control theory. It hardly serves to wave the drowned atolls aside as sites where for some reason the coral larvae failed to catch on, because it seems they did catch on temporarily; else why the submarine atoll topography? If it is asserted that the rising water gained ascendency over coral growth,

FIG. 331.   ELEVATED CORAL REEF, BARBADOS, B. W. I.

The sea cliff, although now far inland, has sea caves and the remains of a beach at its base.

the question arises, Why did the corals fail there and not elsewhere? The assertion that especially violent storms were responsible for a beheading of the coral reefs that are now drowned atolls, or that the extinction of coral growth at such sites has resulted from particular conditions of turbidity, is begging the question. Admission that certain banks (Great Chagos Bank, Indian Ocean; Macclesfield Bank, China Sea) probably originated from downwarping of the reef formations is fatal to the claim that the glacial control theory has general applicability.

A further refutation of the universal significance of the glacial control theory derives from the existence of uplifted coral reefs. Despite the seeming paradox, the fact of sufficient uplift during the period of reef growth to raise reefs in some places to elevations of 1000 feet above sea level actually gives support to the subsidence theory. For if uplifts can have been so great during this time, obviously subsidence of similar measure may have occurred.

The west side of the island of Barbados rises by a series of steps, each one a coral platform (Fig. 331), to the altitude of 1000 feet. The foundation of Barbados is unmetamorphosed sediments, not volcanics. The successive uplifts may not, hence, be ascribed to localized igneous activity. A movement of the sea bottom is involved. Kambara Island, of the Fiji group, is an elevated atoll, with lagoon and reef-rim topography, lifted over 300 feet above sea level. Christmas Island in the Indian Ocean consists of a volcanic base with a cover of uplifted coral reefs rising in steps to the altitude of 1200 feet. There are also reefs uplifted to lesser heights; for example, one on the north coast of Cuba has an elevation of about 30 feet above sea level and, in places, is a mile wide.

Review. The widespread occurrence, the completeness of gradational stages exhibited, and the extremely distinctive characteristics that are the mark of the barrier and atoll reefs compellingly suggest their development under a specific and uniform set of circumstances. The challenge to understanding thus implied is still most adequately met by the subsidence theory. But this theory has not yet been finally confirmed at even a single site by data from a boring that proves undisturbed reef structure at depths significantly greater than 300 feet. However, embayed shore lines behind barrier reefs unmodified by sea cliffs resulting from recent wave attack; drowned atolls (subsidence faster than the rate of coral upgrowth); an adequate mechanism to account for the expansion of the lagoons and the development of their accordant floors; and the presence of uplifted reefs at such high altitudes that an equivalent measure of sinking would satisfy the subsidence requirement for atolls, are phenomena that, considered collectively, strongly attest the verity of the subsidence theory. It also seems entirely in accordance with isostatic theory that an isolated volcanic cone should sink slowly beneath the waves, and thus acquire first a fringing reef, then a barrier reef, and finally have its former presence marked by an enduring atoll.

In behalf of the other theories it may, however, be said that submerged flat-topped platforms do rise from the sea floor to altitudes so near sea level as to make them fitting sites for coral colonization. Painstaking, detailed investigation (Ladd, H. S., and Hoffmeister, J. E., 1936, pp. 89–92) has led to the conclusion, on paleontological and biological evidence chiefly, that the antecedent-platform concept, supplemented by a significant amount of marine abrasion in Pleistocene glacial times, should not be ruled out of consideration when the coral-reef problem is attacked. A reef crown built up around the edges of such a platform would make it, independently of antecedent barrier or fringing reefs, an atoll. But barrier reefs far out from island shores would then be explicable only by lowering of the sea level under glacial control. Further, with glacial lowering of sea level the corals may have been enabled to establish themselves on many banks that were previously beyond their depth. Indeed, the glacial lowering may have destroyed existing atolls, which reformed as sea level rose again. In such instances there would be glacial "control" but behind it, in time, there could still be the disappearing island and the subsidence theory. In accordance with this inference the embayed coasts behind barrier reefs could be of preglacial or glacial origin and have escaped modification because the barrier reef rising with the waters from the 300-foot minimal level would shut off wave attack throughout postglacial time. If, finally, further borings show the base of atoll reefs generally to be at approximately 300 feet below sea level, the control-functioning of the glacial eustatic shifts of sea level will be rather certainly indicated.

SUMMARY

Reef-building corals thrive only where a number of specific environmental conditions are satisfied. This greatly restricts the distribution of coral reefs. The remains of other lime-secreting organisms commonly comprise a large part of the coral-reef mass.

Fringing reefs and coral crusts develop along shallow tropical coasts in clear waters, and coral banks cap submarine platforms. A shallow lagoon separates the inner edge of a barrier reef from the shore line. In atolls a lagoon, also shallow, is surrounded by a wall-like ring of coral reef. The barrier reefs and atoll rings grow freely seaward but die off on the lagoon side.

Barrier reefs and atolls are very simply accounted for by the subsidence theory. If this theory holds, the atoll reefs must have great vertical thickness. As yet the postulated thicknesses have not been finally demonstrated.

A glacial-control theory derives its main support from the facts that the barrier-reef and atoll lagoons appear to have a maximal depth of 300 feet and flat floors. It is maintained that the existing barrier and atoll reefs have been built up since Pleistocene glacial times on the outer edges of wave-eroded plat-forms made, or leveled off, at the 300-foot depth when sea level was lowered because water was locked up in the continental ice sheets. The absence of cliffed headlands behind barrier beaches and the existence of submerged atolls are circumstances difficult to explain by the glacial-control theory. A combination of the several theories may provide the general answer that is sought for in the coral-reef problem.

BIBLIOGRAPHY

CLASSICAL

Darwin, C. R. (1842) *The Structure and Distribution of Coral Reefs,* Smith, Elder and Company, London.

Murray, J. (1880) *On the Structure and Origin of Coral Reefs,* Proceedings Royal Society of Edinburgh, Vol. 10, pp. 505–518.

Jukes-Browne, A. J., and Harrison, J. B. (1891) *The Geology of Barbados, Part I, The Coral Rocks of Barbados and Other West Indian Islands,* Quarterly Journal Geological Society of London Vol. 47, pp. 197–250.

Saville-Kent, W. (1893) *The Great Barrier Reef of Australia,* W. H. Allen, London.

Sollas, W. J. (1899) *Funafuti: The Study of a Coral Atoll,* Annual Report of the Smithsonian Institution for 1899, pp. 389–406.

Hinde, G. J., and Others (1904) *The Atoll of Funafuti, Report on the Materials of the Borings,* Royal Society of London.

RECENT

Vaughn, T. W. (1919) *Corals and the Formation of Coral Reefs,* Annual Report of the Smithsonian Institution for 1917, pp. 189–276.

Chamberlin, R. T. (1924) *The Geological Interpretation of the Coral Reefs of Tutuila, American Samoa,* Publication 340, Carnegie Institute of Washington, pp. 170–176.

Davis, W. M. (1928) *The Coral Reef Problem,* Special Publication No. 9, American Geographical Society, New York.

Gardiner, J. S. (1931) *Coral Reefs and Atolls,* The Macmillan Company, London.

Kuenen, P. H. (1933) *Geology of Coral Reefs,* Report of the Snellius Expedition, Utrecht, Netherlands, Vol. V, Part II.

Daly, R. A. (1934) *The Changing World of the Ice Age,* Yale University Press, New Haven.

Ladd, H. S., and Hoffmeister, J. E. (1936) *A Criticism of the Glacial-Control Theory,* Journal of Geology, Vol. 44, pp. 74–92.

Chapter Twenty-two

KARST TOPOGRAPHY

Introduction. Limestone yields freely to the solvent action of water; dolomite somewhat less so. The rate of solution of both these rocks is much greater when the water is charged with carbon dioxide. Rain, as it falls, collects some carbon dioxide from the air. As precipitation soaks into the ground the water gets more carbon dioxide from the decomposing organic matter that, varying with soil type and occurrence, makes up different proportions of the soil substance. When the water reaches bedrock, in regions underlain by limestone of considerable thickness, it tends to open channels which progressively conduct more and more of the drainage to subterranean courses. That is to say, the solvent power of the charged water, percolating downward along joint fissures or pores of the rock, is such that the channels of underground-drainage escape are enlarged so rapidly that rills, brooks, and even creeks lose their surface flow to them, and surface drainage shrinks in volume (Figs. 332, 333). Valley development by normal stream erosion and weathering processes then ceases. Only transverse streams of large volume (drainage collected from sources outside the limestone area) are able to persist in open-surface channels. The Ohio River where it crosses the limestone region of southern Indiana and central-northern Kentucky, and the Tarn River (Fig. 111) in the Causses of France may be cited as examples of such through streams.

The sequence of topographic forms that result from the dominance of the solution process, and of the underground escape of drainage, is referred to as the *karst cycle*. The term derives from the Jugoslav *kras*, meaning "stone," which is the root for the Italian place name, Carso (Fig. 334), applied to the region some 300 miles long, 50 miles wide, and, in places, 8000 feet high, extending along the northeastern coast of the Adriatic Sea, all composed of limestone, where karst phenomena have their most

Fig. 332. UNDERGROUND SOLUTION OF TULLY LIMESTONE, SALMON CREEK, NEW YORK

The underside of the ledge, across the center of the picture, is dissolved away by the water of the creek seeping along the stratification plane between this bed and the bed below it. The water has descended to this level through joint planes down from the surface bed of the creek above the fall site.

564

comprehensive development. The French word *causses*, referring to areas on the south of the central upland of France, is
sometimes used in the generic sense as the equivalent of "karst."
Not so well known as either the Dinaric (Adriatic) or French

FIG. 333. DETAIL OF THE SOLUTION ACTION ON THE STRATIFICATION-PLANE SUR-
FACE OF THE TULLY LIMESTONE

A fragment of the rock is turned up to show the irregular solution of the
limestone to form channels for the passage of the water. Cavern development in miniature.

karst areas, but perhaps as characteristically developed, is the
karst region of Jamaica, B. W. I., which has its focus in the
"cockpit" country of the island (Rappenecker, C., 1936).

In some respects the expression of less extreme development,
in the sense of structure and stage, in others the expression of

climatic difference, are karst regions in central Kentucky, central Florida, in northern Yucatan, and in Barbados and Puerto Rico in the West Indies, and at numerous other sites in nearly all parts of the world.

Rock Solution. It should not be inferred from the content of the preceding paragraphs that limestones and dolomites are the only rock materials that yield freely to solution. Solution is a

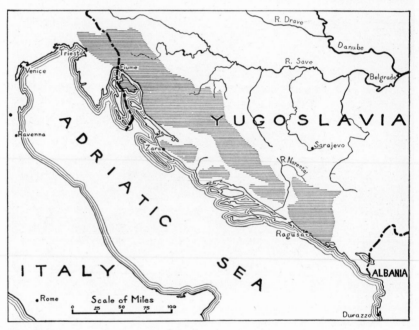

FIG. 334. THE ADRIATIC KARST REGIONS
The ruled areas are the karst country. Drawing by Walter Williams.

factor in the decomposition and disintegration of practically all rocks but ordinarily other processes so far surpass solution in efficacy that solution action does not distinctively affect surface forms.

There are certain exceptions. Where beds of readily soluble rock salt and gypsum are near enough to the surface of the land to be reached by circulating underground water, the surface over such beds may settle irregularly because of the progressive removal of its underground support. This phenomenon is known as *solution subsidence* (Fig. 335). If the depressions due to solution subsidence have bottoms below the level of the local water table, ponds are formed. A solution-subsidence tract from dissolving of rock-salt beds occurs around the village of Union Springs, New York. Another area of similar origin is found at the southern base of the Harz Mountains in Germany. The importance of such deep, underground solution of salt and gypsum beds in creating sinks and basins is being increasingly recognized. Such collapse is inferred for the sinks in the Meade Basin, Kansas

FIG. 335. SOLUTION SUBSIDENCE, ST. JACOB'S WELL, KANSAS
Probably results from underground solution of salt beds. Photograph by H. T. U. Smith.

(Frye, J. C. and Schoff, S. L., 1941) and for the Pecos Basin in New Mexico (Morgan, A. M., 1941).

Beneath a cover of Pleistocene marine sands Florida is underlain by limestones largely made up of shell and coral detritus. The covering sands are extremely porous and permeable; the limestone hardly less so. In consequence the limestones dissolve almost as freely as rock salt or gypsum beds. Accordingly all the central, higher part of Florida is pitted with lakes (Fig. 336) and dry basins, *sink holes,* unconnected by surface drainage. The general yield of the underlying limestone induces this widespread subsidence, though probably not so suddenly or frequently as is

FIG. 336. SINK HOLE LAKE, GREEN HEAD, NEAR BRISTOL, FLORIDA

The surface cover of sand is clearly illustrated.

suggested by one author's statement that in certain sections "one must be on the lookout in driving through the country for newly formed sinks."

Uplifted coral reefs have much the same composition and structure as the Florida limestones. In arid climates they tend to retain their original form for long periods. Even in humid regions such reefs are rather enduring relief features because their extreme permeability causes them to function like sieves. The water escapes at the lower edges of the reefs. Seepage at the bases of the outer scarps promotes the formation of gullies by headward erosion through solution-sapping. *Pocket valleys,* with vertical head and side walls, and a nearly flat floor, are, in time, opened by this process. Good examples of such valleys notch the uplifted coral-reef platforms that make up the whole west side of the island of Barbados. Pocket valleys of similar origin are also of widespread occurrence in northwestern Florida where they are known as *steep-heads* (Plate VI). The ample and continuous supply of underground water in Florida commonly gives rise to a spring of large volume, at the base of the steep-head.

Eventually the interiors of the uplifted coral reefs are riddled to the point of crumbling from removal, by solution, of their substance. Uneven collapse then leads to the formation of residual conical summits, resembling haystacks, called *pepino hills* (Fig. 337) in Puerto Rico, *Mogotes* in the Isle of Pines (Carlson, F. A., 1942, p. 21 and 24). The pepino hills themselves are honeycombed with caves. Equivalent forms in the French Causses are called *buttes temoines,* in the Adriatic karst, *hums.*

Where massive limestone, barren of soil, is exposed to beating rains, its surface, both along joint planes and in the unfissured areas between such breaks, tends to develop furrows separated by rounded and knife-edge ridges of relatively low relief. This surficial development called *karren* (not to be confused with kar, a glacial cirque) is known to the French as *lapies,* to the British as *clints.* Exceptionally, where there is frequent laving by heavy tropical rains, differential solution and rill flow bring about the development of karren in rocks of other types. Sandstones on the east coast of Barbados (Fig. 338) have this type of surface, and in Hawaii it is reported to develop on steep walls of basalt (Fig.

FIG. 337. PEPINO HILLS, BAYAMON REGION, NORTH SIDE OF PUERTO RICO
Photographer unknown.

Fig. 338.   LAPIES IN SANDSTONE, BARBADOS, B. W. I.
Developed by beating tropical rains.

Fig. 339.   KARREN FLUTING OF LAVA ROCK, HALAWA FALLS, MOLOKAI, T. H.

A region of heavy tropical rains. The large amphitheatre heads of these valleys result from progressive dissolution of intervening ridges of the lava rock. Photograph from The 11th. Photo Section, Wheeler Field, Honolulu, T. H.

339) (Palmer, H. S., 1927). In these instances the vigor of the solution attack is so great that other weathering processes, normally dominant in the disintegration and decomposition of such rock types, are completely superseded.

The Topography of Chalk. The geomorphic circumstances of the famous chalk regions of southern England and northeastern France somewhat resemble those of central Florida. The particularly marked characteristics of chalk are its ability to imbibe, like the Florida limestones, and to hold, unlike the Florida rock, very large quantities of water. Much of the water supply of London has for many years been derived from wells in the chalk beds which pass under the city in a synclinal trough. The chalk emerges north and northwest of London to form the Chiltern Hills, south of the city as the North Downs. It appears again in France across the Channel.

Although the chalk is extremely permeable and is nearly pure limestone its ability to hold water appears greatly to inhibit solution action. Trunk streams originating outside the chalk districts are able to maintain their flow and deepen their valleys as they cross these limestone belts. Their downcutting gradually lowers the water table. Tributary valleys within the chalk then tend to be dewatered by seepage into their floors and become *bournes,* or *dry valleys.* Bournes carry surface water intermittently at times of heavy precipitation. They, and the completely waterless dry valleys, give the chalk regions their particular topographic aspect. In extreme cases the discordance at the point of junction of a dry tributary with a main stream is sufficiently abrupt to create a *dry hanging valley.*

Dolines. Careful observation indicates that active movement of water within chalk is along obscure, close-spaced, and discontinuous joint planes. In massive limestones joint fissures are commonly clearly discernible, are spaced at appreciably wide intervals, and penetrate the rock to considerable depths without offset. Solution action, accordingly, tends to be concentrated along the lines of these breaks (Fig. 340). Their enlargement (Fig. 341) in this manner may be regarded as incipient karren.

Where differential solution of limestone has been especially effective, commonly where two joint planes intersect, some surface water finds an underground drainage route. Such sites, after lateral enlargement at the top, become generally **dolines** (Fig. 342), and have variants called *swallow holes* and sink holes. "Swallow hole" is a British term and refers to somewhat cylindrical, dry holes (Wooldridge, S. W., and Morgan, R. S., 1937, pp. 280–283) in the chalk which are inferred to "swallow" surface drainage at times of heavy rains. "Sink hole" is an American term applied to shallow, commonly marshy or pond-basin depressions of circular outline where runoff collects and later disappears

Fig. 340. SOLUTION ACTION ALONG JOINT PLANES IN MASSIVE LIMESTONE, JAMESVILLE, NEW YORK
Incipient karren forms.

by slow seepage underground or by evaporation. In Kentucky sink holes of irregular outline resulting from the collapse of part of a cave roof are fairly common. Both swallow holes and sink holes are characteristic developments in flatlying, undisturbed, homogeneous limestone masses.

The doline, of which the swallow hole and sink hole are variants, is the initial and fundamental unit of karst topography. The type doline has the form of a funnel top and occurs in the Adriatic karst. There, as in the French causses, the rocks have been subjected to orogenic deformation. Structural differences,

ᴀᴛᴇ VI. Steep Heads and Pinnate Drainage Pattern. Part of the Holt, Florida, quadrangle
p of the United States Geological Survey. Horizontal scale 1/62,500, contour interval 10 feet.
e abrupt terminations of the steep heads is strikingly illustrated. The cover mass is sand, the
dermass limestone from which springs of large volume emerge at the heads. The pinnate pat-
n probably reflects systems of joints in the limestone.

accordingly, affect the doline development. Dolines range in size and form from mere chimneylike shafts, called *jamas,* which may be 300 or more feet deep, to the representative funnel-shaped occurrences ranging from 30 to 400 feet in diameter and 6 to 75 feet deep. Single dolines occur, but more commonly dolines are observed to dot the landscape in numbers up to a hundred or more to the square mile. Some indication of arrangement along structure lines is then to be noted.

FIG. 341. ADVANCED SOLUTION IN MASSIVE LIMESTONE, WARO, WHANGAREI, NEW ZEALAND
Photograph by C. A. Cotton.

In areas where the rock is barren of a vegetation cover and of a soil, as in the high-altitude Adriatic karst, the dolines tend to be steep-sided and deep, with ribbed and fluted karren sides. Where there is forest growth, hence a soil cover, the dolines develop as smoothly rounded, broad, shallow basins. Slow solution takes place under the soil; the insoluble residuum of the rock is added to the soil thickness; there is soil creep toward the center of the depression.

Exceptionally the dolines drain through a free opening of

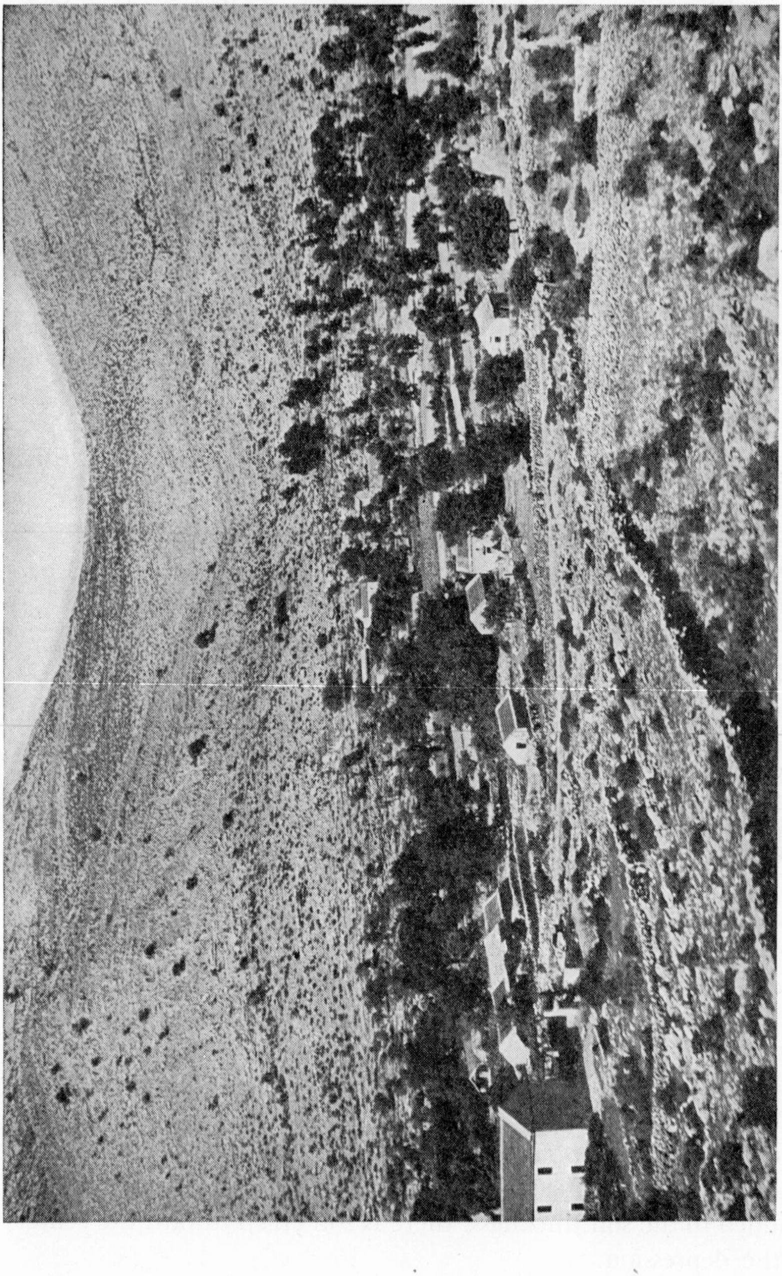

FIG. 342. DOLINE, YUGOSLAVIA

circular outline at the bottom of the depression. More commonly collapse of the bottom into a horizontal passage clogs the outlet with rock debris, or with soil and organic waste. The escape of water in such instances is by seepage, with resultant temporary ponding of heavy precipitation.

Uvalas. A number of small, steep-sided dolines may in time coalesce by lateral enlargement to form a greater basin (Fig. 343) of irregular outline and gentler slopes. The underground drain-

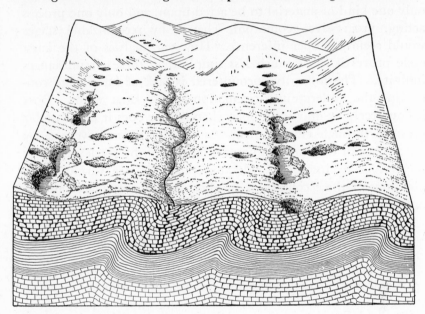

FIG. 343.   DOLINES AND UVALAS

At several sites along the valley courses the dolines have merged to become uvalas. Underground drainage is actively dissolving the folded limestone. Drawing by Elizabeth Burckmyer.

age is then concentrated on the lowest hollow. Where this has happened on a large scale the resulting extensive depression is called a *uvala.* Because joint fissures ordinarily follow a regular pattern, uvalas tend to be elongated hollows aligned with the fissure system. In some instances uvalas may be the trace of earlier surface-valley courses, or the result of piecemeal collapse, from their roofs toward the land surface, of subterranean horizontal galleries. Uvalas thus formed are called *valley sinks* in America and occur in the cavern regions of central Kentucky.

The Karst Cycle. It is interesting to note that geomorphologists who are loath to adopt the cycle scheme as a general framework for the analysis of all land forms resulting from degradational processes, do attempt a systematization of karst phenomena on the cycle basis. Presumably they are influenced to apply the cycle concept to the karst because in this instance the structure is uniformly limestone and because solution is the dominating, if not the sole process, affecting topographic development. With only one kind of material to be acted upon, and only one process acting, progressive geomorphic change by recognizable stages would seem a proper inference. However analysis of the karst cycle proves it to be much less simple than these circumstances indicate. The difficulty encountered is lack of knowledge concerning the underground circulation of the karst water. Does it flow freely by gravity in open channels, or does it move under pressure through closed tubes? Is its circulation governed by the surface of the water table as a base level, by sea level, or by impervious or insoluble beds at depth? Or are various combinations of these conditions in effect at different places and at different times?

Opposed to the idea of free circulation in open channels is the fact that water in the karst lands disappears underground in more places and in larger volume than reappears. However there is some degree of correlation between the times of sediment clouding of surface water and turbidity of that emerging from springs. But tests made by chlorination and by introducing salt and coloring matter to inflowing water showed that from 10 to 60 hours elapsed before the tagged liquid outflowed at points only a few miles remote, though at considerably lower altitudes, from the sites where the foreign matter was added. This slow movement tends to invalidate the idea of direct, unrestricted flow. Accordingly some observers maintain that karst water circulates like ground water elsewhere, only more freely because solution opens larger passages. Other karst investigators assert that the water "rains" vertically through the rock until it comes to the level of the water-table surface and that only below this is there horizontal movement. Evidence of pressure flow in closed passages, independent of each other and of the general ground water level, is found in the fact that the floors of high-level basins are flooded by outlet pipes before those at lower levels are similarly inundated.

Whatever answers are made to the problem of karst-water circulation, other factors and sequences in the karst geomorphic cycle are well established. For its initiation and characteristic development great thicknesses of limestone raised well above sea level must be present. The karst cycle may begin before a cover of insoluble rock has been completely removed, as in Kentucky, where, in the Mammoth Cave district, a porous sandstone permits surface water to gain entrance to the underlying limestone.

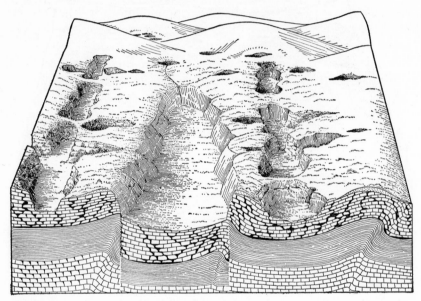

FIG. 344.   END OF YOUTH IN THE KARST CYCLE

The drainage is all underground. A considerable volume of the limestone has been dissolved away. A polje has resulted from the graben faulting of the central section. Drawing by Elizabeth Burckmyer.

Karren flutings on bare rock surfaces, and scattered dolines, are the first topographic features to appear. The stage of youth comprises the period during which the dolines increase in number and are individually enlarged. When, eventually, every portion of former surface-stream runoff has been diverted to underground courses (Fig. 344), when doline slopes are substituted for valley sides, and valley lines become valley sinks the stage of youth is ended.

During maturity the landscape is converted to uvalas and hums

(Fig. 345). **Blind valleys** are developed on uvala floors. These
have steep sides and a steep wall for a terminus. At the base
of the steep wall the surface flow disappears underground. The
channel section is inferred to develop by progressive infall, from
the interior, of horizontal solution galleries. Blind valleys differ
from pocket valleys in that the latter develop where underground
water emerges in greater or less volume.

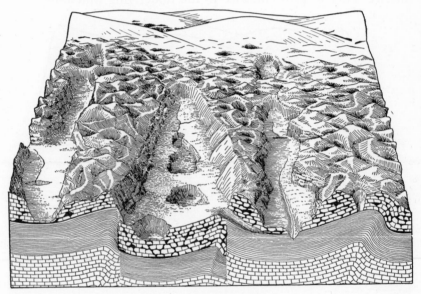

FIG. 345. LATE MATURITY IN THE KARST CYCLE

The whole landscape is converted to dolines and uvalas. Solution action
extends to the level of the impervious (ruled) layer. The form of the polje
remains practically unmodified because there is no surface drainage to erode
the declivities. Ponore (center section) convey drainage underground to
lower levels. Drawing by Elizabeth Burckmyer.

Old age sees the reduction of ridges between uvalas, the complete isolation of residual hums, and the general lowering of the
surface to an altitude near the ground-water level, assuming that
this governs the karst cycle as a base level. In the end stage,
either at base level or in contact with insoluble rock, surface
streams resume and the landscape has the aspect of a peneplain,
except that it shows a dot pattern, the last remainders of the hums
(Fig. 346), instead of the low linear divides of the fluvial-cycle
end form.

Poljes. In the outline of the karst cycle, as given, no account is taken of diastrophic changes that may occur while the cycle is in progress. If the level of the water-table surface, or sea level, is regarded as base level for the karst cycle, then sinking of the land in sufficient measure could be expected to terminate the karst cycle and convert some of the doline and uvala basins to lakes. Uplift, *per contra*, would re-energize the karst process and provide for a larger vertical measure of karst relief. These effects

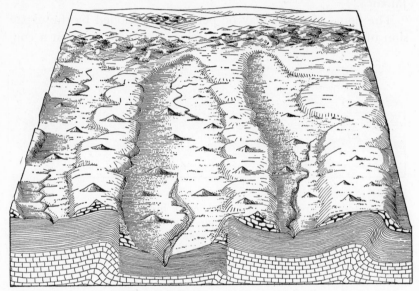

FIG. 346.   OLD AGE IN THE KARST CYCLE

The limestone has been nearly all consumed, only hums remain. The surface has been lowered generally to the level of the insoluble beds and surface drainage is being re-established. Drawing by Elizabeth Burckmyer.

are analogous to those resulting in the fluvial cycle from the same causes.

But different from the fluvial cycle, diastrophism in the course of karst evolution may put an enduring mark of its own on the topography. When the karst cycle has advanced to the stage of late youth, valley development is terminated. If, then, block-faulting occurs, no subaerial processes operate to destroy the horsts or grabens that result. Under the fluvial cycle these tend to be erased; the horsts are worn down, the grabens aggraded. In the karst they remain unmodified for long periods.

The distinctive vast depressions in the karst called *poljes* (Fig. 344) are interpreted as grabens.   Poljes are vertical-walled, closed basins, commonly of elliptical outline and with flat alluvial floors. They have areas up to 100 square miles in extent and have independent surface drainage systems on their floors.   They frequently have a central lake, and may have irregular borders resulting from the headward retreat of pocket valleys where springs emerge.   Poljes occur in the Adriatic karst and in Jamaica.

The floors of poljes may be periodically flooded by the expansion of the central lake (Rappenecker, C., 1936) or from a com-

Fig. 347.   CAVERN DEVELOPMENT BY UNDERGROUND RIVERS

The layers, *A*, are shale; *B*, limestone; *D*, indicates a doline; *E*, a cavern entrance. The horizontal galleries are determined by the shale layers (or relatively insoluble beds, of impure limestone) and the grade level of the transverse stream. The natural bridge has resulted from enlargement of adjoining uvalas. Modified from N. S. Shaler.

pletely dry condition.   Sediment is thus spread about to make the level floors.   Such inundation is from water brought in, apparently under pressure, by *ponore,* pipelike, lateral passages which may function alternately to pour in or draw off water.   The rises are associated with periods of exceptionally heavy rainfall.

Caverns and Natural Bridges.   Although *caverns* are subterranean occurrences, therefore, strictly speaking, not geomorphic phenomena, they are included in the discussion because their development affects surface forms.   A generally horizontal passageway through rock is, somewhat ludicrously, said to be a cavern when its diameter is sufficiently large to permit a man to crawl through.

It was long customary to ascribe the excavation of cavern passages to the erosive action of waters circulating over and at the cave-floor level. This view is still defended (Swinnerton, A. C., 1932). Where transverse rivers cross a region with karst drainage the outlets of the subterranean courses could be into the trunk stream at ground-water levels. Galleries of cavern passages at different levels, the upper ones dry, might result from the down-cutting of the transverse stream (Fig. 347). The approximate horizontality of the levels of the galleries could be indicative of strata more resistant than average to the erosive and solvent action of the subterranean streams.

But instead of the somewhat tubular tunnels that might be expected to result from such erosion, cavern passages usually ex-hibit great variations in size of cross section, have very irregular floors, and are nearly all in course of filling with flowstone and dripstone. Constriction rather than enlargement is taking place (Fig. 348). No difference in rock composition can be detected at the horizons of the several gallery levels. Large water-filled pits extend below the water-table level. It is difficult to reconcile these observed conditions with the free-drainage theory of cavern excavation.

If, in accordance with what is known of karst hydrography, the opening of the lateral cavern passages is regarded as a function of the ground-water circulation, a much more satisfactory correla-tion of theory and observation results (Figs. 332, 333). In its upper levels the ground water moves under varying local pressure heads. Passages of great diversity in altitude, size, and form may be opened. Moreover, the water is held constantly in contact with all the rock surface of the tube through which it moves. The slow mass transudation insures solution to the full capacity of the large volume of water involved. Below the active upper movement a very sluggish circulation may dissolve pits to inde-terminate, great depths. As crystal formation would be facili-tated by such conditions crystal caverns are considered to have been developed at such deep-seated sites. The different gallery levels are to be regarded as evidence of successive uplifts of the land, with concurrent lowering of the ground-water level to new, local base levels, as these were established from deepening of the valleys of the revived trunk streams. (The downcutting of nearby through-flowing streams without uplift would not give rise to definite gallery levels.) In harmony with such history the upper-

FIG. 348. FILLING OF CAVERN PASSAGES WITH DRIPSTONE, FLOWSTONE, AND FALLEN BLOCKS
Photograph from Endless Caverns, New Market, Virginia.

level galleries begin to fill with flowstone and dripstone, and by infalling of their ceilings as soon as they are drained of ground water.

It is, however, possible for the cavern passages to be enlarged above the water-table level by infalling of their ceilings, if the fallen fragments are dissolved in the waters at the floor, whether in streams or as ground water. The great domes of the Carlsbad Cavern in New Mexico may best be explained as of such origin. The similar, but much smaller *cenotes* of northern Yucatan belong in the same class. Cenote infalling extends to the surface, making an open cistern, as the word "cenote" denotes.

Some uvalas may have resulted from the unroofing of caverns

FIG. 349.   NATURAL BRIDGE, VIRGINIA

on a large scale. Certain water gaps in the Folded Appalachian region may be of this origin (Fridley, H. M., 1939, 1940). If such unroofing is a common occurrence it apparently takes place all at once because there are no well-authenticated examples of natural bridges that are remnants of a cavern roof. Natural Bridge, Virginia, has been so interpreted (Fig. 349) but is much more probably the remainder of a local, subsurface, solution diversion of the stream which passes under the bridge (Malott, C. A., and Shrock, R. R., 1930). The deepening of the valley above and below the bridge, giving the arch its height, has resulted from normal stream erosion and weathering after the -subterranean passageway had been opened by solution along a short reach of the stream's course. Natural Tunnel, Virginia (Fig. 350) (Woodward, H. P., 1936), is interpreted to have the same history of development. The two sites differ in that at Natural Tunnel

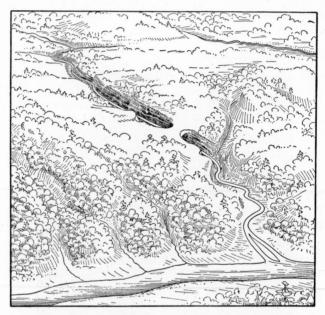

FIG. 350.   DEVELOPMENT OF NATURAL TUNNEL, VIRGINIA

The Clinch River, foreground, received a tributary with a steep descent, right hand lower corner.   Other drainage, top of diagram, originally reached the Clinch by a long parallel course of low gradient.   By underground solution-percolation water from the headwaters of the upper level drainage was diverted in ever larger volume to the head of the steep gradient stream by subterranean flow.   This eventually resulted in complete piracy of the headwaters of the low gradient stream.   By further erosion, and collapse of the roof, the natural tunnel was left.   Drawing by Elizabeth Burckmyer.

a considerable section of the valley retains its tunnel cover.   In both instances there appears to have been diversion of drainage, by a short, steep-gradient tributary to a master stream, from the headwaters of a longer competing tributary.   This piracy was at first by subterranean courses and later in an open channel.   The Natural Bridge and Natural Tunnel persist as relics of the one-time tunnel course.

New River at Fort Lauderdale, Florida, is locally reported to have depths up to 50 or more feet in places although the land there is only 10 to 15 feet above sea level. The present surface stream is inferred to have resulted from the geologically recent unroofing by solution and infall of the course of a subterranean drainage of large volume developed in the limestone of these parts. With uplift of the land, and a deep entrenchment of the stream, natural bridge and tunnel sections might be brought to light along the valley of the New River.

SUMMARY

Two common rocks, limestone and dolomite, are readily dissolved by water charged with carbon dioxide. This gas is available to precipitation and to underground water from the air and from the soil. Percolating downward, such acidulated water enlarges pores and fissures in limestone to the end that all drainage is diverted to subterranean courses. The karst cycle is then fully operative.

General underground solution in very permeable, porous rocks causes widespread, irregular, surface subsidence. Isolated residual hills called "hums" mark an end stage of such yield. Under solution attack bare, massive rock develops ribbed and fluted surfaces, called "karren."

The ability of chalk to hold as well as to imbibe water permits chalk regions to retain surface drainage until the water table has been lowered by the downcutting of trunk streams. Tributaries then become bournes, or dry valleys.

Dolines are the characteristic items of representative karst topography. The type form of the doline is a basin, shaped and functioning like a funnel top to direct drainage underground through a hole at the center of the hollow. Dolines vary greatly in the steepness of their slopes and in areal extent. By lateral enlargement they coalesce to form uvalas.

The karst cycle begins with karren and single dolines; it arrives at maturity when the dolines are united in uvalas, and all drainage escapes through underground channels. Old age sees a reduction of the surface to the ground-water level, with residual hums appearing as isolated summits.

Underground solution is little effective in erasing relief resulting from diastrophism, particularly graben-faulting, occurring after the karst cycle is in effect. Vast, vertical-walled, closed depressions, with level, alluviated floors, called "poljes," are attributed to such tectonic movement. Poljes are alternately flooded and drained by water flowing under pressure through ponore.

The manner in which lateral solution passages are enlarged to cavern dimensions is in dispute. One view is that this takes place below the water-table level; the other, that it can be accomplished by subterranean stream flow and weathering. There is consensus of opinion that cavern enlargement occurs by infall from the ceiling, but that natural bridges either do not result from this process, or, if ever so formed, do not long survive.

BIBLIOGRAPHY

CLASSICAL

Shaler, N. S. (1890) *The Topography of Florida*, Bulletin Museum of Comparative Zoology, Vol. 16, pp. 139–158.

Cvijic, J. (1893) *Das Karstphänomen*, Penck's Geographische Abhandlungen, Vol. 5, pp. 49–330.

Martel, E. A. (1893) *The Land of the Causses*, Appalachia, Vol. 7, pp. 18–30, 130–149.

RECENT

Grund, A. (1914) *Der Geographische Zyklus im Karst*, Zeitschrift der Gesellschaft für Erdkunde zu Berlin, Vol. for 1914, pp. 621–640.

Sellards, E. H. (1914) *Some Florida Lakes and Lake Basins*, Florida State Geological Survey, 6th Annual Report, pp. 115–159.

Sanders, E. M. (1921) *The Cycle of Erosion in a Karst Region*, Geographical Review, Vol. 11, pp. 593–604.

Cvijic, J. (1924) *The Evolution of Lapies*, Geographical Review, Vol. 14, pp. 26–49.

Jillson, W. R. (1924) *American Karst Country*, Pan American Geologist, Vol. 42, pp. 37–44.

Palmer, H. S. (1927) *Lapies in Hawaiian Basalts*, Geographical Review, Vol. 17, pp. 627–631.

Lobeck, A. K. (1929) *The Geology and Physiography of the Mammoth Cave National Park*, Kentucky Geological Survey, Series 6, Vol. 31, pp. 327–399.

Davis, W. M. (1930) *Origin of Limestone Caverns*, Bulletin Geological Society of America, Vol. 41, pp. 475–628.

Malott, C. A., and Shrock, R. R. (1930) *Origin and Development of Natural Bridge, Va.,* American Journal of Science, 5th Series, Vol. 19, pp. 256–273.

Swinnerton, A. C. (1932) *Origin of Limestone Caverns,* Bulletin Geological Society of America, Vol. 43, pp. 663–693.

Lehman, O. (1932) *Die Hydrographie des Karstes,* Enzyklopedia der Erdkunde, (Oskar Kende), F. Deuticke, Wien und Leipzig.

Wright, F. J. (1934) *The Newer Appalachians of the South,* Part I, Denison University, Scientific Laboratories: Journal, Vol. 29, pp. 1–105.

Dicken, S. N. (1935) *Kentucky Karst Landscapes,* Journal of Geology, Vol. 43, pp. 708–728.

Fig. 351. VOLCANIC REGION, AUVERGNE, FRANCE
Photographer unknown.

Chapter Twenty-three

LAND FORMS FROM VOLCANICITY

Introduction. Volcanic force is endogenic and, as such, gives rise to constructional land forms. These may be so large as to constitute geomorphic units of first importance. On the other hand, volcanic features may be small and superimposed on landscapes of a geomorphic development quite unrelated to volcanicity. The lesser volcanic items may, however, be so numerous as to give a distinctive topographic aspect to wide districts, which are then known as *volcanic regions.* The Auvergne Region (Fig. 351) of Central France, and an area at the eastern end of the island of Java, are representative examples of volcanic regions.

Either as geomorphic units, basic to further landscape evolution, or as incidental elements in territories whose main development is of another kind, the volcanic forms comprise many items deserving notice.

Nature of Volcanicity. The mechanism of volcanicity is not the concern of the student of geomorphology. It suffices for him to know that molten rock, magma, may be intruded into solid rock, or it may be extruded, either quietly as a hot fluid, or explosively as fragments, at the surface of the earth. The intruded masses, after cooling, acquire geomorphic significance only as they are later exposed by subaerial denudation. The extruded materials are of immediate consequence as geomorphic items. Broadly speaking, all extruded volcanic stuff is *lava* (Fig. 352); but ordinarily this word is used only to refer to material that emerges from a vent in a fluid or pasty state. The fragmented material of explosive eruption is collectively referred to as *pyroclastics* (Fig. 353), of which the components are styled *volcanic bombs, lapilli, volcanic ash,* and *volcanic dust,* in decreasing order of size. When deposited, beds of the coarser frag-

589

mentary stuff are called *volcanic breccia,* of the finer, *tuff.* Another general term for pyroclastics is *volcanic cinders.*

Lava Plateaus.   In Iceland, in 1783, on a line marked by the
Laki volcano, a fissure called the "Skaptar Cleft," 20 miles long,
opened in the surface of the earth.   From this fissure 3 cubic
miles of lava poured out and spread, 100 feet deep, to points
40 miles distant from the source.   Two hundred and seventy
square miles of country were covered.   This is the grandest, with

FIG. 352.   LAYERED LAVA, KILAUEA CALDERA, HAWAII

regard to volume of outpouring, volcanic eruption within historic time.   From geologic evidence it is clear that the plateaus
of Iceland, to an estimated thickness of over 10,000 feet, were
built up by similar eruptions of earlier periods.   The uplands
of Iceland are only a portion of a far vaster area, upbuilt by
lava flows, which once extended from northeastern Ireland, the
Western Isles of Scotland, the Orkney and Faroe Islands to Iceland.   Much of this great mass has since been eroded away or
has subsided beneath the sea.   In other places lava plateaus of
vast dimensions remain intact.   One is the Columbia Lava Plateau

of northwestern United States.   Another is the Deccan Region of northwest India; a third lies west of the Ivesti Mountains in East Africa; a fourth, the Ahaggar, is in the center of the Sahara The Columbia Lava Plateau extends over 100,000 square miles in Washington, Oregon, and Idaho.   Some authorities assert that the area of all flows in this general region is over 200,000 square miles.   The Deccan Region of India has an area of 200,000 square miles.   In both places the lava is 4000 or more feet thick.   The

FIG. 353.   PYROCLASTICS, RIM OF THE CRATER OF VESUVIUS, ITALY

Ahaggar of the Sahara, a plateau 155 miles wide and 6600 feet high, is less well-known.

As there is no evidence that the Columbia lava flows were laid down in water, the outpourings, which came at intervals of hundreds, perhaps thousands of years, and ranged from 10 to 200 feet thick, must have built up the plateau to a height of at least 4000 feet on a land base, for this is the thickness of the lava cover.   Where the Columbia Plateau is unmodified by subsequent weathering or stream dissection, as in its eastward extension known as the Snake River Plain, the topographic surface is that of the uppermost lava flow and is a nearly horizontal plain. The lava, when emitted, was very fluid and evidently submerged the country under the fiery fluid as a flood of water of equal volume in a closed basin would make a lake. Keeping its appropriate level the lava wraps around the spurs of mountains and extends between them as bays. Isolated summits were converted to islands, called *steptoes,* by the seas of molten rock. In part the regions flooded by lava had a high relief previous to the eruptions. Downstream from the Snake River Plain the Snake River has eroded a canyon which cuts through the lava flows into the basement rock. The underlying rock is granite, and in places rises, with steep slopes, 2500 feet up the canyon walls. Such summits are covered by a thickness of 1000 to 2000 feet of the flat-lying lava beds. The course of the river itself is consequent upon the lava surface; the canyon cut is a magnificent example of super-imposition in progress.

Volcanic Rifts. It is inferred that the Columbia lava floods came from fissures. They are considered to be analogous with the Iceland eruption in 1783. Further evidence of their origin by welling from fissures is their vast extent of horizontal surface, and that fragmental volcanic material is almost lacking. There is, also, positive indication of such origin. In the Craters of the Moon National Monument in Idaho, a number of cones and craters are strung along a line, the Great Rift Zone, which is inferred to be the site of a fissure from which the floods of lava spread across the country. Hobbs (1912) likens such cones to anthills distributed along the crack between two blocks of a concrete pavement. Very recent flows on the Snake River Plain seem to have emerged from localized centers now marked by low domes 200 to 300 feet high, 8 to 10 miles in diameter.

Fissure eruptions may, on the other hand, be explosive and then give rise to *volcanic rifts.* In Iceland these are open rents, called *ḡja,* one of which, the Eldgja, is over 18 miles long and is 600 feet deep in places. In 1886, at Tarawera in New Zealand, a nearly continuous trench about 9 miles long, in places over 500 feet wide at the top, and having depths extending from 300 to 1400 feet below the surface was opened by an explosive eruption. No lava was emitted. The ejected material consisted solely of fragments and fine powder derived in part from the shattering of

previously existing volcanic rock, destroyed in the formation of
the rift. This debris is recognizable as a layer of deposit extending across 4000 square miles of country. Near the fissure this bed
attains the thickness of 170 feet.

Inversion of Relief. Intermediate between the fissure eruptions, which build up great plateaus by lava floods, and those
which merely create rifts by explosion, are the eruptions that
pour out enough lava to fill valleys and bring about considerable
modification of drainage courses and of drainage development.
These are common occurrences. Streams are blocked so that
lakes form in the valley above the lava dam; their flow is diverted
to new channels along the borders of the lava sheet. Somewhat
regularly the cooled lava proves to be a rock more resistant to
weathering and erosion than that which it covers and abuts. The
lava is on the one hand permeable and on the other hand hard,
so that it lets water through instead of suffering decomposition,
and, because of its hardness, fails to yield readily to erosion. In
consequence of these circumstances, areas that at remote periods
have experienced lava filling of their valleys not uncommonly
exhibit *inversion of relief.* A stream if diverted by a lava
flow may cut channels on either side of the lava mass filling its
former valley. The earlier valley floor is then converted to a
raised upland and sometimes appears as a large mesa. The
borders of the lava-capped summit areas tend to develop steep
slopes because successive lava flows provide a layered structure
(Fig. 352), and because there may be beds of volcanic ash between
the lava layers. Such structure favors recession of the side of the
lava mass by weathering escarpments (Fig. 155), hence the development of vertical walls, or a series of terraces. If the lava
capping is sufficiently massive and resistant, the general degradation of the surrounding areas may make the topographic inversion
very complete. Conspicuous examples occur on the western slopes
of the Sierra Nevada in California, in the Auvergne Region (Fig.
351) of France and in Hesse, Germany.

Volcanic Cones. Filling of valleys with lava commonly proceeds from more or less circular vents instead of from fissure
eruptions. Ordinarily these localized vents are also the sites
about which *volcanic cones* are built up.

Volcanic cones differ greatly in form in accordance with the kind of material erupted from the volcanic vent. Those vents which emit lavas having nearly the degree of fluidity of the ones that give rise to extensive lava flows build *shield cones* (Fig. 354), of which the Hawaiian Islands are the type examples. Shield cones may rise to great heights but they are very broad of base and have very gentle slopes. Thus Mauna Loa rises 30,000 feet above the sea floor on which it rests. But the island of Hawaii,

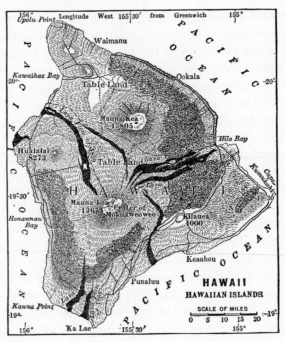

FIG. 354. MAP OF HAWAII
A broad shield cone built up by lava flows about
three vents.

of which Mauna Loa and Mauna Kea are the summits, is over 50 miles wide at sea level, the plane of which is at about one-half the height of the mass, and the whole island from sea floor to summits is composed of lava. The slopes from sea level upward to 10,000 feet altitude on Mauna Loa increase in steepness from 2 degrees to 10 degrees, but the top is flatter again. The island as a whole makes a vast mound corresponding to a shield in form. The fluid lava, escaping commonly from fissures in the sides of Mauna Loa, spreads thinly and flows far down the slopes (Fig.

355). A single flow may be 30 miles long; one was measured to be over a mile wide and to average 20 feet in thickness. The tops of these flows when unweathered may be wide fields of lava of the *pahoehoe* type (Fig. 356), having undulating shiny surfaces, or of *aa,* made up of jagged blocks, developed when flowing lava below the surface breaks up the upper crust.

Fig. 355. LAVA FLOW, APRIL 1926, FROM MAUNA LOA, HAWAII

The village is Hoopuloa which was later overwhelmed. Photograph from U. S. Army Air Service, copyright by the War Department.

Dome cones differ from shield cones in that they are much steeper, have narrower bases, and are built up by lavas that emerge in a pasty rather than in a fluid state. The difference in the nature of the lava arises from difference in composition. The fluid lavas are basaltic, or basic, the pasty ones siliceous, or acid. These pasty materials pile up immediately around the vent thus forming a high dome. Lassen Peak (Fig. 357) in California is cited as a representative example of a dome cone. The celebrated *puys* (Fig. 351) of the Auvergne Region of France are perfect examples, in miniature, of dome cones. The Bogosloff Islands in the Bering Sea are the summits of a dome cone that rose in historic times.

If the magma is even less fluid, or, perhaps, if the volume of gases in a pasty lava is great, the material is erupted explosively in fragments. The finer dust of such outbursts is drifted away by the winds but the coarser pieces rain back to form a ring about the orifice. The ring is built up until it forms a *cinder cone*

FIG. 356.   PAHOEHOE LAVA, KILAUEA CALDERA, HAWAII

(Fig. 358) with the vent in the center. Commonly a number of eruptions are required to develop a large cinder cone. However, rather tremendous results may come from a single outburst. It is related that the site of Monte Nuovo, a cinder cone near Naples, Italy, was, previous to September 29, 1538, the shore of a shallow lake on a plain. On that day an eruption of hot fragments and ashes began and when it had ended, after a week's time, a cinder cone over 2000 feet in diameter at the base and over 400 feet high had been built up. An equally famous and more modern instance of rapid construction of a cinder cone is that of Jorullo in Mexico. The location of Jorullo is southwest of Mexico City, about half way to the Pacific Coast, on the southern slope of the Mexican Plateau. At the end of September, 1759, explosive out-bursts began at a site where no indications of a volcanic vent had been noted. By November of that year a cone 820 feet high with

FIG. 357. MT. LASSEN, CALIFORNIA, A DOME CONE
In eruption 1914-1915. Photographer unknown.

a circular crater had been built up. Later eruptions, including lava emissions, raised Jorullo to the altitude of 1300 feet.

Cinder cones on the west side of Death Valley, California, have the appearance of being the result of a single eruption (Fig. 359). Mingled with the volcanic fragments at their summits are water-rounded quartz pebbles, the surfaces of which are in part spalled off, testifying to the intense sudden heat to which the gravel beds, through which the eruption passed, were subjected (v. Engeln, O. D., 1932).

Cinder cones are steep because the angle of repose of the angular material of which they are composed may be as high as 40 degrees. They seldom attain heights greater than 1000 feet, but nevertheless are usually prominent features in the landscape.

The highest, most imposing volcanic cones are almost without exception *composite cones*. Composite cones result from inter-

FIG. 358.   RED MOUNTAIN, A CINDER CONE, OWENS VALLEY, CALIFORNIA

changing eruption of lava and fragmentary materials. Assume that a lava eruption first builds up a shield or dome base. On this a cinder cone is erected. A succeeding lava eruption injects the loose cinder mass with ribs (dikes) of molten rock which harden in place. Near the summit of the cinder cone a lava flow breaks out and flows down the slope. A cinder eruption follows. The present day Vesuvius provides a perfect demonstration of such alternations. In time a very high cone, composed of volcanic fragments, filled in between and held up by ribs of solid rock, lava dikes and flows, is built up. The lava framework

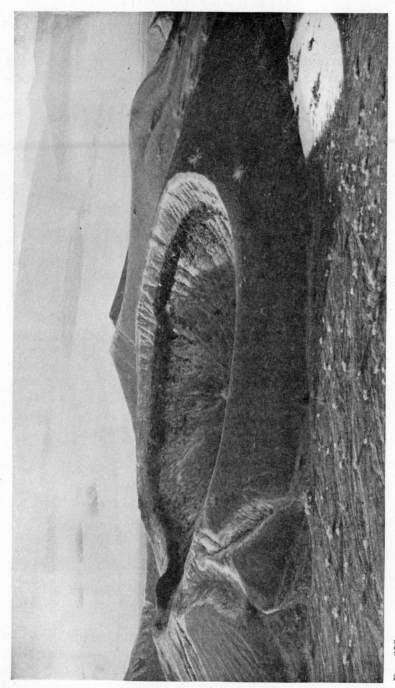

Fig. 359. UBEHEBE CRATER, DEATH VALLEY, CALIFORNIA
The bowl-shaped crater of a cinder cone.

of a composite cone, or *stratovolcano* may be likened to the steel structure of a skyscraper building.

The form of these composite cones, while they are still growing, is one of rare scenic beauty. The mountain is symmetrically dis-

FIG. 360. COLIMA, MEXICO, A REPRESENTATIVE COMPOSITE CONE
Photograph by Otto Brehme.

posed about the orifice at the top. Toward this summit the slopes extend in sweeping concave curves, gentle at the base, steepening regularly upward. Fujiyama (Fig. 253) in Japan is universally known as a nearly perfect example of such development and

FIG. 361. PART OF THE CALDERA OF KILAUEA, HAWAII

The steep cliff and flat floor are characteristically shown.

attractiveness. Mt. Edgecomb near Sitka, Alaska, and Mayon in the Philippine Islands, are rivals of Fujiyama. All the great cones of the United States are composite cones, Shasta, Rainier, Hood, Adams, as are also Popocatepetl in Mexico, Chimborazo in South America (Fig. 360). The profiles vary in steepness in accordance with the proportions of cinder and lava; thus Chimborazo with much fragmentary material is steep; Aetna in Sicily, chiefly lava, has gentler slopes. Practically all of the island of Java is made up of volcanic cones, chiefly cinder and composite erections.

Craters and Calderas. Orifices at the summits of volcanic cones vary greatly in form and size. Dome cones lack a visible opening. Those of composite cones tend to be narrow and deep; of cinder cones, broader and bowl-shaped (Fig. 359). These smaller openings are called *craters.* The openings of shield cones are characteristically vast and are called *calderas.* Mauno Loa in Hawaii, and Kilauea on its flank, present perfect examples of functioning calderas. The shortest diameter of the Mauna Loa caldera is over 2 miles, that of Kilauea over 1 mile.

Between eruptions the calderas of shield cones exhibit flat floors of frozen lava bounded by a steep cliff composed of the edges of lava flows broken across. In Kilauea the whole caldera floor rises and falls (Fig. 361). Its surface level varies from 400 to 1000 feet below the rim. The rim and the floor, in their present form, are said to date from 1840 when an eruption from low in the outer side of the cone was accompanied by faulting down and subsidence of its top.

Ancient Calderas. The functioning calderas of the Hawaiian cones are far surpassed in size by long inactive pits in the Alaskan Peninsula. The Hawaiian pits are probably due to subsidence. Calderas of similarly great dimensions in the Alaskan Peninsula appear, however, to be the product of explosive eruptions. Of such, Aniakchak, over 13 miles in diameter, is a representative example (Plate VII).

Emi Kusi is a caldera 9 miles in diameter at an elevation of 11,000 feet forming the summit of the Tibesti volcanic massif in the east-central part of the Sahara. Rising steam from its floor indicates that the volcanic energy has not completely died out.

Crater Lake (Fig. 362) in Oregon has caldera proportions. It is 6 miles in diameter and 4000 feet deep from the rim to the

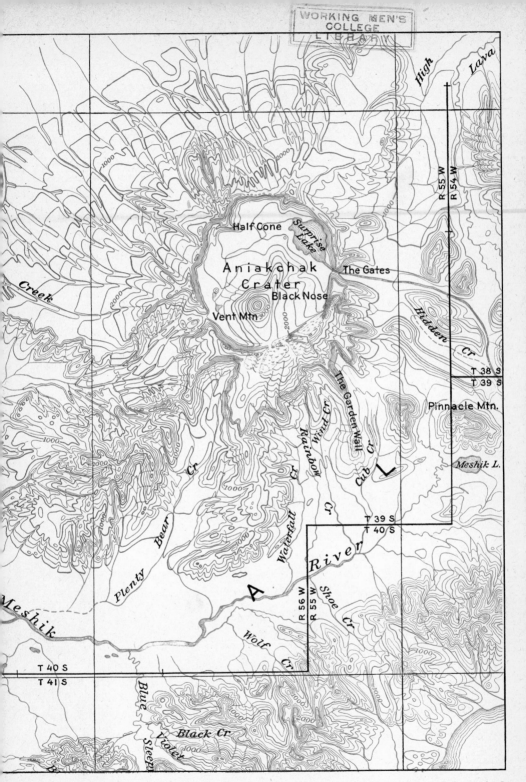

PLATE VII. Aniakchak Crater. Part of the Kanatak District, Alaska Peninsula Map of the United
States Geological Survey. Horizontal Scale, 1/250,000, contour interval 200 feet. Shows the great
caldera due to an explosive eruption, consequent streams descending the cone in a radial pattern,
incipient glacierization on the south side of the caldera rim, a graded glacial trough, probably
from Pleistocene glaciation, at the head of Plenty Bear Creek, and the glacio-fluvial aggradation
of the valley floor of Meshik River.

bottom of the lake. This caldera has been attributed both to collapse and explosion. In support of its origin by collapse it is pointed out that valleys, with glacially striated sides, begin abruptly as broad notches in the rim, and that no great accumulation of volcanic fragments is present on the lower slopes. It is inferred that the glaciated valleys must have had a continuation to reservoir areas, snow fields, on higher slopes now gone. The explosion possibility remains, however, because calderas in Alaska are at present occupied by ice domes from which outlet glaciers pour through gaps in the rim. In the Pleistocene glacial period the Crater Lake caldera could have been functioning in like manner. Again, if composed of fine ash, the explosive ejecta from Crater Lake may have been conveyed far and wide by the wind. Deposits of pumice, a glass froth commonly ejected in explosive

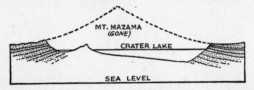

FIG. 362.   CRATER LAKE, OREGON, WITH RESTORATION OF THE INFERRED FORMER CONE, NAMED MT. MAZAMA

eruptions, of considerable extent and thickness occur in the region surrounding Crater Lake, and may well be part of the material blasted out to form the depression. The seemingly conflicting evidence is reconciled in an explanation advanced by H. Williams (1939). It is that the caldera collapse occurred not more than a few thousand years ago and was preceded by violent eruptions of pumice and scoria. Before that the cone had been deeply eroded by Pleistocene and post-Pleistocene glaciers.

Maare. The historically recent eruption of Krakatau, or Krakatoa (Fig. 363), provided direct evidence of the possible explosive origin of calderas. Krakatau is an island in the straits of Sunda, between Java and Sumatra. In May, 1883, a series of volcanic explosions converted two-thirds of the island to dust and spread the debris over hundreds of thousands of square miles of the surrounding seas. Where the central, highest parts of the island had been, there was afterwards water 900 feet deep. The eruption of Bandai San in Japan, in 1888, in two hours time blew

Fig. 363.   Krakatoa after the 1883 eruption

away one-half of a cone 2000 feet high.   Still more terrifically destructive was the eruption of Tamboro, on the island of Sumbawa, east of Java, in 1815.   It has been computed that over 30

Fig. 364.   Maar, Eifel region, Germany, Lake Gemunden
Photographer unknown.

cubic miles of rock were exploded, a volume equal to 100 cones the size of Vesuvius.

Such explosive outbursts, but of less magnitude, in areas of low relief give rise to circular pits called *maare* (Fig. 364).   Maare

are especially numerous in the Eifel region west of the Rhine Valley. in Germany. The depressions are commonly water-filled and range from one-fourth to one-half mile in diameter. A low wall of debris, composed chiefly of the exploded bedrock penetrated by the blast, but including a little volcanic matter, surrounds the maar.

The origin of Meteor Crater (Fig. 365) near Winslow, Arizona, has long been a matter for dispute. It is a pit almost a mile wide

FIG. 365.   METEORITE CRATER, NEAR WINSLOW, ARIZONA
Photograph from Spence Air Photos.

and 500 feet deep in a region of volcanic activity. However, the presence of iron meteorites within the depression and scattered over the surrounding plateau area rather clearly indicates the meteorite origin of the crater. A vast number of smaller, very shallow, pits in the coastal plain areas of North Carolina, South Carolina, and Georgia were, according to some investigators, produced by the impact of a meteorite swarm.

These depressions are locally known as *bays.* Typically the bays are elliptical in outline, a few hundred feet to nearly a mile in length, 5 or 10 feet deep, with gentle side slopes leading to a flat bottom. Their axes have a remarkably regular northeast to southwest trend. Meteor Crater is surrounded by a rim which rises 150 feet above the general level of the country. The bays either lack rims or have only a low sandy ridge on the southeast side. In opposition to the meteorite hypothesis of their origin it is argued that the bays occur chiefly on flat interfluves where drainage seeps underground, that they are solution depressions, and derive their elongation and orientation from structural lines in the underlying beds. Unless success attends efforts made to discover buried meteorite fragments under their floors the evidence at hand points to the solution theory of origin as the correct interpretation of the bays (MacCarthy, G. R., 1937).

Cone-in-cone, or Nested Craters. Not uncommonly composite volcanic cones have a compound form. The best known example is Vesuvius. Before the great explosive eruption of 79 A.D., which buried Pompeii under 30 or more feet of ash, the cone of Vesuvius had a crater of the caldera type, and was called "Monte Somma." The eruption of 79 A.D. destroyed a large part of the Somma ring. A series of eruptions since then, partly of lava, partly of fragments, have built up the modern cone of Vesuvius, inside and rising above what remains of the rim, called a "caldera" by some authors, of the ancient Somma. An approach to Vesuvius from the north now is first over the slopes of the old Somma, then across the rim of the old crater (altitude 3729 feet), into a valley called the *atrio* (3142 feet), behind the rim, then up lava slopes and finally up the cinder slopes of the modern cone (4267 feet). On the floor of the modern cone a small secondary cinder cone was building about the actual vent in 1930 during a period of very slight activity.

Such compounding is part of the development of many composite cones. When it is obvious the feature is referred to as *cone-in-cone,* or *nested craters* (Fig. 366). Sometimes, however, an old cone is partly blown away but no new cone is built up in the explosion crater. The cone then has a truncated summit. Such development may be regarded as a small-scale phase of the explosion caldera phenomenon. Not uncommonly *parasitic,* or *adventive* cones develop around vents opened in the side of the main cone. Shastina on the side of Mount Shasta in California is a noteworthy example. Such cones are also conspicuous on the slopes of Mount Aetna, in Sicily.

Fig. 366.   NESTED CRATERS, MODERN, OF VESUVIUS (ERUPTIONS OF 1930)

FIG. 367. SPINE OF MOUNT PELÉE, MARTINIQUE, MARCH 25, 1903
Photograph by E. O. Hovey.

Volcanic Spines.   An ephemeral feature, but one that is imposing during the period of its existence and one that when first known was thought to be unique, is the *volcanic spine.*   The fact of volcanic spines was learned at the time of the Mont Pelée eruption in Martinique in 1902 (Fig. 367).   The main outburst of that eruption was an enormous volume of gas and ash, both fiery hot.   Lesser eruptions, similar in kind, followed for over a year. As the eruptive activity died down a mass of pasty lava was pushed upward out of the crater, after the manner of stiff tooth paste emerging from a tube under pressure from the fingers.   The column of lava rose until it towered as a monumental obelisk more than 1000 feet above the crater rim.   It is thought that the great gaseous explosions of the main subsequent eruptions came out horizontally from beneath an older lava plug which had filled the core of the upper part of the cone to a considerable depth.   So interpreted, the spine would be the old plug slowly raised up by the volcanic forces.   A similar case is that of the eruption of Lassen Peak in California in 1915.   There were then two great horizontal blasts from beneath an old lava plug which was lifted up 300 feet.   But the Pelée spine may have been composed of new, very stiff lava hardening as it was made to emerge. The dome which rose in the crater of Tarumai, on Hokkaido Island, Japan, in 1909 is a parallel instance of such emergence.

However it originated, the resulting obelisk in Pelée was of such small strength that, either from slight internal explosions or from weathering, it has since crumbled down completely.   The eruption of Santa Maria volcano in Guatemala, in 1922, produced a spine, much like that of Pelée, which also crumbled quickly.

Dissection of Volcanic Cones.   The posteruptive degradational history of a volcanic cone is commonly much emphasized in geologic textbook writing.   Presumably special attention is given this topic because the sequence in the sculpture of the cones is readily appreciated and affords a convincing demonstration of geomorphic principles.

When the volcanic constructional processes cease, or become subordinate to degradational action, the sides of a cone become furrowed by radial consequent streams.   This is the stage of youth in the erosional history of a volcanic cone as a new geomorphic unit.   It could be expected that cinder cones, because of their loose construction, would yield almost at once to the destructive processes. Instead they are found to retain the perfect symmetry of their constructional development over long periods, especially if situated in arid climates. Their permeability and the siliceous nature of the fragments composing cinder cones account for this durability. Even the characteristically heavy downpours of desert regions sink underground as they fall on such cones, leaving its constructional slopes undisturbed. It is only as slow chemical weathering gives rise to clayey mineral substances, which serve to close the larger pores, that surface runoff becomes effective.

Originally numerous, subequal, consequent-stream furrows on the sides of a cone are in time replaced by a comparatively few deep and wide valleys, *barrancas*. This change results from abstraction, that is, the underground loss of drainage and eventual merging by slope retreat of shallow consequents into a neighboring deeper consequent; and from the growth of insequent tributaries to the larger consequents. In Hawaii the combining of a number of small consequent valleys into a single very large one gives rise to tremendously deep and wide canyons (Fig. 339), separated by very sharp ridges.

If, in a composite cone, persistent layers of weak materials, for example, tuff beds, are present, short subsequent valleys partially ringing the cone will develop from the more rapid yield of these less resistant beds. Exceptionally strong intruded lavas, on the other hand, may be weathered into relief to form dike ridges (Figs. 153, 154). Such ridges are very prominent in the Spanish Peaks of Colorado and in the Highwood Mountains of central Montana. Gently inclined lava beds on the lower slopes of a cone, built up largely by emissions of fluid flows, are dissected to triangular plateaus which the French call *planèzes*. The Cantal Cone in the Auvergne region of France shows planèzes typically developed. Further dissection converts the planèzes to mesas by cutting them off at the head from the central mass of the cone.

When great barrancas trench the upper slopes of a cone and its lower levels are much divided into planèzes and mesas the stage of full maturity is reached in cone dissection.

From maturity through old age, relief is, in the main, softened.

The divides are rounded, the valley floors and sides are graded to easy slopes.   All this is in accord with the normal course of the fluvial geomorphic cycle.   There is, however, a notable departure from the regular sequence.   This is the inversion of relief that gives extraordinary prominence to a particular type of monadnock, the *volcanic neck,* or *volcanic plug.*   At the site of the original crater depression, the lava filling of the throat of the volcano, below the bottom of the crater, is commonly made up of so much more durable rock than that composing the outer cone of accumulation, that it very effectively resists the erosional processes.   Unlike a volcanic spine, the volcanic neck (Fig. 159) which then stands out remains intact long after the remainder of the cone has been destroyed.   The Devil's Tower or Mato Tepee, Wyoming, in the Black Hills district (Fig. 175) is a famous example of this effect (Dutton, C. E., and Schwartz, J. M., 1936).   (Some geomorphologists consider the Mato Tepee to be a narrow dome, others a laccolith, still others a butte, that is an erosion remnant of a once-extensive lava flow.)

When even the volcanic neck has crumbled down, the end of the old-age stage in cone dissection is reached.   Ultimately only the leveled-off outcrop of the volcanic rock of the throat of the vent, interrupting the country rock of a region, gives evidence of the former volcanic activity.   The *pipes* of the Kimberley diamond mines of South Africa are thought to be of such origin.

Minor Geomorphic Results of Volcanicity.   Where streams have cut through lava flows or sills, *lava palisades* are commonly a feature of the valley sides.   The homogeneous lava substance, cooling and contracting, develops hexagonal jointing in marked perfection.   The lava beds bisected by river erosion display this structure prominently as a palisade (upright posts) wall in the valley slope.   The Palisades of the Hudson (Fig. 368) opposite the north end of New York City are the best known occurrence of this phenomenon.   The lower Yellowstone River valley in Yellowstone National Park affords very good examples.   The Giants Causeway (Fig. 369) in the north of Ireland and Fingals Cave in western Scotland are other developments resulting from such hexagonal jointing of lava beds.   Faulted and tilted lava beds isolated by erosion give rise to *trap ridges* (Fig. 216), of which Mount Tom and Mount Holyoke in the Connecticut Valley are examples. These show the palisade structure on their broken edges.

Sometimes lava breaks out in such volume from the flanks of a cinder cone as to carry away its side. A *breached cone* is thus developed. Examples of these are found in the Mont Dore Province in Central France. If the waves of the sea break through a cone so as to permit the water to enter its crater a

FIG. 368. LAVA PALISADES OF THE HUDSON
An intruded sill brought into relief by erosion. Photographer unknown.

volcanic harbor is formed. An instance of this is St. Paul's Rocks in the Atlantic. Another very perfect volcanic harbor is that of the island of Ischia in the Bay of Naples (Fig. 370).

Geysers and *hot springs*, as such, are phenomena more pertinent to the field of dynamic geology than to that of geomorphology. The water and steam they emit are commonly heated by contact with, or by gaseous emanations from, buried, still hot, lava flows. But in rising toward the surface the hot water and steam dissolve quantities of mineral substance from the rocks they pass through. Much of this mineral substance is deposited when the waters emerge. If the waters have passed through limestones such deposits may form great terraces, like those of Mammoth Hot Springs (Fig. 371) in Yellowstone National Park. Elsewhere in the same park hot-spring deposits of siliceous mineral make extensive basin fills because the superheated vapor serves to dissolve even quartz. Similar deposits of notable size also occur in the New Zealand geyser and hot-spring regions. Around some

Fig. 369.   GIANT'S CAUSEWAY, IRELAND
Photographer unknown.

hot springs and around the mouths of geysers, low *geyser cones* of siliceous sinter are regularly built up. Like these are the *mud volcano cones,* comprised of clay thrown out by steam jets. Rise of less violent steam currents cooks the rock to pools of thin mud, called *paint pots* in recognition of the vivid colors of the mud that are induced by the chemical reactions incidental to the cooking.

Number and Distribution of Volcanic Cones. A careful count by Sapper of all volcanic vents known to be active within historic time gave 97 in the Atlantic-Indian Ocean hemisphere, 353 in the

Pacific half of the earth's surface (Fig. 372). In addition there are probably several thousand cones dormant or extinct in so far as human records reveal their histories.

The preponderance in numbers of active volcanoes in the Pacific hemisphere is made more significant by the plan of their distribution. For the most part the cones are items in a ring encircling the Pacific Basin. Although the spacing between the

FIG. 370. HARBOR OF ISCHIA, ITALY, A VOLCANIC CRATER
Vesuvius is seen in the distance. Photographer unknown.

vents is uneven it is nevertheless obvious that they are situated at, or behind, the break line between the vast depressed area comprising the bottom of the Pacific Ocean basin and the mountainous lands that, in general, border its shores. Regions of crustal instability appear also to be the sites of volcanic activity. Furthermore, the vents are associated with faulting more than with folding. When folding predominates volcanoes appear commonly on one or both sides of the deformed belts. Thus while the Alps lack volcanoes, the Mediterranean area south of the Alps is closely dotted with active and extinct vents.

Aside from the Pacific girdle the only other general line of distribution of volcanoes that may be traced is one extending vaguely east and west around the earth, north of the equator. The Mediterranean region is part of this. It continues through the Caucasus, has representation in central Asia, appears again in Hawaii, cuts across Central America, includes the Lesser Antilles of the West Indies, and comes back to the Mediterranean through the Cape Verde and Canary Islands and the Azores.

From these two general belts an association seems to be indi-

FIG. 371.   MAMMOTH HOT SPRINGS, YELLOWSTONE NATIONAL PARK
Photograph by W. H. Jackson.

cated with the seas. However volcanic vents are present far inland, as on the plateaus of Arizona and the highlands of Africa. Great volcanic piles occur in the center of the Sahara. Whether active or extinct the fact of the continued existence of the volcanic masses as cones or plateaus, despite the intensive attack by degrading processes to which they are subject, is indicative of the large part that volcanic activity has played in the recent geologic history of the earth.

It is therefore not unfitting that a book on geomorphology should close with a chapter devoted to a discussion of the forms produced by volcanic action. The geologic ages appear to extend

over a period of two billion years. During the major part of all
that time the lands appear to have been plains of low relief.
To be sure there were great orogenies before those whose effects
are now visible but if geomorphologists had existed in any of
the almost interminable eras when the monotonous landscapes
prevailed over all the earth they could only have speculated
about vanished mountain ranges and imposing volcanic cones.
They might not have been able even to conceive such relief

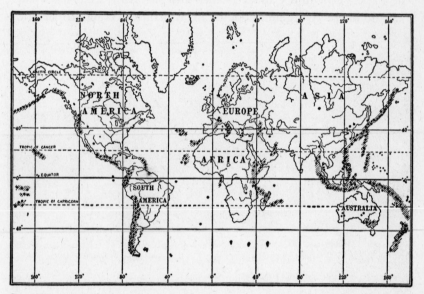

FIG. 372.   DISTRIBUTION OF VOLCANOES

The shaded sections indicate the main areas of volcanism, the dots active or
recently extinct vents.

features. But it so happens that thinking man came on the
scene during the closing phases of a geologic period of great
endogenic activity. Mountain ranges and plateaus were then being heaved up; the earth's crust was being broken and faulted
into great disordered blocks. Accompanying these large disturb-
ances there was much volcanic activity which has not yet completely died down. Of this volcanism the isolated volcanic cones
are the earmarks and the magnificent monuments.

Perhaps, indeed, it was the stimulus derived from the then
so rapidly changing earth, coupled with the climatic drive im-

posed by the Pleistocene glacial period, which ended not over 30,000 years ago, that caused man to develop his present capacities. Had the primeval ancestors of modern man been compelled to wander for untold ages through monotonous forests or grass- lands, stretching across endless plains, man might always have remained an uncouth and unenterprising being. But in a chang- ing geomorphic environment mankind changed also to meet the new conditions. Certain it is that the environment greatly affected human history. Indeed the records of the earliest civilizations in Europe show men struggling with ice and with flood and with destruction by fire. That struggle is not yet finished. Under- standing of man and his activities should not be regarded as complete unless it includes a knowledge of the geomorphic back- grounds.

SUMMARY

Land forms from volcanicity may have the importance of geo- morphic units or be only incidental items in the landscape. Chief significance attaches to materials extruded. The greatest volcanic effort is expended in the outpouring of lava from fissures in sufficient volume to build up lava plateaus. Explosive outbursts have created long and deep open rifts. Where country rock is less resistant to degradation than superimposed lava masses dif- ferential erosion may bring about noteworthy inversions of relief.

Volcanic cones are erected around vents having a point loca- tion and are the representative volcanic forms. Volcanic cones vary in shape in accordance with the type of material erupted. Openings at the summits of cones range in size from small craters to vast calderas, the latter developing by subsidence or explosion. A single short explosive outburst may produce a pit without building up any semblance of a cone. Cones of complex form are produced by a series of unlike eruptions.

In the role of geomorphic unit the volcanic cone provides an ideal site for observation of the progress of the fluvial geomorphic cycle. Distinctive stages of dissection are readily recognizable. Minor volcanic phenomena may give rise to conspicuous topo- graphic features. Geysers and hot springs associated with volcanic activity bring dissolved mineral substance to the surface in large enough volume to produce terraces, basin-fills, and low cones.

Four-fifths of the historically active volcanic cones are located in and around the basin of the Pacific Ocean. Such distribution is indicative of an association of volcanoes with regions of diastrophic unrest. But important vents appear in apparently stable areas. The recent geologic past is one of much greater crustal instability and volcanism than that of the major part of geologic time.

BIBLIOGRAPHY

CLASSICAL

Scrope, P. (1858) *On the Geology and Extinct Volcanoes of Central France,* 2nd ed. J. Murray, London.

Dutton, C. E. (1884) *Hawaiian Volcanoes,* 4th Annual Report, United States Geological Survey, Washington, pp. 75–219.

Russell, I. C. (1893) *Lava Plateau of the Columbia and Snake Rivers.* Bulletin United States Geological Survey, Washington, No. 108.

Russell, I. C. (1897) *Volcanoes of North America,* The Macmillan Company, New York.

Hovey, E. O. (1903) *The New Cone of Mt. Pelée and the Gorge of the Riviére Blanche,* American Journal of Science, 4th Series, Vol. 16, pp. 269–281.

Heilprin, A. (1904) *The Tower of Pelée,* J. B. Lippincott and Company, Philadelphia.

RECENT

Bell, J. M. (1906) *The Great Tarawera Volcanic Rift, New Zealand,* Geographical Journal, Vol. 27, pp. 369–382.

Johnson, D. W. (1907) *Volcanic Necks of the Mt. Taylor Region, New Mexico,* Bulletin Geological Society of America, Vol. 18, pp. 303–324.

Jaggar, T. A., Jr. (1908) *The Evolution of Bogosloff,* Bulletin American Geographical Society, Vol. 40, pp. 385–400.

Davis, W. M. (1912, 2nd ed., 1924) *Die Erklärende Beschreibung der Landformen, Vulkanische Formen,* pp. 316–351, B. G. Teubner, Leipzig-Berlin.

Jillson, W. R. (1917) *Physiographic Effects of the Volcanism of Mt. St. Helens, Washington,* Geographical Review, Vol. 11, pp. 398–405.

Sapper, K. T. (1927) *Vulkankunde,* J. Engelhorn's Nachfolger, Stuttgart.

Stearns, H. T. (1928) *Craters of the Moon National Monument, Idaho,* Geographical Review, Vol. 14, pp. 362–372.

Tyrrell, G. W. (1931) *Volcanoes,* T. Butterworth Ltd., London.

Fairchild, H. L. (1930) *Nature and Fate of the Meteor Crater Bolide,* Science, New Series, Vol. 72, pp. 463–467.

v. Engeln, O. D. (1932) *The Ubehebe Craters and Explosion Breccias in Death Valley, California,* Journal of Geology, Vol. 40, pp. 726–734.

Smith, W. D., and Swartzlow, C. R. (1936) *Mount Mazama: Explosion versus Collapse,* Bulletin Geological Society of America, Vol. 47, pp. 1809–1830.

Williams, H. (1941) *Calderas and their Origin,* University of California Publications, Bulletin of the Department of Geological Sciences, Vol. 25, pp. 239–346.

WORKS TO WHICH REFERENCE IS MADE

(Note: Only those books and papers that are specifically referred to in the text are included in this list. General and topical references will be found in the bibliography at the end of each chapter.)

Adams, F. D. (1938) *The Birth and Development of the Geological Sciences,* The Williams and Wilkins Company, Baltimore.

Alexander, H. S. (1932) *Pothole Erosion,* Journal of Geology, Vol. 40, pp. 305–337.

Ashley, G. H. (1935) *Studies in Appalachian Mountain Sculpture,* Bulletin Geological Society of America, Vol. 46, pp. 1395–1436.

Bailey, E. B. (1939) *Tectonics and Erosion,* Journal of Geomorphology, Vol. 2, pp. 116–120.

Bates, R. E. (1939) *Geomorphic History of the Kickapoo Region, Wisconsin,* Bulletin Geological Society of America, Vol. 50, pp. 819–880.

Behre, C. H., Jr. (1933) *Talus Behavior above Timber in the Rocky Mountains,* Journal Geology, Vol. 41, pp. 785–814.

Betz, Jr., F. and Hess, H. H. (1942) *The Floor of the North Pacific Ocean,* Geographical Review, Vol. 31, pp. 99–116.

Blackwelder, E. (1925) *Exfoliation as a Phase of Rock Weathering,* Journal of Geology, Vol. 33, pp. 793–806.

Born, A. (1930) *Erdkrustenbewegungen,* Handbuch der Geophysik, Band III, Lieferung I, Gebrüder Borntraeger, Berlin.

Bowman, I. (1934) *William Morris Davis,* Geographical Review, Vol. 24, pp. 177–181.

Bryan, K. (1922) *Erosion and Sedimentation in the Papago Country, Arizona,* Bulletin 730, United States Geological Survey.

———— (1934) *Geomorphic Processes at High Altitudes,* Geographical Review, Vol. 24, pp. 655–656.

———— (1940) *The Retreat of Slopes,* Annals Association of American Geographers, Vol. 30, pp. 254–268.

Bucher, W. H. (1939) *Deformation of the Earth's Crust,* Bulletin Geological Society of America, Vol. 50, pp. 421–432.

———— (1940) *Submarine Valleys and Related Geologic Problems of the North Atlantic,* Bulletin Geological Society of America, Vol. 51, pp. 489–512.

Callaghan, E. (1939) *Recent Fault Scarps in the Western Part of the Great Basin,* Bulletin Geological Society of America, Vol. 50, No. 12, Part 2, Abstracts, p. 1948.

Carlson, F. A. (1942) *American Settlement in the Isla de Piños, Cuba,* Geographical Review, Vol. 31, pp. 21–35.

Cole, W. S. (1930) *The Interpretation of Intrenched Meanders,* Journal of Geology, Vol. 38, pp. 423–436.

—— (1941) *Nomenclature and Correlation of Appalachian Erosion Surfaces,* Journal of Geology, Vol. 49, pp. 129–148.

Cotton, C. A. (1922–26) *Geomorphology of New Zealand,* Dominion Museum, Wellington, New Zealand.

—— (1941) *The Longitudinal Profiles of Glaciated Valleys,* Journal of Geology, Vol. 49, pp. 113–128.

Crickmay, C. H. (1933) *The Later Stages of the Cycle of Erosion,* Geological Magazine, Vol. 70, pp. 337–347.

Daly, R. A. (1905) *The Accordance of Summit Level Among Alpine Mountains,* Journal of Geology, Vol. 13, pp. 105–125.

—— (1915) *The Glacial-Control Theory of Coral Reefs,* Proceedings American Academy of Arts and Sciences, Vol. 51, pp. 155–251.

—— (1934) *The Changing World of the Ice Age,* Yale University Press, New Haven.

—— (1939) *Regional Departures from Ideal Isostasy,* Bulletin Geological Society of America, Vol. 50, pp. 387–420.

—— (1940) *Strength and Structure of the Earth,* Prentice-Hall, Inc., New York.

Davies, L. M. (1940) *Note on Three Himalayan Rivers,* Geological Magazine, Vol. 77, pp. 410–412.

Davis, W. M. (1889a) *The Rivers and Valleys of Pennsylvania,* National Geographic Magazine, Vol. 1, pp. 183–253. Also *Geographical Essays,* 1909, pp. 413–484, Ginn and Company, Boston.

—— (1889b) *The Drainage of Cuestas,* Proceedings of the Geologists' Association, Vol. XVI, pp. 75–93.

—— (1894) *Physical Geography as a University Study,* Journal of Geology, Vol. 2, pp. 66–100. Also *Geographical Essays,* pp. 165–192, Ginn and Company, Boston.

—— (1899) *The Peneplain, Geographical Essays,* 1909, pp. 350–380, Ginn and Company, Boston.

—— (1902) *Base-Level, Grade, and Peneplain,* Journal of Geology, Vol. X, pp. 77–111. Also *Geographical Essays,* 1909, pp. 381–412, Ginn and Company, Boston.

—— (1905) *The Geographical Cycle in an Arid Climate,* Journal of Geology, Vol. 13, pp. 381–407. Also *Geographical Essays,* 1909, pp. 296–322, Ginn and Company, Boston.

—— (1909) *Geographical Essays,* Ginn and Company, Boston.

—— (1912) *Die erklärende Beschreibung der Landformen,* B. G. Teubner, Leipzig.

—— (1923) *The Cycle of Erosion and the Summit Level of the Alps,* Journal of Geology, Vol. 31, pp. 1–41.

—————— (1924) *Die erklärende Beschreibung der Landformen,* 2nd ed., B. G. Teubner, Berlin.

—————— (1930) *The Peacock Range, Arizona,* Bulletin Geological Society of America, Vol. 41, pp. 293–313.

—————— (1932) *Piedmont Benchlands and Primärrümpfe,* Bulletin Geological Society of America, Vol. 43, pp. 399–440.

—————— (1938) *Sheetfloods and Streamfloods,* Bulletin Geological Society of America, Vol. 48, pp. 1337–1416.

de Martonne, E. (1927) *Regions of Interior-Basin Drainage,* Geographical Review, Vol. 17, pp. 397–414.

Demorest, M. (1939) *Glacial Movement and Erosion: A Criticism,* American Journal of Science, Vol. 237, pp. 594–605.

De Terra, H. (1940) *Some Critical Remarks Concerning W. Penck's Theory of Piedmont Benchlands in Mobile Mountain Belts,* Annals Association of American Geographers, Vol. 30, pp. 241-247.

Du Toit, A. L. (1937) *Our Wandering Continents,* Oliver and Boyd, Edinburgh.

—————— (1940) *An Hypothesis of Submarine Canyons,* Geological Magazine, Vol. 57, pp. 395–404.

Dutton, C. E. (1880) *Report on the Geology of the High Plateaus of Utah,* United States Geographical and Geological Survey of the Rocky Mountain Region (Powell) Washington.

Dutton, C. E., and Schwartz, G. M. (1936) *Notes on the Jointing of the Devil's Tower, Wyoming,* Journal of Geology, Vol. 44, pp. 717–728.

Eaton, H. N. (1919) *Some Subordinate Ridges of Pennsylvania,* Journal of Geology, Vol. 27, pp. 121–127.

Elston, E. D. (1917–1918) *Potholes, Their Variety, Origin and Significance,* Scientific Monthly, Vol. 5, pp. 554–567, Vol. 6, pp. 37–53.

v. Engeln, O. D. (1911) *Phenomena Associated with Glacier Drainage and Wastage,* Zeitschrift für Gletscherkunde, Vol. 6, pp. 104–150.

—————— (1932) *The Ubehebe Craters and Explosion Breccias in Death Valley, California.* Journal of Geology, Vol. 40, pp. 726–734.

—————— (1937a) *Rock Sculpture by Glaciers: A Review,* Geographical Review, Vol. 27, pp. 478–482.

—————— (1937b) *Scarp of the High Sierra Nevada,* Pan-American Geologist, Vol. 68, pp. 333–339.

—————— (1938a) *Glacial Geomorphology and Glacier Motion,* American Journal of Science, Vol. 35, pp. 426–440.

—————— (1938b) *Large, Sharply Defined Terminal Moraine Ridges,* Comptes Rendus du Congrès International de Géographie, Amsterdam, 1938, Vol. 2, Section 2a, pp. 210–213.

—————— (1940) *A Particular Case of Knickpunkte,* Annals Association of American Geographers, Vol. 30, pp. 268–271.

Farmin, R. (1937) *Hypogene Exfoliation in Rock Masses,* Journal of Geology, Vol. 45, pp. 625–635.

Fenneman, N. M. (1936) *Cyclic and Non-Cyclic Aspects of Erosion,* Science, Vol. 83, pp. 87–94.

—— (1938) *Physiography of Eastern United States,* McGraw-Hill Book Company, Inc., New York.

Flint, R. F. (1941) *Ozark Segment of Mississippi River,* Journal of Geology, Vol. 49, pp. 626–640.

Fridley, H. M. (1939) *Solution and Stream Piracy,* Journal of Geology, Vol. 47, pp. 178–188.

—— (1940) *Watergaps by Solution and Piracy: A Reply,* American Journal of Science, Vol. 238, pp. 226–233.

Frye, J. C. and Schoff, S. L. (1941) *Deep-Seated Solution in the Meade Basin and Vicinity, Kansas and Oklahoma,* Bulletin Geological Society of America, Vol. 52, p. 1999.

Fryxell, F. M., Horberg, L., Edmund, R. (1941) *Geomorphology of the Teton Range and Adjacent Basins,* Bulletin Geological Society of America, Vol. 52, p. 1903.

Gerber, E. (1934) *Zur Morphologie wachsender Wande,* Zeitschrift für Geomorphologie, Vol. 8, pp. 213–223.

Gilbert, G. K. (1877) *Report on the Geology of the Henry Mountains (Utah),* United States Geographical and Geological Survey of the Rocky Mountain Region (Powell), Washington.

—— and Gulliver, F. P. (1895) *Tepee Buttes,* Bulletin Geological Society of America, Vol. 6, pp. 333–342.

Glock, W. S. (1932) *Available Relief as a Factor in the Profile of a Land Form,* Journal of Geology, Vol. 40, pp. 74–83.

Gould, L. M. (1935) *The Ross Shelf Ice,* Bulletin Geological Society of America, Vol. 46, pp. 1367–1394.

Gregory, J. W. (1911) *Constructive Waterfalls,* Scottish Geographical Magazine, Vol. 27, pp. 537–546.

Griggs, D. (1939) *A Theory of Mountain Building,* American Journal of Science, Vol. 237, pp. 611–650.

Guyot, E. (1935) *La Théorie des Translationes Cóntinentales et l'Astronomie,* Annales Guebhard-Siverine, an. 11, f.2, pp. 57–73. Neuchatel, Switzerland.

Hess, H. H. (1938) *Gravity Anomalies and Island Arc Structure With Particular Reference to the West Indies,* Proceedings of the American Philosophical Society, Vol. 79, pp. 71–96.

Hobbs, W. H. (1911) *Repeating Patterns in the Relief and in the Structure of the Land.* Bulletin Geological Society of America, Vol. 22, pp. 123–176.

—— (1912) *Earth Features and Their Meaning,* 1st. ed., The Macmillan Company, New York.

Huntington, E., and Goldthwait, J. W. (1903) *The Hurricane Fault in Southwestern Utah,* Journal of Geology, Vol. 11, pp. 46–63.

Hutton, J. (1795) *Theory of the Earth*, William Creech, Edinburgh, Scotland.

Ireland, H. A., Sharpe, C. F. S., and Eargle, D. H. (1939) *Principles of Gully Erosion in the Piedmont of South Carolina*, Technical Bulletin, 633, United States Department of Agriculture.

Jefferson, M. S. (1902) *Limiting Width of Meander Belts*, National Geographic Magazine, Vol. 13, pp. 373–384.

Johnson, D. W. (1919) *Shore Processes and Shoreline Development*, John Wiley & Sons, Inc., New York.

———— (1931) *Stream Sculpture on the Atlantic Slope*, Columbia University Press, New York.

Johnson, W. D. (1901) *The High Plains and their Utilization*, United States Geological Survey, 21st Annual Report, Pt. IV, pp. 601–741.

Johnstone, J. (1928) *An Introduction to Oceanography*, 2nd ed. University Press of Liverpool.

Keindl, J. (1940) *Zur Frage der Entstehung der Ozeanbecken*, Zeitschrift für Geomorphologie, Bd. XI, pp. 1–8.

Kesseli, J. E. (1940) *The Development of Slopes*, Mimeographed, University of California, Berkeley, California.

———— (1941) *Rock Streams in the Sierra Nevada, California*, Geographical Review, Vol. 31, pp. 203–227.

———— (1941) *The Concept of the Graded River*, Journal of Geology, Vol. 49, pp. 561–588.

Keyes, C. R. (1908) *Rock-Floor of Intermont Plains of the Arid Region*, Bulletin Geological Society of America, Vol. 19, pp. 63–92.

Ladd, H. S., and Hoffmeister, J. E. (1936) *A Criticism of the Glacial-Control Theory*, Journal of Geology, Vol. 44, pp. 74–92.

Lawson, A. C. (1894) *The Geomorphogeny of the Coast of Northern California*, Bulletin Department of Geology, University of California, Vol. 1, pp. 241–271.

———— (1938) *The Isostasy of Large Deltas*, Bulletin Geological Society of America, Vol. 49, pp. 401–416.

Leet, L. D. (1940) *Status of Geological and Geophysical Investigations of the Atlantic and Gulf Coastal Plain*, Bulletin Geological Society of America, Vol. 51, pp. 873–886.

Lehmann, O. (1934) *Ueber die morphologischen Folgen der Wandverwitterung*, Zeitschrift für Geomorphologie, Vol. 8, pp. 93–99.

Lyell, C. (1830–32) *Principles of Geology*, John Murray, London.

MacCarthy, G. R. (1937) *The Carolina Bays*, Bulletin Geological Society of America, Vol. 48, pp. 1211–1226.

Machatschek, F. (1934) *Geomorphologie*, B. F. Teubner, Leipzig and Berlin.

———— (1938) *Das Relief der Erde*, Erster Band, Gebrüder Borntraeger, Berlin.

Malott, C. A., and Shrock, R. R. (1930) *Origin and Development of Natural Bridge, Virginia,* American Journal of Science, 5th Ser., Vol. 19, pp. 256–273.

Mather, K. F. (1939) *Earth Structure and Earth Origin,* Science Vol. 50, pp. 65–70.

Matthes, F. E. (1930) *Geologic History of the Yosemite Valley,* Professional Paper 160, United States Geological Survey, Washington.

—— (1939) *History of Faulting Movements at the East Front of the Sierra Nevada as Indicated by Dislocated Moraines,* Bulletin of the Geological Society of America, Vol. 50, No. 12, Part 2, Abstracts, p. 1955.

Maull, O. (1938) *Geomorphologie,* F. Deuticke, Leipzig and Wien.

Maxon, J. H., and Campbell, I. (1935) *Stream Fluting and Stream Erosion,* Journal of Geology, Vol. 43, pp. 729–744.

McGee, W. J. (1897) *Sheetflood Erosion,* Bulletin Geological Society of America, Vol. 8, pp. 87–112.

Meyerhoff, H. A., and Hubbell, M. (1927–1928) *The Erosional Landforms of Eastern and Central Vermont,* Vermont State Geologist, 16th Annual Report, pp. 315–381.

—— and Olmstead, E. W. (1936) *The Origins of Appalachian Drainage,* American Journal of Science, Vol. 32, pp. 21–42.

Meyerhoff, H. A. (1940) *Migration of Erosional Surfaces,* Annals Association of American Geographers, Vol. 30, pp. 247–254.

Monnett, V. E. (1922) *Topographic Criteria of Oil Field Structure,* Bulletin American Association of Petroleum Geologists, Vol. 6, pp. 37–41.

Morawetz, S. O. (1932) *Eine Art von Abtragsvorgang,* Petermanns Mitteilungen, Vol. 78, pp. 231–233.

Mordziol, C. (1910) *Ein Beweis für die Antezedenz des Rheindurchbruchtales,* Zeitschrift der Gesellschaft für Erdkunde zu Berlin, pp. 77–92, 159–173.

Morgan, A. M. (1941) *Solution Phenomena in the Pecos Basin in New Mexico,* Bulletin Geological Society of America, Vol. 52, p. 2005.

National Geographic Society (1939) *National Geographic Society-U. S. Navy Solar Eclipse Expedition, 1937, to Canton Island.* National Geographic Society, Contributed Papers, Solar Eclipse Series, No. 1, Washington.

Nelson, W. A. (1940) *Topography of the Former Continent of Appalachia (From Geologic Evidence),* National Research Council, American Geophysical Union, Transactions of 1940, Part III, pp. 786–796.

Oestreich, K. (1909) *Studien über die Oberflächengestalt des rheinisches Schiefergebirgs, III. Die Verbiegung der rheinischen Hauptterrasse,* Petermanns Mitteilungen, Vol. 55, pp. 57–62.

—— (1938) *Historisches zur Frage der Piedmont Treppe, Compte Rendu,* Congrès International de Géographie, Amsterdam, Tome II–IIa, pp. 162.

Palmer, H. S. (1927) *Lapies in Hawaiian Basalts,* Geographical Review, Vol. 17, pp. 627–631.

Penck, A. (1905) *Climatic Features in the Land Surface,* American Journal of Science (4) Vol. 19, pp. 165–174.

Penck, W. (1924) *Die Morphologische Analyse,* J. Engelhorn's Nachf., Stuttgart.

Pirsson, L. V. (1914) *The Geology of Bermuda Island: the Igneous Platform;* American Journal of Science, 4th Series, Vol. 38 pp. 331–344.

Playfair, J. (1802) *Illustrations of the Huttonian Theory of the Earth,* William Creech, Edinburgh.

Powell, J. W. (1875) *Exploration of the Colorado River of the West,* Smithsonian Institution, Washington.

Rappenecker, C. (1936) *The Regional and Economic Geography of Jamaica, B. W. I.,* Thesis, Cornell University Library, Ithaca, N. Y.

Raymond, E., and Stetson, H. C. (1931) *A New Factor in the Transportation and Distribution of Marine Sediments,* Science, New Series, Vol. 73, pp. 105-106.

Reid, J. A. (1911) *Geomorphogeny of the Sierra Nevada Northeast of Lake Tahoe,* Bulletin Department of Geological Sciences, University of California, Vol. 6.

Renner, G. T., Jr. (1927) *The Physiographic Interpretation of the Fall Line,* Geographical Review, Vol. 17, pp. 276–286.

Rich, J. L. (1938) *Recognition and Significance of Multiple Erosion Surfaces,* Bulletin Geological Society of America, Vol. 49, pp. 1695–1722.

—— (1941) *Buried Stagnant Ice as a Normal Product of a Progressively Retreating Glacier in Hilly Regions,* Bulletin Geological Society of America, Vol. 52, p. 1929.

Rodgers, J. (1937) *Tilting of Proglacial Lakes,* American Journal of Science, Vol. 34, pp. 1–8.

Russell, R. J. (1931) *Geomorphological Evidence of a Climatic Boundary,* Science, Vol. 74, pp. 484–485.

—— (1939) *Louisiana and the Ice Age,* Louisiana Conservation Review, Spring, 1939, pp. 14–16, 18.

—— (1940) *Quaternary History of Louisiana,* Bulletin Geological Society of America, Vol. 51, pp. 1199–1234.

—— (1941) *Lower Mississippi Valley Loess,* Bulletin Geological Society of America, Vol. 52, p. 1931.

Salisbury, R. D. (1919) *Physiography,* 3rd ed. rev., Henry Holt and Company, Inc., New York.

Sanders, E. M. (1921) *The Cycle of Erosion in a Karst Region,* Geographical Review, Vol. II, pp. 593–604.

Shackleton, M. R. (1934) *Europe,* Longmans, Green & Company, London.

Sharp, H. S. (1929) *The Fall Zone Peneplain,* Science, Vol. 69, pp. 544–545.

Shepard, F. P. (1933) *Geological Misconceptions Concerning the Oceans,* Science, Vol. 78, pp. 406–408.

Staub, Rudolf (1928) *Bewegungsmechanismus der Erde,* Gebrüder Borntraeger, Berlin.

Stose, G. W. (1940) *Age of the Schooley Peneplain,* American Journal of Science, Vol. 238, pp. 461–476.

Suess, E. (1888) *Das Antlitz der Erde,* Vol. 2, F. Tempsky, Wien.

Swinnerton, A. C. (1932) *Origin of Limestone Caverns,* Bulletin Geological Society of America, Vol. 43, pp. 663–693.

Taber, S. (1927) *Fault Troughs,* Journal of Geology, Vol. 35, pp. 577–606.

Tarr, R. S., and Martin, L. (1906) *Recent Changes in Level in the Yakutat Bay Region, Alaska,* Bulletin Geological Society of America, Vol. 17, pp. 29–64.

——— (1915) *College Physiography,* The Macmillan Company, New York.

Thompson, H. D. (1939) *Drainage Evolution in the Southern Appalachians,* Vol. 50, pp. 1323–1356, Bulletin Geological Society of America.

Van Bemmelen, R. W. (1930) *Das Permanenzproblem nach der Undationstheorie,* Geologische Rundschau, Vol. 30, pp. 10–20.

Veatch, A. C., and Smith, P. A. (1939) *Atlantic Submarine Valleys of the United States and the Congo Submarine Valley,* Special Paper Number 7, Geological Society of America.

Vening Meinesz, F. A. (1934) *Report of the Gravity Expedition in the Atlantic of 1932 and the Interpretation of the Results,* Netherlands Geodetic Commission, Gravity Expeditions at Sea, 1923–1932, Delft, Netherlands.

Ver Steeg, K. (1930) *Wind Gaps and Water Gaps of the Northern Appalachians, their Characteristics and Significance,* Annals New York Academy of Science, Vol. 32, pp. 87–220.

Von Engeln, O. D. See under E: v. Engeln.

Ward, F. (1930) *The Role of Solution in Peneplanation,* Journal of Geology, Vol. 38, pp. 262–270.

Williams, H. (1939) *Age of Crater Lake, Oregon,* Bulletin Geological Society of America, Vol. 50, Abstracts, p. 1962.

Willis, B. (1895) *The Northern Appalachians,* National Geographic Society Monographs, American Book Company, New York, pp. 169–202.

———— (1928) *Dead Sea Problem: Rift Valley or Ramp Valley:* Bulletin Geological Society of America, Vol. 39, pp. 490–542.

———— (1936) *East African Plateaus and Rift Valleys,* Carnegie Institution of Washington, Publication No. 470, Washington.

Woodward, H. P. (1936) *Natural Bridge and Natural Tunnel, Virginia,* Journal of Geology, Vol. 44, pp. 604–616.

Wooldridge, S. W., and Morgan, R. S. (1937) *The Physical Basis of Geography,* Longmans, Green & Company, London.

INDEX

For the convenience of readers who may wish to follow particular topics through the book the serial succession of pages is given in parentheses at the end of each heading under which numerous items are listed.

629

and valleys, 2; on uniformitarianism, 82.

Hwang Ho basin, loess deposits of, 417.

Icebergs, 471; Antarctic, 475.
Ice cave, 471.
Ice cliffs, 471.
Ice domes, in calderas, 603.
Ice fall, 454.
Iceland, Laki volcano of, 590; volcanic plateaus of, 590; volcanic rift, Eldgja, 592.
Incipient peneplain, 222.
Incised meanders, 205–208.
Indented coast line, 508–511.
Indian leap, 293.
Indus River, as a desert through river, 399.
Inface, 120.
Ingrown meanders, 205–206, 221.
Inherited drainage, 225.
Inner lowland, 120.
Inner vale, 120.
Inselberg, 427–430.
Inselberglandschaft, 428.
Insequent streams, 116; in ancient mountains, 336; in deserts, 408; on till plain, 489.
Interfluves, 137.
Interlocking spurs, 199.
Interruption, of fluvial geomorphic cycle, 220–221.
Intervention, of fluvial geomorphic cycle, 220–221.
Intrenched meanders, 205–208, 221.
Inversion of relief, 322, 324; by dissection of volcanic cones, 609; by lava flows, 593; in Folded Appalachians, 342.
Ireland, former glacier in, 473; lava plateau of, 590.
Ireland, H. A., on young valleys, 115.
Ischia, Italy, volcanic harbor of, 610.
Island arcs, 42–45.
Islands, coral, 63; large, 39–40; orogenic, 42–45; small, 40–42.
Isle of Pines, Cuba, mogotes of, 569.
Isostasy, 26–27; and geosynclines, 313; of Hawaii, 40; of Mississippi River delta, 254.
Ivesti Mountains, Africa, lava plateau near, 591.

Jamaica, B. W. I., karst region of, 565; poljes of, 580.

Jamas, 573.
James River, headwater erosion of, 350, 352.
Java, as a volcanic region, 589; volcanic cones of, 602.
Jefferson, M. S., on limiting width of meander belt, 144.
Johnson, D. W., on crenulate shore lines, 527; on superimposition theory of Appalachian drainage, 356–357.
Johnson, W. D., on Great Plains, 153.
Joint-plane falls, 185–186.
Joint planes, in relation to rock cities, 295–296.
Joints, 162–163, 165, 167; hexagonal, 609.
Jorullo, Mexico, as a cinder cone, 596–597.
Junctions, accordant, 175–177; accordant, restoration of after glaciation, 461; discordant, 179–185.
Jura Mountains, Switzerland, concordant border on northwest side of, 306; consequent drainage development on, 314; in stage of youth of fluvial cycle, 324; structure of, 314–316.
Jutland, west coast of a graded shore line, 541.
Juxtaposition, of beds, etc., 157.

Kalahari Desert, Africa, as a Trade Wind desert, 402; bornhardts of, 429.
Kambara, Fiji Islands, as an elevated atoll, 559.
Kame moraines, 494.
Kame terrace, 494.
Kames, 493–494.
Kar, 447.
Kar-niveau, 448–450; development of, 452.
Karren, 569; incipient, 571.
Karst, structure of, 63; circulation of ground water in, 576.
Karst geomorphic cycle, 563, 576–579; and diastrophism, 579–580; stage of youth, 577; stage of maturity, 577–578; stage of old age, 578.
Karst regions, examples of, 563, 565–566.
Keindl, J., on hypothesis of expanding earth, 35.
Kentucky, Mammoth Cave district of, 577; sink holes of, 572; valley sinks of, 575.

Nappes, 64, 332.

Narai Island, Fiji Islands, coral reefs of, 555.

Nashville Dome, Tennessee, as a dome structure, 64; erosional history of, 307–309.

National Geographic Society, eclipse expedition of, 552.

Natural Bridge, Virginia, origin of, 583–584.

Natural bridges, 212.

Natural levees, 146–147.

Natural Tunnel, Virginia, origin of, 584.

Navajo Mountain, Utah, a laccolithic dome, 307.

Neck, meander, 144.

Negative strip, 44.

Nehrungen, 540.

Nelson, W. A., on Appalachian sediments, 340.

Nested, craters, 606; saucer basins, 62.

Névé line, 471.

New England, ancient mountains of, 336; glacial erratics in, 502; roches moutonnées' modeling of northern mountains of, 483.

Newfoundland, ice cap of in Pleistocene, 498; nature of, 42.

New-Kanawha Rivers, as antecedent streams, 346.

New Mexico, bolsons of, 426.

New River, Fort Lauderdale, Florida, nature of channel of, 585.

New York State, differential glacial erosion in central, 502–503; drumlins of, 491; glacial series in north-central, 497.

New Zealand, geyser deposits in, 611; South Island, loess deposits of, 421; South Island, plain of marine erosion on, 525; volcanic rift at Tarawera, 592–593.

Niagara escarpment, 286.

Niagara Falls, as cap-rock falls, 186–189; as result of glacial diversion, 503; retreat of, 173.

Nick points, 265.

Nieves penitentes, 471.

Nile River, as a desert through river, 399.

Nip, 529.

Nivation, 445–446.

Noncylic erosion, 89.

Normal geomorphic cycle, 106. *See also under:* "Fluvial geomorphic cycle."

Normandy Coast, France, as a falaise coast, 541.

North America, indented northeastern coast of, 508.

North Carolina, "bays" of, 605.

North Downs, England, as a chalk region, 571.

North Minerva Atoll, a representative atoll, 551.

Norway, as zone of Pleistocene glacial erosion, 501; roches moutonnées' modeling of, 483.

Noses, 326–327.

Nunataks, 465; of Spitzbergen, 485.

Oasis, 411.

Obsequent fault-line scarp, 382–383.

Obsequent stream, 127–128.

Ocean basins, 25; origin, 32–35; origin of Atlantic basin, 33–35; origin of Pacific Basin, 33–34; pulsation theory of origin of, 34–35.

Ocean bottoms, relief of the, 38–39.

Ocean deeps, 45–46.

Oceans, extent of, 27–28; sounding of the, 38.

Oestreich, K., on antecedent course of the Rhine River, 230.

Offshore bar, 529–532.

Oghurd, 423.

Ohio, till plain of, 489.

Ohio River, as a through stream, 563; meanders of, 205.

Old age, stage of. *See under:* "Stages of Arid, Fluvial, Glacial, Karst, and Shore-line geomorphic cycles."

Oldland, 114.

Olean, New York, rock city near, 295–296, 298.

Olmstead, E. W., on Folded Appalachian drainage, 347–348.

Ontario, Canada, Highlands of as zone of Pleistocene glacial erosion, 501.

Open valley, 201.

Orinoco River, delta of, 252.

Orkney Islands, lava plateau of, 590.

Orogenic uplift, 198.

Osar, 492.

Oule, 447.

Outer lowland, 120.

Outer vale, 120.

Outlet glaciers, from calderas, 603; function of, 473.

Outliers, 292–295.

Outwash fans, 494, 496.